# Rest Areas &

# Welcome Centers

## *Along US Interstates*

**Published by:**

Roundabout Publications
PO Box 19235
Lenexa, KS 66285

800-455-2207

www.TravelBooksUSA.com
www.RoadNotes.com
www.RVdumps.com

**Please Note**

Every effort has been made to make this book as complete and as accurate as possible. However, there may be mistakes both typographical and in content. Therefore, this text should be used as a general guide to rest areas and welcome centers. Although we regret any inconvenience caused by inaccurate information, the author and Roundabout Publications shall have neither liability nor responsibility to any person or entity with respect to any loss or damage caused, or alleged to be caused, directly or indirectly by the information contained in this book.

Library of Congress Control Number: 2005926742
ISBN: 1-885464-11-8

# Table of Contents

# Introduction

Each year, millions of travelers take to America's Interstate highways. Some are on vacation or a road trip, others are traveling on business, and some are full-time RVers enjoying retirement on the road. Whatever the reason, it's nice to know what services are available along the way. That's what this book is about.

## Rest Areas and Welcome Centers

Rest areas not only offer relief when nature calls but also provide a place for the weary traveler to take a break from driving. You can also walk the family pet or buy a soft drink and snack from a vending machine. Some rest areas, particularly along toll highways, sell food and fuel. These are usually known as service areas or plazas.

Rest area usage rules vary by state and each rest area. Some impose a time limit to how long you can stay. Others allow you to park overnight. A few even have a camping area complete with electric hookups for RVers. If you plan to stay in a rest area for more than a few hours, be sure to read the rules (usually posted near the restrooms).

Welcome centers are most often found just after entering a state. It is here that you can obtain maps and brochures about places to camp, things to see, and things to do while visiting. Most welcome centers are staffed with knowledgeable personnel that can help you better enjoy your visit.

## Interstate Highway Services

In addition to rest areas and welcome centers, this book shows you where some of the more popular services are located. Included are discount stores like Wal-Mart or Target, which are good places to buy items that you forgot to pack. Some of the larger stores also sell groceries or have a fast food restaurant inside. Some, such as Wal-Mart, usually allow RVers to park overnight for free. (Don't assume overnight parking is permitted, check with the store's manager first.)

New to this edition of the book are Cracker Barrel Old Country Store locations. Cracker Barrel has been named the "Best Family Dining Restaurant in America" by a *Choice in Chains* national survey and the "Best Restaurant in America" by the Good Sam Club, the world's largest membership organization of recreational vehicle owners.

Some of the more popular travel centers are also included in *Rest Areas & Welcome Centers*. Travel centers are usually large establishments that provide a host of services. It used to be that these areas catered to truck drivers. Now they offer services not only to truckers but to all travelers. Most have fast food restaurants or home-style restaurants. They offer gasoline and diesel fuel, LP gas, and dump stations for RVers. Travelers can also shop for convenience items, soft drinks, and snacks. Some also allow overnight parking at no charge. Travel centers included in this book are AmBest, Flying J, Love's, Petro, Pilot, and Travel Centers of America.

Another service of interest to RVers is the location of dump stations for emptying holding tanks. The RV Dump Station Locator in the back of the book indicates where dump stations are located along Interstate highways. Most are located in travel centers like Flying J. Others are in rest areas or welcome centers, city and county parks, gas stations, and other places.

## About this Book

*Rest Areas and Welcome Centers* contains a lot of useful information. Knowing how to use this book will enhance the value of the information it contains.

The book is arranged alphabetically by state with Interstate highways listed from lowest to highest. Each Interstate is introduced with a brief description, including its length and general direction of travel within the state. That is followed by a chart indicating the services available along the route (*see Figure 1*).

It is important to note that your direction of travel determines how you read the chart. If you are traveling south or west, read down the chart. If you are traveling north or east, read up the chart. As a reminder of this, you'll find directional arrows to the left of each chart.

## Mile Markers and Exit Numbers

Having a basic understanding of mile markers and exit numbers will make it easier to use this book.

### Mile Markers
Mile markers, or mileposts as they are also known, are the little vertical green signs on the edge of highways. They are placed at one-mile intervals. Mile marker numbering begins at the most southerly or westerly point in a state. For example, if you enter Colorado from New Mexico, mile markers will increase as you travel north through Colorado. Likewise if you were to enter Colorado from Utah, mile markers would increase as you traveled east through Colorado. California is the only state that does not use mile markers. Instead they use a Post Mile system with numbering beginning and ending at county lines.

# Exit Numbers

Interstate exit numbers are determined by one of two methods. The first, and most widely used, is based on the mile marker system. Using this method, the first exit number on an Interstate as you travel north or east is determined by its distance from the state line. For example, if an exit is located between mile markers 4 and 5, it is numbered as Exit #4. The next exit, if located at mile marker 8.7, would be numbered as Exit #8. Thus you would know that you must travel another 4 miles to reach the next exit. Using this method of exit numbering helps to determine the location and distance to a desired exit.

The second method of numbering Interstate exits is the consecutive numbering system, which means Interstate exit numbers begin at the most southerly or westerly point and increase consecutively as you travel north or east. Using this method, the first exit

## Figure 1

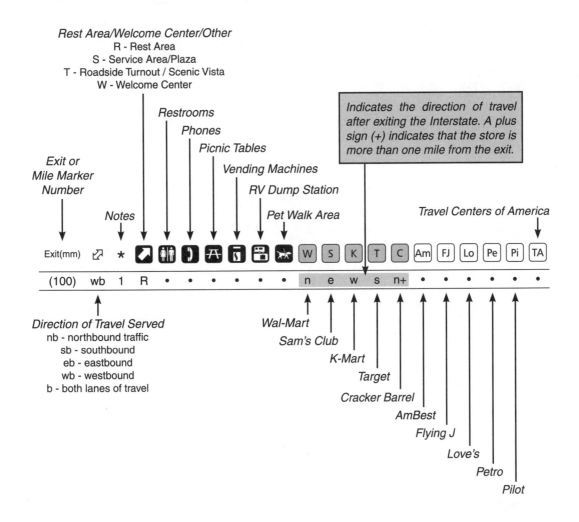

on an Interstate as you travel north or east is Exit #1. Each exit thereafter increases consecutively as #2, #3, #4, and so on. Few states use this method of numbering Interstate exits.

As previously mentioned, California does not use mile markers nor does it indicate exits with a number. This is changing, however. In January of 2002, California began erecting signs displaying exit numbers based on the mile marker system. Completion of this project is expected in 2008. The exit numbers and mile marker numbers used in this book for California are based on the new proposed numbers that California has assigned. Notes at the bottom of each chart will help you identify Interstate exits in California until the re-numbering project is completed.

## Notes

It is our hope that you find this book an invaluable aid as you travel along America's Interstate highways. If you discover errors or additions that need to be made to this book, please let us know. We always welcome comments or suggestions for improvement.

# Hotel / Motel Toll-Free Numbers

Below is a convenient list of toll-free telephone numbers and web sites for selected hotels and motels across the United States.

| Name | Phone | Web Site |
|---|---|---|
| Adams Mark Hotels & Resorts | 800-444-2326 | www.adamsmark.com |
| AmericInn | 800-634-3444 | www.americinn.com |
| AmeriHost Inn | 800-434-5800 | www.amerihostinn.com |
| Baymont Inn & Suites | 866-999-1111 | www.baymontinn.com |
| Best Inn, Suites & Hotels | 800-237-8466 | www.bestinn.com |
| Best Western Hotels | 800-780-7234 | www.bestwestern.com |
| Budget Host | 800-283-4678 | www.budgethost.com |
| Choice Hotels International | 877-424-6423 | www.choicehotels.com |
| Clarion Inn | 877-424-6423 | www.choicehotels.com |
| Comfort Inn & Suites | 877-424-6423 | www.choicehotels.com |
| Country Hearth Inn | 800-848-5767 | www.countryhearth.com |
| Country Inn & Suites | 888-201-1746 | www.countryinns.com |
| Courtyard by Marriott | 888-236-2427 | www.marriott.com |
| Crowne Plaza Hotels & Resorts | 800-227-6963 | www.crowneplaza.com |
| Days Inn | 800-329-7466 | www.daysinn.com |
| DoubleTree Hotel, Suites & Resorts | 800-222-8733 | www.doubletreehotels.com |
| Drury Inn | 800-378-7946 | www.druryhotels.com |
| Econo Lodge | 877-424-6423 | www.choicehotels.com |
| Embassy Suites | 800-362-2779 | www.embassysuites.com |
| Exel Inns | 800-367-3935 | www.exelinns.com |
| Extended StayAmerica | 800-804-3724 | www.extstay.com |
| Fairfield Inn by Marriott | 888-236-2427 | www.marriott.com |
| Fairmont Hotels & Resorts | 800-257-7544 | www.fairmont.com |
| Flag Inn | 877-424-6423 | www.choicehotels.com |
| GuestHouse Inn & Suites | 800-214-8378 | www.guesthouseintl.com |
| Hampton Inn & Suites | 800-426-7866 | www.hamptoninn.com |
| Hawthorne Suites | 800-527-1133 | www.hawthorn.com |
| Hilton Hotels | 800-445-8667 | www.hilton.com |
| Holiday Inn | 800-465-4329 | www.holiday-inn.com |
| Holiday Inn Express | 800-465-4329 | www.hiexpress.com |
| Homewood Suites | 800-445-8667 | www.homewood-suites.com |
| Howard Johnson | 800-446-4656 | www.hojo.com |
| Hyatt Hotels & Resorts | 888-591-1234 | www.hyatt.com |

| Name | Phone | Web Site |
|---|---|---|
| Inter-Continental Hotels & Resorts | 888-303-1758 | www.interconti.com |
| Jameson Inn | 800-526-3766 | www.jamesoninns.com |
| Key West Inn & Suites | 866-253-9937 | www.keywestinn.net |
| LaQuinta Inn | 800-642-4241 | www.laquinta.com |
| Lees Inn & Suites | 800-733-5337 | www.leesinn.com |
| MainStay Suites | 800-424-6423 | www.choicehotels.com |
| Marriott Hotels & Resorts | 888-236-2427 | www.marriott.com |
| Microtel Inn & Suites | 888-771-7171 | www.microtelinn.com |
| Motel 6 | 800-466-8356 | www.motel6.com |
| Omni Hotels | 800-843-6664 | www.omnihotels.com |
| Park Inn Hotels | 888-201-1801 | www.parkhtls.com |
| Passport Inn | 800-251-1962 | www.bookroomsnow.com |
| Preferred Hotels & Resorts | 800-323-7500 | www.preferredhotels.com |
| Quality Inn, Hotels & Suites | 877-424-6423 | www.choicehotels.com |
| Radisson Hotels | 888-201-1718 | www.radisson.com |
| Ramada Inn | 800-272-6232 | www.ramada.com |
| Red Carpet Inn | 800-251-1962 | www.bookroomsnow.com |
| Red Lion Hotel & Inns | 800-733-5466 | www.redlion.com |
| Red Roof Inn | 800-733-7663 | www.redroof.com |
| Renaissance Hotel | 888-236-2427 | www.marriott.com |
| Residence Inn by Marriott | 888-236-2427 | www.marriott.com |
| Ritz-Carlton Hotel | 800-241-3333 | www.ritzcarlton.com |
| Rodeway Inn | 877-424-6423 | www.choicehotels.com |
| Scottish Inns | 800-251-1962 | www.bookroomsnow.com |
| Sheraton Hotels & Resorts | 888-625-5144 | www.sheraton.com |
| Shilo Inn | 800-222-2244 | www.shiloinns.com |
| Shoney's Inn | 800-552-4667 | www.shoneysinn.com |
| Signature Inn | 800-822-5252 | www.signature-inns.com |
| Sleep Inn | 877-424-6423 | www.choicehotels.com |
| Staybridge Suites | 800-238-8000 | www.staybridge.com |
| Super 8 Motel | 800-800-8000 | www.super8.com |
| Travelodge | 800-578-7878 | www.travelodge.com |
| Vagabond Inn | 800-522-1555 | www.vagabondinns.com |
| Wellesley Inn | 877-774-6345 | www.wellesleyinnandsuites.com |
| West Coast Hotels | 800-325-4000 | www.westcoasthotels.com |
| Westin Hotels & Resorts | 888-625-5144 | www.westin.com |
| Westmark Hotel | 800-544-0970 | www.westmarkhotels.com |
| Wingate Inn | 800-228-1000 | www.wingateinns.com |
| Wyndham Hotels & Resorts | 877-999-3223 | www.wyndham.com |

# State Tourism Offices

| State | Phone | Web Site |
|---|---|---|
| Alabama | 800-Alabama | www.touralabama.org |
| Alaska | 800-478-1255 | www.travelalaska.com |
| Arizona | 866-275-5816 | www.arizonaguide.com |
| Arkansas | 800-Natural | www.arkansas.com |
| California | 800-GoCalif | www.visitcalifornia.com |
| Colorado | 800-Colorado | www.colorado.com |
| Connecticut | 800-CTBound | www.ctbound.org |
| Delaware | 866-2-VisitDE | www.visitdelaware.com |
| Florida | 888-735-2872 | www.visitflorida.com |
| Georgia | 800-VisitGA | www.georgia.org |
| Hawaii | 808-531-0244 | www.gohawaii.com |
| Idaho | 800-VisitID | www.visitid.org |
| Illinois | 800-2Connect | www.enjoyillinois.com |
| Indiana | 888-Enjoy-IN | www.enjoyindiana.com |
| Iowa | 888-472-6035 | www.traveliowa.com |
| Kansas | 800-2Kansas | www.travelks.com |
| Kentucky | 800-225-8747 | www.kentuckytourism.com |
| Louisiana | 800-677-4082 | www.louisianatravel.com |
| Maine | 888-624-6345 | www.visitmaine.com |
| Maryland | 866-MDWelcome | www.mdisfun.org |
| Massachusetts | 800-227-Mass | www.massvacation.com |
| Michigan | 800-644-2489 | www.michigan.org |
| Minnesota | 888-Tourism | www.exploreminnesota.com |
| Mississippi | 866-See-Miss | www.visitmississippi.org |
| Missouri | 800-519-2100 | www.visitmo.com |
| Montana | 800-VisitMT | www.visitmt.com |
| Nebraska | 877-Nebraska | www.visitnebraska.org |
| Nevada | 800-Nevada8 | www.travelnevada.com |
| New Hampshire | 800-Fun-In-NH | www.visitnh.gov |
| New Jersey | 800-NisitNJ | www.visitnj.org |
| New Mexico | 800-733-6396 | www.newmexico.org |
| New York | 800-Call-NYS | www.iloveny.com |
| North Carolina | 800-VisitNC | www.visitnc.com |
| North Dakota | 800-435-5663 | www.ndtourism.com |
| Ohio | 800-Buckeye | www.discoverohio.com |
| Oklahoma | 800-652-6552 | www.travelok.com |
| Oregon | 800-547-7842 | www.traveloregon.com |

| State | Phone | Web Site |
|---|---|---|
| Pennsylvania | 800-VisitPA | www.visitpa.com |
| Rhode Island | 800-556-2484 | www.visitrhodeisland.com |
| South Carolina | 803-734-1700 | www.discoversouthcarolina.com |
| South Dakota | 800-S-Dakota | www.travelsd.com |
| Tennessee | 615-741-2159 | www.tnvacation.com |
| Texas | 800-452-9292 | www.traveltex.com |
| Utah | 800-Utah-Fun | www.utah.com |
| Vermont | 800-Vermont | www.1-800-vermont.com |
| Virginia | 800-VisitVA | www.virginia.org |
| Washington | 800-544-1800 | www.experiencewashington.com |
| West Virginia | 800-Call-WVA | www.wvtourism.com |
| Wisconsin | 800-432-8747 | www.travelwisconsin.com |
| Wyoming | 800-255-5996 | www.wyomingtourism.org |

# Alabama

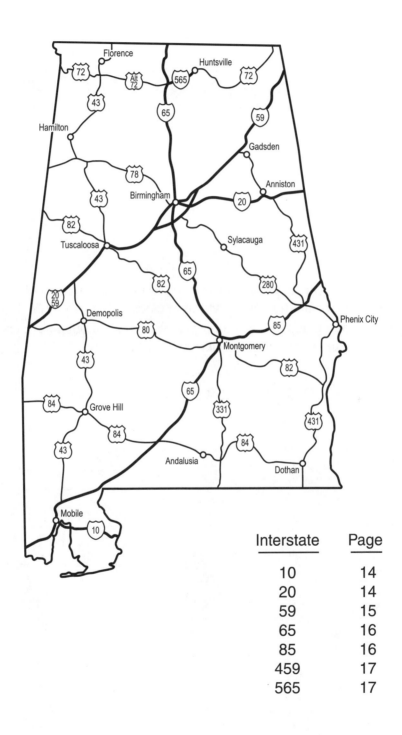

| Interstate | Page |
|:---:|:---:|
| 10 | 14 |
| 20 | 14 |
| 59 | 15 |
| 65 | 16 |
| 85 | 16 |
| 459 | 17 |
| 565 | 17 |

Interstate 10 in Alabama runs east to west for 67 miles from the Florida state line to the Mississippi state line. Eastbound travelers should read up the chart. Westbound travelers read down the chart.

E ↕ W

| Exit(mm) | ↗ | ★ | 🔲 | 🚻 | ☎ | ⛱ | ⛽ | 🏪 | 🐾 | W | S | K | T | C | Am | FJ | Lo | Pe | Pi | TA |
|---|---|---|---|---|---|---|---|---|---|---|---|---|---|---|---|---|---|---|---|---|
| (66) | wb | | W | • | • | • | • | • | • | | | | | | | | | | | |
| 53 | b | | | | | | | | | | | | | | | | • | | | |
| 44 | b | | | | | | | | | | | | | | | | | • | | |
| 35 | b | | | | | | | | | s+ | | | | | | | | | | |
| 17 | b | | | | | | | | | n | | | | | | | | | | |
| 15b | b | | | | | | | | | | n | | | | | | | | | |
| 13 | b | | | | | | | | | | | | | | | | | | • | |
| 4 | b | | | | | | | | | | | | | | | | | | | • |
| (1) | eb | | W | • | • | • | • | • | • | | | | | | | | | | | |

Interstate 20 in Alabama runs east to west for approximately 215 miles from the Georgia state line to the Mississippi state line. A portion of the highway from Birmingham to Mississippi is also I-59. Eastbound travelers should read up the chart. Westbound travelers read down the chart.

E ↕ W     E ↕ W

| Exit(mm) | ↗ | ★ | 🔲 | 🚻 | ☎ | ⛱ | ⛽ | 🏪 | 🐾 | W | S | K | T | C | Am | FJ | Lo | Pe | Pi | TA |
|---|---|---|---|---|---|---|---|---|---|---|---|---|---|---|---|---|---|---|---|---|
| (213) | wb | | W | • | • | • | • | • | • | | | | | | | | | | | |
| 188 | b | | | | | | | | | | | | n | | | | | | | |
| 185 | b | | | | | | | | | s | | | | | | | | | | |
| 158b | wb | | | | | | | | | s | | | | | | | | | | |
| 158 | eb | | | | | | | | | s | | | | | | | | | | |
| 144 | b | | | | | | | | | s | | | n | | | | | | | |
| 133 | b | | | | | | | | | s | s | | | | | | | | | |
| 132 | wb | | | | | | | | | | s | | | | | | | | | |
| 132b | eb | | | | | | | | | | s | | | | | | | | | |
| 123 | b | | | | | | | | | | | | | | | | | | • | |
| 118 | b | 1 | | | | | | | | s+ | | | | | | | | | | |
| 108 | b | | | | | | | | | s | | | n | | | | | | | |
| 104 | b | | | | | | | | | | | | | | | | • | | | |
| 100 | b | | | | | | | | | | | | | | | | | • | | |
| (85) | b | | R | • | • | • | • | • | • | | | | | | | | | | | |
| 77 | | | | | | | | | | | | | | | | | | | | • |
| 76 | | | | | | | | | | | | | n | | | | | | • | |
| 73 | | | | | | | | | | s | s | | | | | | | | | |

| | Exit(mm) | ↗ | ★ | ⬈ | 🚻 | ☎ | ⛱ | ⛽ | 🏪 | 🐾 | W | S | K | T | C | Am | FJ | Lo | Pe | Pi | TA |
|---|---|---|---|---|---|---|---|---|---|---|---|---|---|---|---|---|---|---|---|---|---|
| E ↕ | 71a | | | | | | | | | | | | s | | | | | | | | |
| | (39) | wb | | R | • | • | • | • | • | • | | | | | | | | | | | |
| ↕ W | (38) | eb | | R | • | • | • | • | • | • | | | | | | | | | | | |
| | (.5) | eb | | W | • | • | • | • | • | • | | | | | | | | | | | |

1) Wal-Mart is on Aaron Aronov Dr.

---

**59** Interstate 59 in Alabama runs north to south for 242 miles from the Georgia state line to the Mississippi state line. A portion of the highway from Birmingham to Mississippi is also I-20. Northbound travelers should read up the chart. Southbound travelers read down the chart.

| | Exit(mm) | ↗ | ★ | ⬈ | 🚻 | ☎ | ⛱ | ⛽ | 🏪 | 🐾 | W | S | K | T | C | Am | FJ | Lo | Pe | Pi | TA |
|---|---|---|---|---|---|---|---|---|---|---|---|---|---|---|---|---|---|---|---|---|---|
| | (241) | sb | | W | • | • | • | • | • | • | | | | | | | | | | | |
| | 218 | b | | | | | | | | | w | | w | | w | | | | | | |
| | 181 | b | | | | | | | | | | | | | w | | | | | | |
| N ↕ | (168) | sb | | R | • | • | • | • | • | • | | | | | | | | | | | |
| | (165) | nb | | R | • | • | • | • | • | • | | | | | | | | | | | |
| ↕ S | 141 | b | | | | | | | | | w | w | | | e | | | | | | |
| | 134 | b | | | | | | | | | w | | | | | | | | | | |
| | 123 | b | | | | | | | | | | | | | | | | | | • | |
| | 118 | b | 1 | | | | | | | | e+ | | | | | | | | | | |
| | 108 | b | | | | | | | | | e | | | | w | | | | | | |
| | 104 | b | | | | | | | | | | | | | | | | • | | | |
| | 100 | b | | | | | | | | | | | | | | | | | • | | |
| N | (85) | b | | R | • | • | • | • | • | • | | | | | | | | | | | |
| ↕ | 77 | b | | | | | | | | | | | | | | | | | | | • |
| ↕ | 76 | b | | | | | | | | | | | | w | | | | | | • | |
| S | 73 | b | | | | | | | | | e | e | | | | | | | | | |
| | 71a | b | | | | | | | | | | | e | | | | | | | | |
| | (39) | sb | | R | • | • | • | • | • | • | | | | | | | | | | | |
| | (38) | nb | | R | • | • | • | • | • | • | | | | | | | | | | | |
| | (.5) | nb | | W | • | • | • | • | • | • | | | | | | | | | | | |

1) Wal-Mart is on Aaron Aronov Dr.

Interstate 65 in Alabama runs north to south for 367 miles from the Tennessee state line to Interstate 10. Northbound travelers should read up the chart. Southbound travelers read down the chart.

| Exit(mm) | ↗ | ★ | 🅿 | 🚻 | ☎ | 🍴 | ⛽ | 🏪 | 🐾 | W | S | K | T | C | Am | FJ | Lo | Pe | Pi | TA |
|---|---|---|---|---|---|---|---|---|---|---|---|---|---|---|---|---|---|---|---|---|
| (364) sb | | W | • | • | • | • | • | • | • | | | | | | | | | | | |
| 351 b | | | | | | | | | | w | | | | e | | | | | | |
| 334 b | | | | | | | | | | | | | | | | | | | • | |
| 310 b | | | | | | | | | | | | | | e | | | | | | |
| (302) b | | R | • | • | • | • | • | • | • | | | | | | | | | | | |
| 271 b | | | | | | | | | | e | | | | w | | | | | | |
| 264 b | | | | | | | | | | | | | | | | • | | | | |
| 256b sb | | | | | | | | | | | | e | | | | | | | | |
| 256 nb | | | | | | | | | | | | e | | | | | | | | |
| 255 b | | | | | | | | | | w | w | | | | | | | | | |
| 246 b | | | | | | | | | | | | | | w | | | | | | |
| 231 b | | | | | | | | | | e | | | | | | | | | | |
| (213) b | | R | • | • | • | • | • | • | • | | | | | | | | | | | |
| 205 b | | | | | | | | | | w+ | | | | | | | | | | |
| 181 b | | | | | | | | | | | | | | w | | | | | | |
| 179 b | | | | | | | | | | w+ | | | | | | | | | | |
| 168 b | | | | | | | | | | | | | | | | | | | | • |
| (133) b | | R | • | • | • | • | • | • | • | | | | | | | | | | | |
| 130 b | | | | | | | | | | w | | | | w | | | | | | |
| (89) sb | | R | • | • | • | • | • | • | • | | | | | | | | | | | |
| (85) nb | | R | • | • | • | • | • | • | • | | | | | | | | | | | |
| 19 b | | | | | | | | | | | | | | | | | | | • | |
| 13 b | | | | | | | | | | e | | | | | | | | | | |
| 4 b | | | | | | | | | | e | | | | e | | | | | | |
| 3 b | | | | | | | | | | | w | e | | | | | | | | |

Interstate 85 in Alabama runs north to south for 80 miles from the Georgia state line to I-65 in Montgomery. Northbound travelers should read up the chart. Southbound travelers read down the chart.

| Exit(mm) | ↗ | ★ | 🅿 | 🚻 | ☎ | 🍴 | ⛽ | 🏪 | 🐾 | W | S | K | T | C | Am | FJ | Lo | Pe | Pi | TA |
|---|---|---|---|---|---|---|---|---|---|---|---|---|---|---|---|---|---|---|---|---|
| 79 b | | | | | | | | | | e | | | | | | | | | | |
| (78) sb | | W | • | • | • | • | • | • | • | | | | | | | | | | | |
| 70 b | | | | | | | | | | | | | | | | | • | | | |
| 62 b | | | | | | | | | | | | | | w | | | | | | |

| Exit(mm) | ↗ | ★ | ⬈ | 👫 | 🚻 | ⛽ | ⛺ | 🅿 | 🐾 | W | S | K | T | C | Am | FJ | Lo | Pe | Pi | TA |
|---|---|---|---|---|---|---|---|---|---|---|---|---|---|---|---|---|---|---|---|---|
| (44) | b | R | • | • | • | • | • | • |  |  |  |  |  |  |  |  |  |  |  |  |
| 22 | b |  |  |  |  |  |  |  |  |  |  |  |  |  |  |  |  |  | • |  |
| 6 | b |  |  |  |  |  |  |  |  | e | w |  |  | e |  |  |  |  |  |  |

Interstate 459 is a 33-mile route in Birmingham. It begins on I-59 at Exit 106 and ends on I-59 at Exit 137. Northbound travelers should read up the chart. Southbound travelers read down the chart.

| Exit(mm) | ↗ | ★ | ⬈ | 👫 | 🚻 | ⛽ | ⛺ | 🅿 | 🐾 | W | S | K | T | C | Am | FJ | Lo | Pe | Pi | TA |
|---|---|---|---|---|---|---|---|---|---|---|---|---|---|---|---|---|---|---|---|---|
| 32 | b |  |  |  |  |  |  |  |  |  |  |  | e |  |  |  |  |  |  |  |
| 13 | b |  |  |  |  |  |  |  |  | s | s |  |  |  |  |  |  |  |  |  |

Interstate 565 in Alabama is a 21-mile route between Decatur and Huntsville. Northbound travelers should read up the chart. Southbound travelers read down the chart.

| Exit(mm) | ↗ | ★ | ⬈ | 👫 | 🚻 | ⛽ | ⛺ | 🅿 | 🐾 | W | S | K | T | C | Am | FJ | Lo | Pe | Pi | TA |
|---|---|---|---|---|---|---|---|---|---|---|---|---|---|---|---|---|---|---|---|---|
| 19a | b |  |  |  |  |  |  |  |  | s |  |  |  |  |  |  |  |  |  |  |
| 8 | b |  |  |  |  |  |  |  |  |  | s |  |  |  |  |  |  |  |  |  |

# Arizona

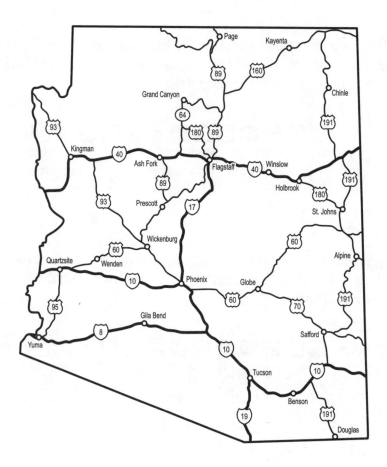

| Interstate | Page |
|:----------:|:----:|
| 8 | 19 |
| 10 | 19 |
| 15 | 20 |
| 17 | 20 |
| 19 | 21 |
| 40 | 21 |

Interstate 8 in Arizona runs east to west for about 178 miles from Interstate 10 to the California state line. Eastbound travelers should read up the chart. Westbound travelers read down the chart.

| Exit(mm) | ⤴ | ★ | ◣ | 🚻 | ☎ | ⛺ | ⛽ | ♻ | 🐾 | W | S | K | T | C | Am | FJ | Lo | Pe | Pi | TA |
|---|---|---|---|---|---|---|---|---|---|---|---|---|---|---|---|---|---|---|---|---|
| (150) wb | T | | | | • | | | | | | | | | | | | | | | |
| (149) eb | T | | | | • | | | | | | | | | | | | | | | |
| 115 b | | | | | | | | | | | | | | | | | | • | | |
| (85) wb | R | | | • | • | • | • | | • | | | | | | | | | | | |
| (84) eb | R | | | • | • | • | • | | • | | | | | | | | | | | |
| (56) b | R | | | • | • | • | • | | • | | | | | | | | | | | |
| (22) b | T | | | | | | | | | | | | | | | | | | | |
| 2 b | | | | | | | | | | n | n | | s | n | | | | | | |

E ↕ W

Interstate 10 in Arizona runs east to west for about 391 miles from the New Mexico state line to the California state line. Eastbound travelers should read up the chart. Westbound travelers read down the chart.

| Exit(mm) | ⤴ | ★ | ◣ | 🚻 | ☎ | ⛺ | ⛽ | ♻ | 🐾 | W | S | K | T | C | Am | FJ | Lo | Pe | Pi | TA |
|---|---|---|---|---|---|---|---|---|---|---|---|---|---|---|---|---|---|---|---|---|
| (389) b | R | | | • | • | • | • | | • | | | | | | | | | | | |
| 340 b | | | | | | | | | | | | | | | | | | | • | |
| (320) b | R | | | • | • | • | • | | • | | | | | | | | | | | |
| 248 b | | | | | | | | | | | | | n | | | | | | | |
| 246 b | | | | | | | | | | | s | | s | | | | | | | |
| 208 b | | | | | | | | | | | | | | | | | • | | • | |
| 203 b | | | | | | | | | | | | | | | | | | | | • |
| 200 b | | | | | | | | | | | | | | | | | • | • | | |
| 194 b | | | | | | | | | | | s+ | | s | | | | | | | |
| (183) wb | R | | | • | • | • | • | | • | | | | | | | | | | | |
| (181) eb | R | | | • | • | • | • | | • | | | | | | | | | | | |
| 160 b | | | | | | | | | | | | | s | | | | | | | |
| 159 b | | | | | | | | | | | | n | s | | | | | | | |
| 157 b | | | | | | | | | | | n | | | | | | | | | |
| 146 b | | | | | | | | | | | | s | | | | | | | | |
| 137 b | | | | | | | | | | | | | | | | | • | | | |
| 136 b | | | | | | | | | | | n | | | | | | | | | |
| 135 b | | | | | | | | | | | | n | | | | | | | | |
| 133 b | | | | | | | | | | | | | | | | | | | • | |
| 129 b | | | | | | | | | | | n | | | | | | | | | |

E ↕ W

| Exit(mm) | ⛽ | ★ | ⬈ | 🚻 | ♿ | ⛱ | ⛽ | 🏪 | 🐾 | W | S | K | T | C | Am | FJ | Lo | Pe | Pi | TA |
|---|---|---|---|---|---|---|---|---|---|---|---|---|---|---|---|---|---|---|---|---|
| 128 | b | | | | | | | | | | | | n | n | | | | | | |
| 114 | b | | | | | | | | | | | | | | | | | | • | |
| 103 | b | | | | | | | | | | | | | | | | | | | • |
| (86) | b | | R | • | • | • | • | | • | | | | | | | | | | | |
| (52) | b | | R | • | • | • | • | | • | | | | | | | | | | | |
| 17 | b | | | | | | | | | | | | | | | | | • | | • | |
| (4) | b | | R | • | • | • | • | | • | | | | | | | | | | | |
| 1 | b | | | | | | | | | | | | | | | • | | | | | |

*(Left margin direction indicator: E ↕ W)*

Interstate 15 in Arizona runs north to south for about 29 miles from the Utah state line to the Nevada state line. Northbound travelers should read up the chart. Southbound travelers read down the chart.

| Exit(mm) | ⛽ | ★ | ⬈ | 🚻 | ♿ | ⛱ | ⛽ | 🏪 | 🐾 | W | S | K | T | C | Am | FJ | Lo | Pe | Pi | TA |
|---|---|---|---|---|---|---|---|---|---|---|---|---|---|---|---|---|---|---|---|---|
| (21) | sb | 1 | T | | | | | | | | | | | | | | | | | |
| (16) | b | 1 | T | | | | | | | | | | | | | | | | | |
| (15) | nb | 1 | T | | | | | | | | | | | | | | | | | |
| (14) | nb | 1 | T | | | | | | | | | | | | | | | | | |
| (10) | nb | 1 | T | | | | | | | | | | | | | | | | | |

*(Left margin direction indicator: N ↕ S)*

1) Truck parking.

Interstate 17 in Arizona runs north to south for about 147 miles from I-40 in Flagstaff to I-10 in Phoenix. Northbound travelers should read up the chart. Southbound travelers read down the chart.

| Exit(mm) | ⛽ | ★ | ⬈ | 🚻 | ♿ | ⛱ | ⛽ | 🏪 | 🐾 | W | S | K | T | C | Am | FJ | Lo | Pe | Pi | TA |
|---|---|---|---|---|---|---|---|---|---|---|---|---|---|---|---|---|---|---|---|---|
| (312) | sb | 1 | T | | | | | | | | | | | | | | | | | |
| (297) | b | | R | • | • | • | • | | • | | | | | | | | | | | |
| (252) | b | 1 | R | • | • | • | • | | | | | | | | | | | | | |
| 217b | b | | | | | | | | | | | | | w | | | | | | |
| 214 | b | | | | | | | | | | | | w | | | | | | | |
| 212 | b | | | | | | | | | | | w | | | | | | | | |
| 206 | b | | | | | | | | | | | | w | | | | | | | |

*(Left margin direction indicator: N ↕ S)*

1) Scenic Vista.

Interstate 19 runs north to south for approximately 64 miles (103 kilometers) from Interstate 10 in Tucson to the Mexico border. Instead of the mile marker system, Interstate 19 uses kilometers. Northbound travelers should read up the chart. Southbound travelers read down the chart.

| Exit(mm) | ↗ | ★ | 🢅 | 🚻 | ☎ | ⛱ | ⛽ | 🚮 | 🐾 | W | S | K | T | C | Am | FJ | Lo | Pe | Pi | TA |
|---|---|---|---|---|---|---|---|---|---|---|---|---|---|---|---|---|---|---|---|---|
| 98 | b | | | | | | | | | | | | w | | | | | | | |
| 95b | sb | | | | | | | | | w | | | | | | | | | | |
| 95 | nb | | | | | | | | | w | | | | | | | | | | |
| 69 | b | | | | | | | | | e | | | | | | | | | | |
| (54 km) | b | | R | • | • | • | • | | • | | | | | | | | | | | |
| 12 | b | | | | | | | | | | | | | | | | | | • | |
| 4 | b | | | | | | | | | e | | e | | | | | | | | |

N ↕ S

Interstate 40 in Arizona runs east to west for 360 miles from the New Mexico state line to the California state line. Eastbound travelers should read up the chart. Westbound travelers read down the chart.

| Exit(mm) | ↗ | ★ | 🢅 | 🚻 | ☎ | ⛱ | ⛽ | 🚮 | 🐾 | W | S | K | T | C | Am | FJ | Lo | Pe | Pi | TA |
|---|---|---|---|---|---|---|---|---|---|---|---|---|---|---|---|---|---|---|---|---|
| 359 | b | | W | • | • | • | • | | • | | | | | | | | | | | |
| (316) | b | | T | | | • | | | | | | | | | | | | | | |
| 283 | b | | | | | | | | | | | | | | | | • | | | |
| 277 | b | | | | | | | | | | | | | | | | | • | | |
| 255 | b | | | | | | | | | | | | | | | | • | | | |
| 253 | b | | | | | | | | | n | | | | | | | | | | |
| (235) | b | 1 | R | • | • | • | • | | • | | | | | | | | | | | |
| 198 | b | | | | | | | | | | n | | n | | | | | | | |
| 195b | b | | | | | | | | | n | | n | n | | | | | | | |
| (183) | wb | | R | • | • | • | • | | • | | | | | | | | | | | |
| (182) | eb | | R | • | • | • | • | | • | | | | | | | | | | | |
| (155) | wb | | T | | | | | | | | | | | | | | | | | |
| 66 | b | | | | | | | | | | | | | | | | | • | | |
| 59 | b | | | | | | | | | | | | | | | | • | | | |
| 53 | b | | | | | | | | | | | n | | | • | | | | | |
| 51 | b | | | | | | | | | n | | | n | | | | | | | |
| 48 | b | | | | | | | | | | | | | | | | | | | • |
| (23) | b | | R | • | • | • | • | | • | | | | | | | | | | | |
| 9 | b | | | | | | | | | | | | | | | | | | • | |

E ↕ W

1) Vending westbound only.

# Arkansas

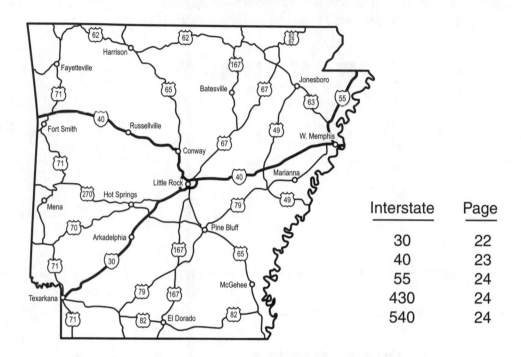

| Interstate | Page |
|---|---|
| 30 | 22 |
| 40 | 23 |
| 55 | 24 |
| 430 | 24 |
| 540 | 24 |

Interstate 30 in Arkansas runs east to west from Interstate 40 in North Little Rock to the Texas state line. The highway is approximately 143 miles long. Eastbound travelers should read up the chart. Westbound travelers read down the chart.

| Exit(mm) | ⤴ | ★ | 🧭 | 🚻 | 🍴 | 🏕 | ⛽ | 🏪 | 🎇 | W | S | K | T | C | Am | FJ | Lo | Pe | Pi | TA |
|---|---|---|---|---|---|---|---|---|---|---|---|---|---|---|---|---|---|---|---|---|
| 131 | b | | | | | | | | | | s | | | | | | | | | |
| 123 | b | | | | | | | | | | n | | | | | | | | | |
| 121 | b | | | | | | | | | | | | | | | | | | • | |
| 118 | b | | | | | | | | | | s | | | | | | | | | |
| 98a | b | | | | | | | | | | s | | | | | | | | | |
| (93) | b | R | • | • | • | • | | • | | | | | | | | | | | | |
| 78 | b | | | | | | | | | | | | n | | | | | | | |
| 73 | b | | | | | | | | | | n | | | | | | | | | |
| (56) | b | R | • | | • | • | | • | | | | | | | | | | | | |
| 46 | b | | | | | | | | | | | | | | | | • | | | |
| 44 | b | | | | | | | | | | | | | | | | | | | • |
| 30 | b | | | | | | | | | | n | | | | | | | | | |
| 7 | b | | | | | | | | | | | | | | | | | • | | |
| (1) | eb | W | • | • | • | • | | • | | | | | | | | | | | | |

E
↕
W

Interstate 40 in Arkansas is about 285 miles long. It runs east to west from the Tennessee state line to the Oklahoma state line. Eastbound travelers should read up the chart. Westbound travelers read down the chart.

| Exit(mm) | ↗ | ★ | ◆ | 🚻 | ☎ | 🍽 | ⛽ | 🏠 | 🐾 | W | S | K | T | C | Am | FJ | Lo | Pe | Pi | TA |
|---|---|---|---|---|---|---|---|---|---|---|---|---|---|---|---|---|---|---|---|---|
| 280 | b | | | | | | | | | | | | | | | | • | • | • | |
| 278 | b | 1 | | | | | | | | | s | | s | | | | | | | |
| 276 | eb | | | | | | | | | | s | | | | | | | | | |
| (274) | wb | | W | • | • | • | | | • | | | | | | | | | | | |
| 260 | b | | | | | | | | | | | | | | | | | | | • |
| (243) | wb | | R | • | • | • | • | | • | | | | | | | | | | | |
| 241a | b | | | | | | | | | | s | | | | | | | | | |
| (235) | eb | | R | • | • | • | • | | • | | | | | | | | | | | |
| 233 | b | | | | | | | | | | | | | | | | | • | | |
| 216 | b | | | | | | | | | | s | | | | | | | | | |
| (199) | b | | R | • | | • | • | | | | | | | | | | | | | |
| 161 | b | | | | | | | | | | | | | | | | | • | • | • |
| 156 | b | | | | | | | | | | | | n | | | | | | | |
| 155 | b | 2 | | | | | | | | | | n | | | | | | | | |
| 152 | b | | | | | | | | | n | | | | | | | | | | |
| 127 | b | | | | | | | | | | | | | n | | | | | | |
| 125 | b | | | | | | | | | | s | | n | | | | | | | |
| 108 | b | | | | | | | | | | s | | | | | | | | | |
| 107 | b | | | | | | | | | | | | | | | | | • | | |
| 84 | b | | | | | | | | | | s | s | | | • | | | • | | |
| 81 | b | | | | | | | | | | | | s | | | | | | | |
| (72) | wb | | R | • | • | • | • | | • | | | | | | | | | | | |
| (70) | wb | 3 | T | | | | | | | | | | | | | | | | | |
| (68) | eb | | R | • | • | • | • | | • | | | | | | | | | | | |
| 58 | b | | | | | | | | | | s | | | | | | | | | |
| 37 | b | | | | | | | | | | | | | | | | | • | | |
| (36) | b | | R | • | • | • | | | • | | | | | | | | | | | |
| 13 | b | | | | | | | | | | s | | n | | | | | | | |
| 5 | b | | | | | | | | | | n | | | | | | | | | |
| (2) | eb | | W | • | • | • | • | | • | | | | | | | | | | | |

*1) Wal-Mart is on W Service Rd. 2) One mile north of exit off US 167. 3) Scenic Vista.*

Interstate 55 in Arkansas runs north to south for 72 miles from the Missouri state line to the Tennessee state line. A small stretch of I-55 in West Memphis is also I-40. Northbound travelers should read up the chart. Southbound travelers read down the chart.

| Exit(mm) | ↗ | ★ | 🔀 | 🚻 | ♿ | ⛽ | ☎ | 🏪 | 🐾 | W | S | K | T | C | Am | FJ | Lo | Pe | Pi | TA |
|---|---|---|---|---|---|---|---|---|---|---|---|---|---|---|---|---|---|---|---|---|
| (68) sb | W | | | • | | • | | • | | | | | | | | | | | | |
| 67 b | | | | | | | | | | e | | | | | | | | | | |
| (45) nb | R | | • | | | • | | | • | | | | | | | | | | | |
| (35) sb | R | | • | | • | | • | | | • | | | | | | | | | | |
| 278 b | | | | | | | | | | w | | w | | | | | | | | |
| 4 b | | | | | | | | | | | | | | | | | • | | • | • |

N ↕ S

Interstate 430 in Arkansas is a 13-mile route in Little Rock. Northbound travelers should read up the chart. Southbound travelers read down the chart.

| Exit(mm) | ↗ | ★ | 🔀 | 🚻 | ♿ | ⛽ | ☎ | 🏪 | 🐾 | W | S | K | T | C | Am | FJ | Lo | Pe | Pi | TA |
|---|---|---|---|---|---|---|---|---|---|---|---|---|---|---|---|---|---|---|---|---|
| 8 b | | | | | | | | | | | | w | | | | | | | | |
| 6 b | | | | | | | | | | | w | | | | | | | | | |

Interstate 540 in Arkansas runs north to south for 72 miles from I-40 in Alma to US 71 in Bentonville. Northbound travelers should read up the chart. Southbound travelers read down the chart.

| Exit(mm) | ↗ | ★ | 🔀 | 🚻 | ♿ | ⛽ | ☎ | 🏪 | 🐾 | W | S | K | T | C | Am | FJ | Lo | Pe | Pi | TA |
|---|---|---|---|---|---|---|---|---|---|---|---|---|---|---|---|---|---|---|---|---|
| 86 b | | | | | | | | | | e | | | | | | | | | | |
| 62 b | | | | | | | | | | w | | | | | | | | | | |

# California

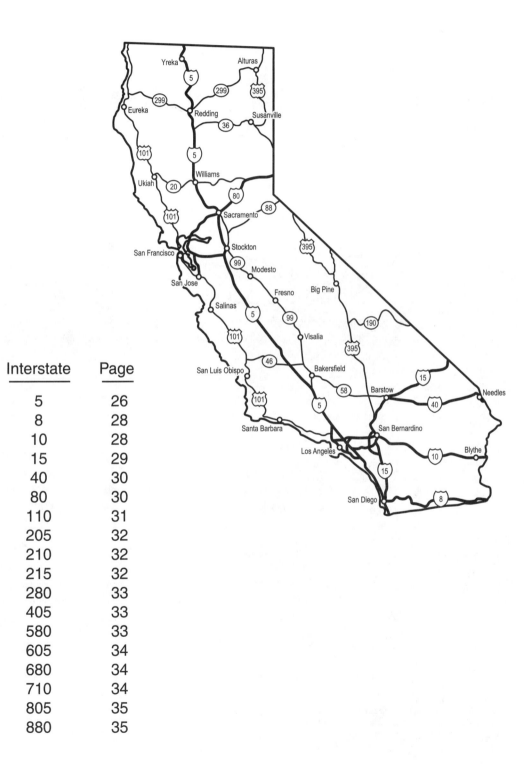

Interstate 5 in California runs north to south for about 797 miles from the Oregon state line to the Mexico border. Northbound travelers should read up the chart. Southbound travelers read down the chart.

| Exit(mm) | ↗ | ★ | icon1 | icon2 | icon3 | icon4 | icon5 | icon6 | icon7 | W | S | K | T | C | Am | FJ | Lo | Pe | Pi | TA |
|---|---|---|---|---|---|---|---|---|---|---|---|---|---|---|---|---|---|---|---|---|
| 786 | b | 1 | R | • | • | • | • | | • | | | | | | | | | | | |
| (780) | sb | 2 | T | | | | | | | | | | | | | | | | | |
| 773 | b | 3 | | | | | | | | w | | | | | | | | | | |
| 753 | b | 4 | R | • | • | • | • | | • | | | | | | | | | | | |
| (723) | nb | 2 | T | | | | | | | | | | | | | | | | | |
| (705) | sb | | R | • | • | • | • | | | | | | | | | | | | | |
| (694) | nb | | R | • | • | • | | | • | | | | | | | | | | | |
| 678a | b | 5 | | | | | | | | | e | | e | | | | | | | |
| 677 | b | 6 | | | | | | | | | | e | | | | | | | | | |
| 673 | b | 7 | | | | | | | | | | | | | | | | | | | • |
| 667 | b | 8 | W | • | | | | | | | | | | | | | | | | |
| (656) | b | | R | • | • | • | • | | • | | | | | | | | | | | |
| 647a | b | 9 | | | | | | | | w | | w | | | | | | | | |
| (633) | b | | R | • | • | • | • | | • | | | | | | | | | | | |
| 630 | b | 10 | | | | | | | | | | | | | | | | | • | | • |
| (608) | b | | R | • | • | • | • | • | • | | | | | | | | | | | |
| 603 | b | 11 | | | | | | | | w | | | | | | | | | | | |
| (583) | b | | R | • | • | • | | | • | | | | | | | | | | | |
| (557) | b | | R | • | • | • | • | | • | | | | | | | | | | | |
| 554 | b | 12 | | | | | | | | | | | | | | | | | • | | |
| 536 | b | 13 | | | | | | | | | e | | e | | | | | | | | |
| (529) | sb | | R | • | • | • | | | • | | | | | | | | | | | |
| 485 | b | 14 | | | | | | | | | | | | | | | | • | | | |
| 481 | b | 15 | | | | | | | | | | | e+ | | | | | | | | |
| (445) | b | | R | • | • | • | • | • | • | | | | | | | | | | | |
| (430) | nb | 2 | T | | | | | | | | | | | | | | | | | |
| (423) | sb | 2 | T | | | | | | | | | | | | | | | | | |
| 407 | b | 16 | | | | | | | | | | | | | | | | | | • | • |
| (386) | b | | R | • | • | • | • | | • | | | | | | | | | | | |
| (320) | b | | R | • | • | • | • | | • | | | | | | | | | | | |
| 278 | b | 17 | | | | | | | | | | | | | | | | | • | | • |
| (259) | b | | R | • | • | • | | | • | | | | | | | | | | | |
| 257 | b | 18 | | | | | | | | | | | | | | | | | | | • |
| 219b | b | 19 | | | | | | | | | | | | | | | | | | • | |
| 219a | b | 20 | | | | | | | | | | | | | | | | | | | • |
| (206) | b | | R | • | • | • | • | • | • | | | | | | | | | | | |
| 205 | b | 21 | | | | | | | | | | | | | • | | | | | |

N ↕ S

| Exit(mm) | ↗ | ★ | | | | | | | | W | S | K | T | C | Am | FJ | Lo | Pe | Pi | TA |
|---|---|---|---|---|---|---|---|---|---|---|---|---|---|---|---|---|---|---|---|---|
| 176 | b | 22 | | | | | | | | | | | | | | | | | • | |
| 167 | b | 23 | | | | | | | | w | | | | | | | | | | |
| 154 | b | 24 | | | | | | | | | | | e | | | | | | | |
| 147a | b | 25 | | | | | | | | | | | w | | | | | | | |
| 146b | b | 26 | | | | | | | | | | e | | | | | | | | |
| 122 | b | 27 | | | | | | | | | | | e | | | | | | | |
| 112 | b | 28 | | | | | | | | e | | | | | | | | | | |
| 105b | b | 29 | W | • | • | | | | | | | | | | | | | | | |
| 104b | b | 30 | | | | | | | | | | | e | | | | | | | |
| 101a | b | 31 | | | | | | | | | | e | | | | | | | | | |
| 100 | b | 32 | | | | | | | | | | | e | | | | | | | |
| 91 | b | 33 | | | | | | | | | | e | | | | | | | | | |
| 90 | b | 34 | | | | | | | | | | | e | | | | | | | |
| 78 | b | 35 | | | | | | | | | | w | | | | | | | | | |
| (63) | sb | 2 | T | | | | | | | | | | | | | | | | | |
| (60) | b | | R | • | • | • | • | • | • | | | | | | | | | | | |
| 54a | b | 36 | W | • | | | | | | | | | | | | | | | | |
| 51b | b | 37 | | | | | | | | e | | | e | | | | | | | |
| 44 | b | 38 | T | | | | | | | | | | | | | | | | | |
| (39) | sb | 2 | T | | | | | | | | | | | | | | | | | |
| 6 | b | 39 | | | | | | | | | | | e | | | | | | | |

1) CA 96 / Klamath River Road
2) Scenic Vista
3) CA 3 / Fort Jones / Etna / Yreka
4) Weed Airport Road
5) CA 44 / Hilltop Drive / Lassen Nat'l Park
6) Redding / Cypress Avenue
7) Knighton Road / Redding Airport
8) Deschutes Road / Factory Outlets Drive
9) South Main Street
10) South Avenue
11) CA 162 / Willows / Oroville
12) County Road 8
13) County Road 102
14) CA 12 / Lodi
15) Eight Mile Road
16) CA 33 / Gilroy
17) CA 46 / Lost Hills / Wasco
18) CA 58 / Bakersfield
19) Laval Road West
20) Laval Road East

21) Frazier Mountain Park Road
22) Lake Hughes Road / Castalc
23) Lyons Avenue / Pico Canyon Road
24) Osborne Street
25) Scott Road
26) Burbank Blvd
27) Pioneer Blvd / Imperial Highway
28) Euclid Street
29) Main Street
30) Santa Ana Blvd / Grand Avenue
31) Tustin Ranch Road
32) Jamboree Road
33) El Toro Road
34) Alicia Parkway
35) Camino Estrella
36) CA 76 East
37) CA 78 East / Vista Way
38) La Costa Avenue / Scenic Vista
39) Palomar Street

Interstate 8 in California runs east to west for 172 miles from the Arizona state line to Sunset Cliffs Blvd in San Diego. Eastbound travelers should read up the chart. Westbound travelers read down the chart.

| Exit(mm) | ⬚ | ★ | ↗ | 👫 | ☎ | 🍴 | ▦ | 🍱 | 🐾 | W | S | K | T | C | Am | FJ | Lo | Pe | Pi | TA |
|---|---|---|---|---|---|---|---|---|---|---|---|---|---|---|---|---|---|---|---|---|
| (155) | b | | R | • | | • | | | • | | | | | | | | | | | |
| 114 | b | 1 | | | | | | | | n+ | | n+ | | | | | | | | |
| (108) | b | | R | • | • | • | | • | • | | | | | | | | | | | |
| (75) | eb | | T | | | • | | | | | | | | | | | | | | |
| 51 | b | 2 | R | • | • | • | | • | • | | | | | | | | | | | |
| (37) | eb | 3 | T | | | | | | | | | | | | | | | | | |
| (24) | wb | | T | | | • | | | | | | | | | | | | | | |
| 22 | b | 4 | | | | | | | | s | | | | | | | | | | |
| 17 | wb | 5 | | | | | | | | | | n | | | | | | | | |
| 17a | eb | 6 | | | | | | | | | | n | | | | | | | | |
| 13b | b | 7 | | | | | | | | | | | n | | | | | | | |

(Left margin: E ↕ W)

1) Imperial Avenue
2) Buckman Springs Road
3) Scenic Vista
4) Los Coches Road
5) Magnolia Avenue / SR-67 North
6) Johnson Avenue
7) Jackson Drive

Interstate 10 in California runs east to west for approximately 244 miles from the Arizona state line to CA 1 in Santa Monica. Eastbound travelers should read up the chart. Westbound travelers read down the chart.

| Exit(mm) | ⬚ | ★ | ↗ | 👫 | ☎ | 🍴 | ▦ | 🍱 | 🐾 | W | S | K | T | C | Am | FJ | Lo | Pe | Pi | TA |
|---|---|---|---|---|---|---|---|---|---|---|---|---|---|---|---|---|---|---|---|---|
| 239 | b | 1 | | | | | | | | | | n | | | | | | | | |
| 222 | b | 2 | R | • | • | • | • | • | • | | | | | | | | | | | |
| (159) | b | | R | • | | • | • | • | • | | | | | | | | | | | |
| 146 | b | 3 | | | | | | | | | | | | | | | | • | | • |
| 142 | b | 4 | | | | | | | | | | | s | | | | | | | |
| 130 | b | 5 | | | | | | | | | | | | | | | • | | | |
| 120 | b | 6 | | | | | | | | | | | | | | | | | • | |
| (113) | b | | R | • | • | • | • | • | • | | | | | | | | | | | |
| 96 | b | 7 | | | | | | | | | | s | | | | | | | | |
| (91) | wb | | R | • | • | • | • | | • | | | | | | | | | | | |
| (86) | eb | | R | • | • | • | | | • | | | | | | | | | | | |
| 77a | b | 8 | | | | | | | | | | | s | | | | | | | |
| 76 | b | 9 | | | | | | | | s | | | | | | | | | | | |
| 73 | b | 10 | | | | | | | | | n | | | | | | | | | | |

(Left margin: E ↕ W)

| Exit(mm) | ↗ | * | | | | | | | | W | S | K | T | C | Am | FJ | Lo | Pe | Pi | TA |
|---|---|---|---|---|---|---|---|---|---|---|---|---|---|---|---|---|---|---|---|---|
| 68 | b | 11 | | | | | | | | | n | | | | | | | | | |
| 64 | b | 12 | | | | | | | | | n | | s | | | | | | | |
| 57 | b | 13 | | | | | | | | | n | | | | | | | | | • |
| 53 | b | 14 | | | | | | | | | n | | | | | | | | | |
| 50 | b | 15 | | | | | | | | | | | s | | | | | | | |
| 49 | b | 16 | | | | | | | | | s | | | | | | | | | |
| 37a | b | 17 | | | | | | | | | | | n | | | | | | | |
| 34a | wb | 18 | | | | | | | | | s | | | | | | | | | |
| 34 | eb | 18 | | | | | | | | | s | | | | | | | | | |
| 31b | wb | 19 | | | | | | | | | | | n | | | | | | | |
| 31c | eb | 19 | | | | | | | | | | | n | | | | | | | |
| 29b | b | 20 | | | | | | | | | n | | | | | | | | | |
| 26b | b | 21 | | | | | | | | | n | | | | | | | | | |

1) Lovekin Blvd
2) Wiley's Well Road
3) Dillon Road
4) Monroe Street
5) Ramon Road
6) Indian Avenue
7) Highland Springs Avenue
8) Alabama Street
9) California Street
10) Waterman Avenue
11) Riverside Avenue
12) Sierra Avenue
13) Milliken Avenue
14) 4th Street
15) Mountain Avenue
16) Central Avenue
17) Citrus Street
18) Pacific Avenue
19) Frazier Street
20) Peck Rd / Valley Blvd
21) CA 19 / Rosemead Blvd

Interstate 15 in California runs north to south for about 292 miles from the Nevada state line to San Diego. Northbound travelers should read up the chart. Southbound travelers read down the chart.

| Exit(mm) | ↗ | * | | | | | | | | W | S | K | T | C | Am | FJ | Lo | Pe | Pi | TA |
|---|---|---|---|---|---|---|---|---|---|---|---|---|---|---|---|---|---|---|---|---|
| (270) | b | | R | • | • | • | | | • | | | | | | | | | | | |
| (217) | b | | R | • | • | • | | | • | | | | | | | | | | | |
| 184 | b | 1 | | | | | | | | e | | | | | | | | | | |
| 178 | b | 2 | W | | • | | | | | | | | | | | | • | | • | • |
| 150 | b | 3 | | | | | | | | | w | | | | | | | | | |
| 147 | b | 4 | | | | | | | | e | | | | | | | | | | |
| 141 | b | 5 | | | | | | | | | | | | | | | | • | | |
| 112 | b | 6 | | | | | | | | e | | e | | | | | | | | |
| 110 | b | 7 | | | | | | | | | w | | | | | | | | | |
| 98 | b | 8 | | | | | | | | | | w | | | | | | | | |
| 93 | b | 9 | | | | | | | | w | w | | | | | | | | | |

| Exit(mm) | ⤢ | ★ | | | | | | | | W | S | K | T | C | Am | FJ | Lo | Pe | Pi | TA |
|---|---|---|---|---|---|---|---|---|---|---|---|---|---|---|---|---|---|---|---|---|
| 73 | b | 10 | | | | | | | | e | | | | | | | | | | |
| 65 | b | 11 | | | | | | | | | e | | | | | | | | | |
| 64 | b | 12 | | | | | | | | w | | | | | | | | | | |
| 61 | b | 13 | | | | | | | | | | e | | | | | | | | |
| 59 | b | 14 | | | | | | | | | | e | | | | | | | | |
| 32 | b | 15 | | | | | | | | | e+ | | | | | | | | | |
| 31 | b | 16 | | | | | | | | | | w | | | | | | | | |
| 21 | b | 17 | | | | | | | | | e | | | | | | | | | |
| 8 | b | 18 | | | | | | | | w | | | | | | | | | | |

N ↕ S

1) East Main Street / Barstow
2) Lenwood Road
3) CA 18 West / Palmdale Road
4) Bear Valley Road
5) Joshua Street / Palm Avenue/
   US 395 North
6) CA 66 / Foothill Blvd
7) 4th Street
8) Second Street
9) Ontario Avenue

10) Diamond Drive / Railroad Canyon Road
11) California Oaks Road
12) Murrieta Hot Springs Road
13) CA 79 North
14) Rancho California Road
15) CA 78 / Oceanside / Ramona
16) Valley Parkway
17) Carmel Mountain Road
18) Aero Drive

 Interstate 40 in California runs east to west for 151 miles from the Arizona state line to I-15 in Barstow. Eastbound travelers should read up the chart. Westbound travelers read down the chart.

| Exit(mm) | ⤢ | ★ | | | | | | | | W | S | K | T | C | Am | FJ | Lo | Pe | Pi | TA |
|---|---|---|---|---|---|---|---|---|---|---|---|---|---|---|---|---|---|---|---|---|
| (106) | b | | R | • | • | • | | | • | | | | | | | | | | | |
| (28) | b | | R | • | • | • | | | • | | | | | | | | | | | |
| 1 | b | 1 | | | | | | | | | s | | | | | | | | | |

E ↕ W

1) East Main Street

 Interstate 80 in California runs east to west for 208 miles from the Nevada state line to 7th Street in San Francisco. Eastbound travelers should read up the chart. Westbound travelers read down the chart.

| Exit(mm) | ⤢ | ★ | | | | | | | | W | S | K | T | C | Am | FJ | Lo | Pe | Pi | TA |
|---|---|---|---|---|---|---|---|---|---|---|---|---|---|---|---|---|---|---|---|---|
| (181) | b | 1 | T | | | | | | | | | | | | | | | | | |
| (177) | b | 1 | R | • | • | • | | | • | | | | | | | | | | | |
| (157) | wb | 1 | T | | | | | | | | | | | | | | | | | |

E ↕ W

| Exit(mm) | | ★ | ↗ | 👫 | 📞 | 🍴 | ⛽ | 🏪 | 🐾 | W | S | K | T | C | Am | FJ | Lo | Pe | Pi | TA |
|---|---|---|---|---|---|---|---|---|---|---|---|---|---|---|---|---|---|---|---|---|
| (143) | b | | R | • | • | • | | | • | | | | | | | | | | | |
| 106 | b | 2 | | | | | | | | n+ | | | | | | | | | | |
| 105a | b | 3 | | | | | | | | | s | | | | | | | | | |
| 102 | b | 4 | | | | | | | | | | s | | | | | | | | |
| 96 | b | 5 | | | | | | | | | | | s | | | | | | | |
| 89 | b | 6 | | | | | | | | | | s | | | | | | | | |
| 88 | b | 7 | | | | | | | | n | | | | | | | | | | |
| 85 | b | 8 | | | | | | | | | | | | | • | | | | | |
| 66a | b | 9 | | | | | | | | s | | | | | | | | | | |
| 55 | b | 10 | | | | | | | | s | s | | s | | | | | | | |
| 44 | b | 11 | | | | | | | | | | | s | | | | | | | |
| 43 | b | 12 | | | | | | | | s | | | | | | | | | | |
| (34) | wb | 1 | R | • | • | • | | | • | | | | | | | | | | | |
| 32 | b | 13 | | | | | | | | | | | s | | | | | | | |
| 21 | b | 14 | | | | | | | | | | s | | | | | | | | |
| 20 | b | 15 | | | | | | | | | | | s | | | | | | | |
| 18 | b | 16 | | | | | | | | | | n | | | | | | | | |
| 15 | b | 17 | | | | | | | | | | | s | | | | | | | |

1) Scenic Vista
2) CA 65 / Lincoln / Marysville
3) Eureka Road / Taylor Road
4) Auburn Blvd / Riverside Avenue
5) Madison Avenue
6) Northgate Blvd
7) Truxel Road
8) West El Camino Avenue
9) CA 113 South / Rio Vista / Dixon
10) Monte Vista Avenue / Allison Drive
11) West Texas Street / Rockville Road
12) CA 12 East / Rio Vista / Suisun City / Albernathy Road
13) Redwood Street
14) Appian Way
15) Richmond Parkway / Fitzgerald Drive
16) San Pablo Dam Road
17) Cutting Blvd / Potrero Street

**110** Interstate 110 is a spur route that begins on I-10 in Los Angeles and runs south to CA Hwy 47. It is approximately 25 miles long. Northbound travelers should read up the chart. Southbound travelers read down the chart.

| Exit(mm) | | ★ | ↗ | 👫 | 📞 | 🍴 | ⛽ | 🏪 | 🐾 | W | S | K | T | C | Am | FJ | Lo | Pe | Pi | TA |
|---|---|---|---|---|---|---|---|---|---|---|---|---|---|---|---|---|---|---|---|---|
| 10 | b | 1 | | | | | | | | | w | | | | | | | | | |
| 8 | b | 2 | | | | | | | | | e | | | | | | | | | |
| 5 | b | 3 | | | | | | | | | w | | e | | | | | | | |

1) CA 91
2) Torrance Blvd / Del Amo Blvd
3) Sepulveda Blvd

Interstate 205 begins on I-5 near Tracy and runs west to I-508. It is approximately 13 miles long. Eastbound travelers should read up the chart. Westbound travelers read down the chart.

| Exit(mm) | ↗ | ★ | 🛣 | 🚻 | ☎ | 🍴 | 🛏 | 🏪 | 🚐 | 🐾 | W | S | K | T | C | Am | FJ | Lo | Pe | Pi | TA |
|---|---|---|---|---|---|---|---|---|---|---|---|---|---|---|---|---|---|---|---|---|---|
| 6 | b | 1 | | | | | | | | | n | | | n | | | | | | | |

1) Grantline Road

 Interstate 210 begins on I-10 near San Dimas and runs west to I-5 in San Fernando. It is approximately 49 miles long. Eastbound travelers should read up the chart. Westbound travelers read down the chart.

| Exit(mm) | ↗ | ★ | 🛣 | 🚻 | ☎ | 🍴 | 🛏 | 🏪 | 🚐 | 🐾 | W | S | K | T | C | Am | FJ | Lo | Pe | Pi | TA |
|---|---|---|---|---|---|---|---|---|---|---|---|---|---|---|---|---|---|---|---|---|---|
| 45 | b | 1 | | | | | | | | | | | | s | | | | | | | |
| 44 | b | 2 | | | | | | | | | s | s | | | | | | | | | |
| 35a | b | 3 | | | | | | | | | s | | | | n | | | | | | |
| 29 | b | 4 | | | | | | | | | | | | s | | | | | | | |
| 5 | b | 5 | | | | | | | | | | s | | | | | | | | | |

(E ↕ W)

1) CA 57 South
2) Lone Hill Avenue
3) Mountain Avenue
4) San Gabriel Blvd / Madre Street
5) Maclay Street

 Interstate 215 begins on I-15 near San Bernardino and runs south to I-15 near Murrieta. Northbound travelers should read up the chart. Southbound travelers read down the chart.

| Exit(mm) | ↗ | ★ | 🛣 | 🚻 | ☎ | 🍴 | 🛏 | 🏪 | 🚐 | 🐾 | W | S | K | T | C | Am | FJ | Lo | Pe | Pi | TA |
|---|---|---|---|---|---|---|---|---|---|---|---|---|---|---|---|---|---|---|---|---|---|
| 41 | b | 1 | | | | | | | | | | | | e | | | | | | | |
| 39 | b | 2 | | | | | | | | | w | | | | | | | | | | |
| 33 | b | 3 | | | | | | | | | | | e | | | | | | | | |
| 28 | b | 4 | | | | | | | | | e | e | | | | | | | | | |
| 22 | b | 5 | | | | | | | | | e+ | | | | | | | | | | |
| 10 | b | 6 | | | | | | | | | | | | e | | | | | | | |

(N ↕ S)

1) Orange Show Road / Auto Center Drive
2) Mount Vernon Avenue / Washington Ave
3) 3rd Street / Blaine Street
4) Eucalyptus Avenue / Eastridge Avenue
5) Ramona Expressway
6) Newport Road

Interstate 280 in California runs north to south for about 60 miles from Fourth Street in downtown San Francisco to US 101 in San Jose. Northbound travelers should read up the chart. Southbound travelers read down the chart.

| | Exit(mm) | ↗ | ★ | ▥ | 👫 | ☎ | 🍽 | ⛽ | 🚮 | 🐾 | W | S | K | T | C | Am | FJ | Lo | Pe | Pi | TA |
|---|---|---|---|---|---|---|---|---|---|---|---|---|---|---|---|---|---|---|---|---|---|
| N | 47a | b | 1 | | | | | | | | | | e | | | | | | | | |
| ↕ | (36) | nb | | R | • | • | • | • | | • | | | | | | | | | | | |
| | (31) | b | 2 | T | | | | | | | | | | | | | | | | | |
| S | 7 | b | 3 | | | | | | | | | | w | | | | | | | | |

*1) Serramonte Blvd. 2) Scenic Vista. 3) Saratoga Avenue / Santa Clara*

Interstate 405 runs north to south for about 56 miles. It begins at I-5 in Irvine and ends at I-5 in Sylmar. Northbound travelers should read up the chart. Southbound travelers read down the chart.

| | Exit(mm) | ↗ | ★ | ▥ | 👫 | ☎ | 🍽 | ⛽ | 🚮 | 🐾 | W | S | K | T | C | Am | FJ | Lo | Pe | Pi | TA |
|---|---|---|---|---|---|---|---|---|---|---|---|---|---|---|---|---|---|---|---|---|---|
| | 47 | b | 1 | | | | | | | | | | w | | | | | | | | |
| | 30a | b | 2 | | | | | | | | | | e | | | | | | | | |
| N | 26b | b | 3 | | | | | | | | | | e | w | | | | | | | |
| ↕ | 22 | b | 4 | | | | | | | | | | e | | | | | | | | |
| S | 16 | b | 5 | | | | | | | | | | e | w | | | | | | | |
| | 11b | b | 6 | | | | | | | | | | w | | | | | | | | |
| | 9b | b | 7 | | | | | | | | | | e | | | | | | | | |

*1) Manchester Blvd*          *5) CA 39 / Beach Blvd*
*2) Atlantic Avenue*          *6) Harbor Blvd*
*3) Bellflower Blvd*          *7) Bristol Street*
*4) Seal Beach Blvd / Los Alamitos Blvd*

Interstate 580 runs east to west for 82 miles. It begins on I-5 south of Tracy and ends at US 101 in San Rafael. Eastound travelers should read up the chart. Westbound travelers read down the chart.

| | Exit(mm) | ↗ | ★ | ▥ | 👫 | ☎ | 🍽 | ⛽ | 🚮 | 🐾 | W | S | K | T | C | Am | FJ | Lo | Pe | Pi | TA |
|---|---|---|---|---|---|---|---|---|---|---|---|---|---|---|---|---|---|---|---|---|---|
| E | 54 | b | 1 | | | | | | | | | | s | | | | | | | | |
| ↕ | 52 | b | 2 | | | | | | | | s | | | | | | | | | | |
| | 46 | b | 3 | | | | | | | | s | s | | | | | | | | | |
| W | 44a | b | 4 | | | | | | | | | | n | | | | | | | | |

*1) 1st Street / Springtown Blvd*          *3) Hacienda Drive*
*2) North Livermore Avenue / Central Livermore*          *4) San Ramon Road*

Interstate 605 runs north to south for 25 miles from Huntington Drive in Duarte to I-405 in Los Alamitos. Northbound travelers should read up the chart. Southbound travelers read down the chart.

| Exit(mm) | ↗ | * | 🏔 | 🚻 | 🅿 | ⛽ | 🔧 | 💾 | 🐴 | W | S | K | T | C | Am | FJ | Lo | Pe | Pi | TA |
|---|---|---|---|---|---|---|---|---|---|---|---|---|---|---|---|---|---|---|---|---|
| 10 | b | 1 | | | | | | | | | | | | w | | | | | | |
| 3 | b | 2 | | | | | | | | | | w | w | | | | | | | |

1) Firestone Blvd
2) Carson Street

 Interstate 680 runs north to south for 71 miles from I-80 near Fairfield to US 101 in San Jose. Northbound travelers should read up the chart. Southbound travelers read down the chart.

| Exit(mm) | ↗ | * | 🏔 | 🚻 | 🅿 | ⛽ | 🔧 | 💾 | 🐴 | W | S | K | T | C | Am | FJ | Lo | Pe | Pi | TA |
|---|---|---|---|---|---|---|---|---|---|---|---|---|---|---|---|---|---|---|---|---|
| 52 | b | 1 | | | | | | | | | | w | w | | | | | | | |
| 47 | b | 2 | | | | | | | | | | | e | | | | | | | |
| 34 | b | 3 | | | | | | | | | | | e | | | | | | | |
| 29 | b | 4 | | | | | | | | | | | w | | | | | | | |
| 6 | b | 5 | | | | | | | | | | | e | | | | | | | |
| 2b | b | 6 | | | | | | | | | | w | | | | | | | | |

N ↑↓ S

1) Concord Avenue
2) North Main Street
3) Bollinger Canyon Road
4) Stoneridge Drive
5) Landess Avenue / Montague Expressway
6) McKee Road

 Interstate 710 runs north to south for 29 miles between Valley Boulevard in Alhambra and East Shoreline Drive in Long Beach. Northbound travelers should read up the chart. Southbound travelers read down the chart.

| Exit(mm) | ↗ | * | 🏔 | 🚻 | 🅿 | ⛽ | 🔧 | 💾 | 🐴 | W | S | K | T | C | Am | FJ | Lo | Pe | Pi | TA |
|---|---|---|---|---|---|---|---|---|---|---|---|---|---|---|---|---|---|---|---|---|
| 13 | b | 1 | | | | | | | | | | | e | | | | | | | |

1) Firestone Blvd

Interstate 805 runs north to south for 31 miles between I-5 near Del Mar and I-5 near the Mexico border. Northbound travelers should read up the chart. Southbound travelers read down the chart.

| Exit(mm) | ⤴ | ★ | 🏞 | 🚻 | ♿ | 🍽 | ⛽ | 🏨 | 🐾 | W | S | K | T | C | Am | FJ | Lo | Pe | Pi | TA |
|---|---|---|---|---|---|---|---|---|---|---|---|---|---|---|---|---|---|---|---|---|
| 22 | b | 1 | | | | | | | | | | e | | | | | | | | |
| 2 | b | 2 | | | | | | | | e | | | | | | | | | | |

*1) Clairemont Mesa Blvd*
*2) Palm Avenue*

Interstate 880 runs north to south for about 46 miles between Seventh Street in downtown San Francisco and I-280 in San Jose. Northbound travelers should read up the chart. Southbound travelers read down the chart.

| Exit(mm) | ⤴ | ★ | 🏞 | 🚻 | ♿ | 🍽 | ⛽ | 🏨 | 🐾 | W | S | K | T | C | Am | FJ | Lo | Pe | Pi | TA |
|---|---|---|---|---|---|---|---|---|---|---|---|---|---|---|---|---|---|---|---|---|
| 34 | b | 1 | | | | | | | | w | | | | | | | | | | |
| 30 | b | 2 | | | | | | | | | | | e | | | | | | | |
| 24 | b | 3 | | | | | | | | w | | e | | | | | | | | |
| 23 | b | 4 | | | | | | | | w | | | | | | | | | | |
| 19 | b | 5 | | | | | | | | | | w | | | | | | | | |
| 17 | b | 6 | | | | | | | | | | | w | | | | | | | |
| 8c | b | 7 | | | | | | | | w | | | | | | | | | | |

N ↕ S

*1) CA 112 / Davis Street*
*2) Lewelling Blvd / San Lorenzo*
*3) Whipple Road / Dyer Street*
*4) Alvarado-Niles Road*
*5) CA 84 East / Thornton Avenue*
*6) Mowry Avenue / Central Fremont*
*7) CA 237 West*

# Colorado

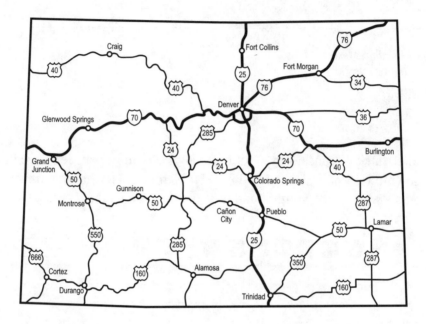

| Interstate | Page |
|:---:|:---:|
| 25 | 37 |
| 70 | 38 |
| 76 | 39 |
| 225 | 39 |

**25** Interstate 25 in Colorado runs north to south for about 300 miles from the Wyoming state line to the New Mexico state line. Northbound travelers should read up the chart. Southbound travelers read down the chart.

| Exit(mm) | 🡕 | * | 🛈 | 🚻 | 💧 | 🍴 | ⛽ | 🏪 | 🐾 | W | S | K | T | C | Am | FJ | Lo | Pe | Pi | TA |
|---|---|---|---|---|---|---|---|---|---|---|---|---|---|---|---|---|---|---|---|---|
| (296) | b | | T | | | | | | | | | | | | | | | | | |
| (268) | b | | W | • | • | • | | | | | | | | | | | | | | |
| (266) | b | | R | • | • | • | | | • | | | | | | | | | | | |
| 257b | b | | | | | | | | | | | | w | w | | | | | | |
| 254 | b | | | | | | | | | | | | | | | • | | | | | |
| 223 | b | | | | | | | | | | | | | w | | | | | | | |
| 221 | b | | | | | | | | | | | | w | | | | | | | | |
| 220 | b | | | | | | | | | w | e | e | | | | | | | | | |
| 207 | b | | | | | | | | | | e | | | | | | | | | | |
| 197 | b | | | | | | | | | | | e | e | | | | | | | | |
| 194 | b | 1 | | | | | | | | w+ | w+ | | | | | | | | | | |
| 184 | b | | | | | | | | | e | | | e | | | | | | | | |
| (171) | b | | R | • | • | • | • | | • | | | | | | | | | | | |
| 150 | b | | | | | | | | | e | e | | | e | | | | | | | |
| 141 | b | | | | | | | | | w | | | | | | | | | | | |
| 138 | b | | | | | | | | | | | | w | | | | | | | | |
| 132 | b | 2 | | | | | | | | e+ | | | | | | | | | | | |
| (115) | nb | | R | • | • | • | • | • | • | | | | | | | | | | | |
| (112) | sb | | R | • | • | • | • | • | • | | | | | | | | | | | |
| 110 | b | | | | | | | | | | | | | | | • | | | | | |
| 102 | b | | | | | | | | | | | e | | w | | | | | | | |
| 101 | b | | | | | | | | | e | | w | | | | | | | | | |
| 74 | b | | R | • | • | • | • | | • | | | | | | | | | | | |
| 18 | b | | R | • | • | • | | | • | | | | | | | | | | | |
| 14a | sb | | W | • | • | • | | | | | | | | | | | | | | |
| 14 | nb | | W | • | • | • | | | | | | | | | | | | | | |
| 11 | b | | | | | | | | | w | | | | | | | | | | | |
| (1) | nb | 3 | T | | | | | | | | | | | | | | | | | |

*N ↕ S* (direction indicators at left of chart)

1) Wal-Mart and Sam's Club on Quebec St off CO 470
2) Wal-Mart is on US 85
3) Scenic Vista.

Interstate 70 in Colorado runs east to west for 447 miles from the Kansas state line to the Utah state line. Eastbound travelers should read up the chart. Westbound travelers read down the chart.

| Exit(mm) | | ★ | | 🚻 | ☎ | ⛲ | ⛽ | 🏪 | 🐴 | W | S | K | T | C | Am | FJ | Lo | Pe | Pi | TA |
|---|---|---|---|---|---|---|---|---|---|---|---|---|---|---|---|---|---|---|---|---|
| (437) | wb | | W | • | • | • | • | • | • | | | | | | | | | | | |
| 383 | b | | R | • | • | • | | • | • | | | | | | | | | | | |
| 361 | b | | | | | | | | | | | | | | | | | • | | |
| 359 | b | | | | | | | | | | | | | | | | | | | • |
| (332) | wb | | R | • | • | • | • | | • | | | | | | | | | | | |
| 306 | b | | R | • | • | • | | | • | | | | | | | | | | | |
| 285 | b | | | | | | | | | | | | | | | | | • | | |
| 278 | b | | | | | | | | | | | | | | | | | | | • |
| 276a | b | | | | | | | | | | | | | | | | | | • | |
| 272 | b | | | | | | | | | | | | n | | | | | | | |
| 270 | b | | | | | | | | | | | | | s | | | | | | |
| 269a | b | | | | | | | | | | | n | | | | | | | | |
| 266 | b | | | | | | | | | | | | | | | | | | | • |
| 264 | b | | | | | | | | | | s | | | | | | | | | |
| 262 | b | | | | | | | | | | | | | s | | | | | | |
| 252 | b | | | | | | | | | | s | | | | | | | | | |
| (226) | eb | 1 | T | | | | | | | | | | | | | | | | | |
| (213) | eb | | T | | | | | | | | | | | | | | | | | |
| 203 | b | | | | | | | | | | s | | | | | | | | | |
| (203) | b | 1 | T | | | • | | | | | | | | | | | | | | |
| 190 | b | | R | • | • | • | | | | | | | | | | | | | | |
| (189) | b | | T | | | | | | | | | | | | | | | | | |
| 167 | b | | | | | | | | | | s | | | | | | | | | |
| 163 | b | | R | • | • | • | | • | | | | | | | | | | | | |
| (162) | b | 1 | T | | | | | | | | | | | | | | | | | |
| 129 | b | | R | • | • | • | | | • | | | | | | | | | | | |
| (128) | eb | | T | | | | | | | | | | | | | | | | | |
| 121 | b | | R | • | • | • | | | | | | | | | | | | | | |
| 119 | b | | R | • | • | • | | | | | | | | | | | | | | |
| 116 | b | | | | | | | | | s+ | | | | | | | | | | |
| (115) | eb | | R | • | • | • | | | | | | | | | | | | | | |
| 114 | b | | | | | | | | | | | | n | | | | | | | |
| (108) | b | | T | | | | | | | | | | | | | | | | | |
| 90 | b | | R | • | • | • | • | • | | | | | | | | | | | | |
| 75 | b | | R | • | • | • | | | • | | | | | | | | | | | |
| (50) | eb | | T | | | | | | | | | | | | | | | | | |
| 37 | b | | | | | | | | | s+ | | s+ | | | | | | | | |

E ↕ W

| Exit(mm) | ⤢ | ★ | 🡕 | 👥 | 📞 | 🏕 | 🚻 | 🏪 | 🐾 | W | S | K | T | C | Am | FJ | Lo | Pe | Pi | TA |
|---|---|---|---|---|---|---|---|---|---|---|---|---|---|---|---|---|---|---|---|---|
| 19 | b | | W | • | • | • | | • | • | | | | | | | | | | | |

1) Scenic Vista

Interstate 76 runs east to west from the Nebraska state line to I-70 in Denver. It is about 184 miles long. Eastbound travelers should read up the chart. Westbound travelers read down the chart.

| Exit(mm) | ⤢ | ★ | 🡕 | 👥 | 📞 | 🏕 | 🚻 | 🏪 | 🐾 | W | S | K | T | C | Am | FJ | Lo | Pe | Pi | TA |
|---|---|---|---|---|---|---|---|---|---|---|---|---|---|---|---|---|---|---|---|---|
| 180 | b | | W | • | • | • | • | • | • | | | | | | | | | • | | |
| 125 | b | | R | • | • | • | | • | • | | | | | | | | | | | |
| 82 | b | | | | | | | | | | | s | | | | | | | | |
| 66a | b | | R | • | • | • | • | | • | | | | | | | | | | | |
| 1a | b | | | | | | | | | | | | n | | | | | | | |

E ↕ W (direction indicator)

Interstate 225 is about 12 miles long and runs between I-25 in Denver and I-70 in Aurora.

| Exit(mm) | ⤢ | ★ | 🡕 | 👥 | 📞 | 🏕 | 🚻 | 🏪 | 🐾 | W | S | K | T | C | Am | FJ | Lo | Pe | Pi | TA |
|---|---|---|---|---|---|---|---|---|---|---|---|---|---|---|---|---|---|---|---|---|
| 7 | b | | | | | | | | | | e | e | | e | | | | | | |

# Connecticut

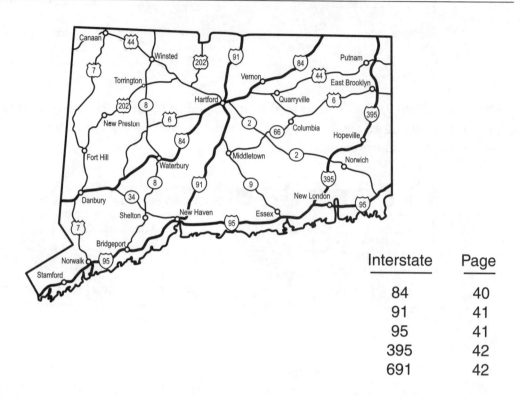

| Interstate | Page |
|---|---|
| 84 | 40 |
| 91 | 41 |
| 95 | 41 |
| 395 | 42 |
| 691 | 42 |

 **84**

Interstate 84 in Connecticut runs east to west for 98 miles from the Massachusetts state line to the New York state line. Exit numbers are based on the consecutive numbering system rather than the mile marker system. Eastbound travelers should read up the chart. Westbound travelers read down the chart.

| Exit(mm) | ↗ | ★ | 🡥 | 🚻 | ☎ | 🍽 | ⛽ | 🛏 | 🐾 | W | S | K | T | C | Am | FJ | Lo | Pe | Pi | TA |
|---|---|---|---|---|---|---|---|---|---|---|---|---|---|---|---|---|---|---|---|---|
| 71 | b | | | | | | | | | | | | | | | | | | | • |
| (85) | b | 1 | W | • | • | • | • | • | • | | | | | | | | | | | |
| 64 | b | | | | | | | | | | | | n | | | | | | | |
| 63 | b | | | | | | | | | | | n | | | | | | | | |
| 62 | b | | | | | | | | | | | | n | | | | | | | |
| (42) | eb | | R | • | • | • | • | • | • | • | | | | | | | | | | |
| 28 | b | | | | | | | | | | | | | | | | | | | • |
| 15 | b | | | | | | | | | | | | n | | | | | | | |
| 8 | b | | | | | | | | | | s | | | s | | | | | | |
| 2 | eb | | W | • | • | • | • | • | • | | | | | | | | | | | |

E ↕ W

1) Welcome Center (westbound), Rest Area (eastbound); no dump station eastbound.

Interstate 91 in Connecticut runs north to south for 58 miles from the Massachusetts state line to I-95 in New Haven. Exit numbers are based on the consecutive numbering system rather than the mile marker system. Northbound travelers should read up the chart. Southbound travelers read down the chart.

| Exit(mm) | ⤢ | ★ | ⬀ | 🚻 | ☎ | ⛱ | ⛽ | 🍴 | 🐾 | W | S | K | T | C | Am | FJ | Lo | Pe | Pi | TA |
|---|---|---|---|---|---|---|---|---|---|---|---|---|---|---|---|---|---|---|---|---|
| 48 | b | | | | | | | | | | | | e | | | | | | | |
| 45 | b | | | | | | | | | e | | | e | | | | | | | |
| 39 | b | | | | | | | | | | | w | | | | | | | | |
| 24 | b | | | | | | | | | w | | | | | | | | | | |
| 21 | b | | | | | | | | | w | | | | | | | | | | |
| (22) | nb | | R | • | • | • | • | • | • | | | | | | | | | | | |
| (15) | sb | | R | • | • | • | • | • | • | | | | | | | | | | | |
| 9 | b | | | | | | | | | | | w | | | | | | | | |
| 8 | b | | | | | | | | | e | | | | | | | | | | |

Interstate 95 in Connecticut runs north to south for 112 miles from the Rhode Island state line to the New York state line. Exit numbers are based on the consecutive numbering system rather than the mile marker system. Northbound travelers should read up the chart. Southbound travelers read down the chart.

| Exit(mm) | ⤢ | ★ | ⬀ | 🚻 | ☎ | ⛱ | ⛽ | 🍴 | 🐾 | W | S | K | T | C | Am | FJ | Lo | Pe | Pi | TA |
|---|---|---|---|---|---|---|---|---|---|---|---|---|---|---|---|---|---|---|---|---|
| (106) | sb | | W | • | • | • | | | | | | | | | | | | | | |
| (100) | nb | 1 | T | | | | | | | | | | | | | | | | | |
| 86 | b | | | | | | | | | w | | | | | | | | | | |
| 82 | b | | | | | | | | | | | | w | | | | | | | |
| 81 | b | | | | | | | | | w | | | | | | | | | | |
| (74) | nb | | W | • | • | • | | | | | | | | | | | | | | |
| (66) | b | 2 | S | • | • | | • | | • | | | | | | | | | | | |
| 56 | b | | | | | | | | | | | | | | | | | | | • |
| (53) | b | 2 | S | • | • | | • | | • | | | | | | | | | | | |
| (41) | b | 2 | S | • | • | • | • | | • | | | | | | | | | | | |
| 40 | b | | | | | | | | | | | | | e | | | | | • | |
| 35 | b | | | | | | | | | | | e | | | | | | | | |
| 33 | b | | | | | | | | | w | | | | | | | | | | |
| (23) | b | 2 | S | • | • | • | • | | • | | | | | | | | | | | |

| Exit(mm) | ↗ | ★ | ⬈ | ♿ | ☎ | ⛺ | ⛽ | 🏪 | 🐎 | W | S | K | T | C | Am | FJ | Lo | Pe | Pi | TA |
|---|---|---|---|---|---|---|---|---|---|---|---|---|---|---|---|---|---|---|---|---|
| (12) | nb | 2 | S | • | • | • | • | | • | | | | | | | | | | | |
| (9) | sb | 2 | S | • | • | • | • | | • | | | | | | | | | | | |

*1) Scenic Vista. 2) Gas, Food Available.*

I-395 is about 56 miles long and runs north to south from the Massachusetts state line to I-95, west of New London. Exit numbers are based on the consecutive numbering system rather than the mile marker system. Northbound travelers should read up the chart. Southbound travelers read down the chart.

| Exit(mm) | ↗ | ★ | ⬈ | ♿ | ☎ | ⛺ | ⛽ | 🏪 | 🐎 | W | S | K | T | C | Am | FJ | Lo | Pe | Pi | TA |
|---|---|---|---|---|---|---|---|---|---|---|---|---|---|---|---|---|---|---|---|---|
| 97 | b | | | | | | | | | w | e | | | | | | | | | |
| (35) | b | R | • | | | | | | | | | | | | | | | | | |
| 84 | b | | | | | | | | | e | | | | | | | | | | |
| (8) | sb | R | • | | • | • | • | | | | | | | | | | | | | |

N ↕ S (directional indicator at left of table)

Interstate 691 runs east to west for 12 miles from Interstate 91 at Exit 18 to Interstate 84 Exit 27. Exit numbers are based on the consecutive numbering system rather than the mile marker system. Eastbound travelers should read up the chart. Westbound travelers read down the chart.

| Exit(mm) | ↗ | ★ | ⬈ | ♿ | ☎ | ⛺ | ⛽ | 🏪 | 🐎 | W | S | K | T | C | Am | FJ | Lo | Pe | Pi | TA |
|---|---|---|---|---|---|---|---|---|---|---|---|---|---|---|---|---|---|---|---|---|
| 6 | wb | | | | | | | | | | | | n | | | | | | | |
| 5 | eb | | | | | | | | | | | | n | | | | | | | |

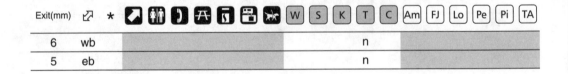

# Delaware

| Interstate | Page |
|:---:|:---:|
| 95 | 43 |

 Interstate 95 in Delaware runs north to south for 23 miles from the Pennsylvania state line to the Maryland state line. Northbound travelers should read up the chart. Southbound travelers read down the chart.

| Exit(mm) | ↗ | ★ | 🅿 | 👫 | 🍴 | ⛽ | 🛏 | 🏪 | 🐾 | W | S | K | T | C | Am | FJ | Lo | Pe | Pi | TA |
|:---:|:---:|:---:|:---:|:---:|:---:|:---:|:---:|:---:|:---:|:---:|:---:|:---:|:---:|:---:|:---:|:---:|:---:|:---:|:---:|:---:|
| 11 | b | | | | | | | | | | | e | | | | | | | | |
| (5) | b | S | • | • | • | • | | | | | | | | | | | | | | |

# Florida

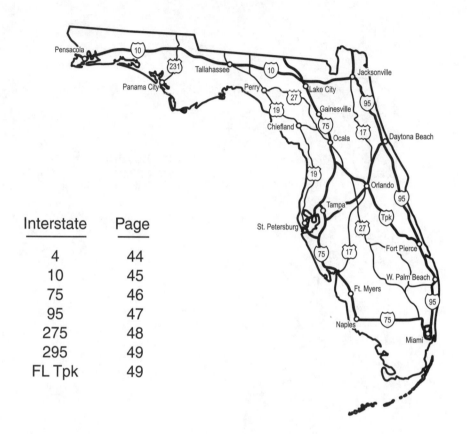

| Interstate | Page |
|:---:|:---:|
| 4 | 44 |
| 10 | 45 |
| 75 | 46 |
| 95 | 47 |
| 275 | 48 |
| 295 | 49 |
| FL Tpk | 49 |

 Interstate 4 runs east to west for 134 miles from I-95 in Daytona Beach to I-275 in Tampa. Eastbound travelers should read up the chart. Westbound travelers read down the chart.

| Exit(mm) | ↗ | * | ↗ | 👥 | 🚻 | 🧺 | 🔋 | 🏧 | 🐾 | W | S | K | T | C | Am | FJ | Lo | Pe | Pi | TA |
|---|---|---|---|---|---|---|---|---|---|---|---|---|---|---|---|---|---|---|---|---|
| (126) eb | | | T | | | | • | | | | | | | | | | | | | |
| 101c wb | | | | | | | | | | | s | | s | | | | | | | |
| 101a eb | | | | | | | | | | | s | | s | | | | | | | |
| 98 b | | | | | | | | | | | | s | s | | | | | | | |
| (95) b 1 | | | R | • | • | • | • | | • | | | | | | | | | | | |
| 78 b | | | | | | | | | | | | | s | | | | | | | |
| 75b b | | | | | | | | | | | | | | n | | | | | | |
| 74a b | | | | | | | | | | | | n | | | | | | | | |
| 64a b | | | | | | | | | | | | | | s+ | | | | | | |

E ↕ W

| Exit(mm) | 🡕 | ★ | 🡒 | 🚻 | ☎ | 🍽 | 🛗 | 🏪 | 🐾 | W | S | K | T | C | Am | FJ | Lo | Pe | Pi | TA |
|---|---|---|---|---|---|---|---|---|---|---|---|---|---|---|---|---|---|---|---|---|
| 55 | b | | | | | | | | | | | | | n | | | | | | |
| 48 | b | | | | | | | | | | | | | n | | | | | | |
| (46) | b | 1 | R | • | • | • | • | | • | | | | | | | | | | | |
| 44 | b | | | | | | | | | | | | | | | | | • | | |
| 33 | b | | | | | | | | | | | | | n | | | | | | |
| 32 | b | | | | | | | | | n+ | n | n | | | | | | | | |
| 10 | b | | | | | | | | | | | | | n | • | | | | | • |

*E ↕ W* (direction indicator at left of rows 46–33)

1) 24hr Security.

Interstate 10 in Florida runs east to west for 370 miles from I-95 in Jacksonville to the Alabama state line. Eastbound travelers should read up the chart. Westbound travelers read down the chart.

| Exit(mm) | 🡕 | ★ | 🡒 | 🚻 | ☎ | 🍽 | 🛗 | 🏪 | 🐾 | W | S | K | T | C | Am | FJ | Lo | Pe | Pi | TA |
|---|---|---|---|---|---|---|---|---|---|---|---|---|---|---|---|---|---|---|---|---|
| (351) | eb | 1 | R | • | • | • | • | | | | | | | | | | | | | |
| (350) | wb | 1 | R | • | • | • | • | | | | | | | | | | | | | |
| 343 | b | | | | | | | | | | | | | | | | | | • | • |
| 335 | b | | | | | | | | | n | | | | | | | | | | |
| (318) | b | 1 | R | • | • | • | • | | • | | | | | | | | | | | |
| (295) | wb | 1 | R | • | • | • | • | | • | | | | | | | | | | | |
| (294) | eb | 1 | R | • | • | • | • | | • | | | | | | | | | | | |
| 283 | b | | | | | | | | | s | | | | | | | | | | |
| (265) | b | 1 | R | • | • | • | • | | • | | | | | | | | | | | |
| (234) | b | 1 | R | • | • | • | | | • | | | | | | | | | | | |
| 203 | b | | | | | | | | | n+ | | | | | | | | | | |
| 199 | b | | | | | | | | | | n | | s | | | | | | | |
| (194) | b | 1 | R | • | • | • | • | | • | | | | | | | | | | | |
| 192 | b | | | | | | | | | | | | | | | | | • | | • |
| (161) | b | 1 | R | • | • | • | • | | • | | | | | | | | | | | |
| 142 | b | | | | | | | | | n | | | | | | | | | • | • |
| (133) | b | 1 | R | • | • | • | | | • | | | | | | | | | | | |
| 120 | b | | | | | | | | | n | | | | | | | | | | |
| 96 | b | 1 | R | • | • | • | | | • | | | | | | | | | | | |
| 85 | b | | | | | | | | | n | | | | | | | | | | |
| (60) | wb | 1 | R | • | • | • | • | | • | | | | | | | | | | | |
| (58) | eb | 1 | R | • | • | • | • | | • | | | | | | | | | | | |
| 56 | b | | | | | | | | | n | | | s | | | | | | | |
| (31) | b | 1 | R | • | • | • | | | • | | | | | | | | | | | |

*E ↕ W* (direction indicators at left of rows 318–283 and 142–96)

| Exit(mm) | ↗ | * | ■ | ■ | ■ | ■ | ■ | ■ | ■ | W | S | K | T | C | Am | FJ | Lo | Pe | Pi | TA |
|---|---|---|---|---|---|---|---|---|---|---|---|---|---|---|---|---|---|---|---|---|
| 10b | b | | | | | | | | | | n | | | | | | | | | |
| 7 | b | | | | | | | | | | | | | s | | | | | | |
| (4) | eb | 1 | W | • | • | • | • | | • | | | | | | | | | | | |

*1) 24hr Security.*

 **75** Interstate 75 in Florida runs north to south for 472 miles from the Georgia state line to the junction with FL 826 in Miami. Northbound travelers should read up the chart. Southbound travelers read down the chart.

| Exit(mm) | ↗ | * | ■ | ■ | ■ | ■ | ■ | ■ | ■ | W | S | K | T | C | Am | FJ | Lo | Pe | Pi | TA |
|---|---|---|---|---|---|---|---|---|---|---|---|---|---|---|---|---|---|---|---|---|
| (470) | sb | | W | • | • | • | • | | • | | | | | | | | | | | |
| 427 | b | | | | | | | | | e | | e | | e | | | | | | |
| (413) | b | | R | • | • | • | • | | • | | | | | | | | | | | |
| 387 | b | | | | | | | | | | | w | | | | | | | | |
| 384 | b | | | | | | | | | e | | | e | w | | | | | | |
| (383) | b | 1 | R | • | • | • | • | | • | | | | | | | | | | | |
| 368 | b | | | | | | | | | | | | | | | | | | • | |
| 358 | b | | | | | | | | | | | | | | | | | | • | |
| 350 | b | | | | | | | | | e | w | e | e | w | | | | | | |
| (346) | b | 1 | R | • | • | • | • | | • | | | | | | | | | | | |
| 341 | b | | | | | | | | | | | | | | | | | | • | |
| 329 | b | | | | | | | | | | | | | | | | | | • | • |
| 314 | b | | | | | | | | | e | | | | | | | | | | |
| (307) | b | | R | • | • | • | • | | • | | | | | | | | | | | |
| 301 | b | | | | | | | | | | | | | e | | | | | | |
| 285 | b | | | | | | | | | | | | | | | | • | | | |
| 279 | b | | | | | | | | | | | | | w | | | | | | |
| (278) | b | 1 | R | • | • | • | • | | • | | | | | | | | | | | |
| 257 | b | | | | | | | | | | e | e | | | | | | | | |
| 240a | sb | | | | | | | | | e | | | | | | | | | | |
| 240 | nb | | | | | | | | | e | | | | | | | | | | |
| (238) | b | 1 | R | • | • | • | • | | • | | | | | | | | | | | |
| 224 | b | | | | | | | | | | | | e | | | | | | | • |
| 220 | sb | | | | | | | | | w | | | w | | | | | | | |
| 220b | nb | | | | | | | | | w | | | w | | | | | | | |
| 210 | b | | | | | | | | | | w | w | | | | | | | | |
| 207 | b | | | | | | | | | w | | | | | | | | | | |
| 193 | b | | | | | | | | | | | | | w | | | | | | |

(Direction indicators in left margin: "N ↕ S" shown beside the 368–350 group and beside the 257–240 group.)

| Exit(mm) | ↗ | ★ | ⬈ | 🚻 | 📞 | ⛱ | 🛢 | 🏧 | 🐾 | W | S | K | T | C | Am | FJ | Lo | Pe | Pi | TA |
|---|---|---|---|---|---|---|---|---|---|---|---|---|---|---|---|---|---|---|---|---|
| 170 | b | | | | | | | | | | | | | w | | | | | | |
| 161 | b | 1 | R | • | • | • | • | | • | | | | | | | | | | | • |
| 141 | b | | | | | | | | | | | | | e | | | | | | |
| 139 | b | | | | | | | | | | | | | | | | | | | • |
| 136 | b | | | | | | | | | w | | | | | | | | | | |
| 131 | b | 1 | R | • | • | • | • | | • | | | | | w | | | | | | |
| 101 | b | | | | | | | | | | | | | w | | | | | | |
| (63) | b | 1 | R | • | • | • | • | | • | | | | | | | | | | | |
| (41) | sb | | T | | | • | | | | | | | | | | | | | | |
| (38) | nb | | T | | | • | | | | | | | | | | | | | | |
| (35) | b | 1 | R | • | • | • | • | | • | | | | | | | | | | | |
| (32) | b | | T | | | • | | | | | | | | | | | | | | |
| 11 | b | | | | | | | | | | | | | e | | | | | | |

*1) 24hr Security.*

Interstate 95 in Florida runs north to south for 382 miles from the Georgia state line to US 1 in Miami. Northbound travelers should read up the chart. Southbound travelers read down the chart.

| Exit(mm) | ↗ | ★ | ⬈ | 🚻 | 📞 | ⛱ | 🛢 | 🏧 | 🐾 | W | S | K | T | C | Am | FJ | Lo | Pe | Pi | TA |
|---|---|---|---|---|---|---|---|---|---|---|---|---|---|---|---|---|---|---|---|---|
| (378) | sb | 1 | W | • | • | • | • | | • | | | | | | | | | | | |
| 360 | b | | | | | | | | | | e | | | | | | | | | |
| 344 | b | | | | | | | | | | | | | w | | | | | | |
| 340 | nb | | | | | | | | | | | e | | | | | | | | |
| (331) | b | 1 | R | • | • | • | • | | • | | | | | | | | | | | |
| 329 | b | | | | | | | | | | | | | | | | | | • | • |
| 318 | b | | | | | | | | | | | | | w | | | | | | |
| 305 | b | | | | | | | | | | | | | | | | • | | | |
| (302) | b | 1 | R | • | • | • | • | | • | | | | | | | | | | | |
| 289 | b | | | | | | | | | w | w | | | e | | | | | | |
| 268 | b | | | | | | | | | e | e | | | w | | | | | | |
| 261a | sb | | | | | | | | | | | | e | e | | | | | | |
| 261 | nb | | | | | | | | | | | | e | e | | | | | | |
| 256 | b | | | | | | | | | | | | e | | | | | | | |
| 249a | sb | | | | | | | | | e+ | | | | | | | | | | |
| 249 | nb | | | | | | | | | e+ | | | | | | | | | | |
| (227) | sb | 1 | R | • | • | • | • | | • | | | | | | | | | | | |
| (225) | nb | 1 | R | • | • | • | • | | • | | | | | | | | | | | |
| 215 | b | | | | | | | | | e | | | w | | | | | | | |

| Exit(mm) | ↕ | ★ | ↗ | 👫 | ☎ | 🍴 | 🏪 | 🖥 | 🐾 | W | S | K | T | C | Am | FJ | Lo | Pe | Pi | TA |
|---|---|---|---|---|---|---|---|---|---|---|---|---|---|---|---|---|---|---|---|---|
| 201 | b | | | | | | | | | | | | | | | | | | • | |
| 191 | b | | | | | | | | | w | | | w | | | | | | | |
| 180 | b | | | | | | | | | e | | e+ | | | | | | | | |
| 176 | b | | | | | | | | | e | | | | | | | | | | |
| (168) | b | 1 | R | • | • | • | • | | • | | | | | | | | | | | |
| 147 | b | | | | | | | | | | | | w | | | | | | | • |
| (133) | b | 1 | R | • | • | • | • | | • | | | | | | | | | | | |
| 131b | b | | | | | | | | | | | | | | • | | | | | |
| 129 | b | | | | | | | | | e | | | w | | | | | | • | |
| (106) | b | 1 | R | • | • | • | • | | • | | | | | | | | | | | |
| 101 | b | | | | | | | | | | | | | e | | | | | | |
| 87a | b | | | | | | | | | e | | | | | | | | | | |
| 77 | b | | | | | | | | | | e | | | | | | | | | |
| 74 | b | | | | | | | | | | | | w | | | | | | | |
| 71 | b | | | | | | | | | | | e | | | | | | | | |
| 60 | b | | | | | | | | | | e | | | | | | | | | |
| 59 | b | | | | | | | | | | | w | | | | | | | | |
| 56 | b | | | | | | | | | | | | w | | | | | | | |
| 51 | b | | | | | | | | | | | e | | | | | | | | |
| 41 | b | | | | | | | | | | | | e | | | | | | | |
| 38a | sb | | | | | | | | | e | | | | | | | | | | |
| 38 | nb | | | | | | | | | e | | | | | | | | | | |
| 36b | sb | | | | | | | | | w | | | | | | | | | | |
| 36 | nb | | | | | | | | | w | | | | | | | | | | |
| 22 | b | | | | | | | | | | | e | | | | | | | | |
| 20 | b | | | | | | | | | | | | w | | | | | | | |

1) 24hr Security.

Interstate 275 runs north to south for about 60 miles from I-75 north of Tampa to I-75 north of Bradenton. Northbound travelers should read up the chart. Southbound travelers read down the chart.

| Exit(mm) | ↕ | ★ | ↗ | 👫 | ☎ | 🍴 | 🏪 | 🖥 | 🐾 | W | S | K | T | C | Am | FJ | Lo | Pe | Pi | TA |
|---|---|---|---|---|---|---|---|---|---|---|---|---|---|---|---|---|---|---|---|---|
| 50 | b | | | | | | | | | w | | | | | | | | | | |
| 49 | b | | | | | | | | | | w | | | | | | | | | |
| 41a | b | | | | | | | | | w | | | | | | | | | | |
| 26 | b | | | | | | | | | | | | | e | | | | | | |
| (13) | b | | R | • | • | • | • | | • | | | | | | | | | | | |
| (7) | b | | R | • | • | • | • | | • | | | | | | | | | | | |

I-295 in Florida forms a partial loop around Jacksonville that is 35 miles long. Exit numbering begins at Saint Augustine Rd and increases in a clockwise direction.

| Exit(mm) | ↗ | ★ | ↰ | 👪 | 🚹 | 📞 | ⛽ | 🛏 | 🍴 | 🐾 | W | S | K | T | C | Am | FJ | Lo | Pe | Pi | TA |
|---|---|---|---|---|---|---|---|---|---|---|---|---|---|---|---|---|---|---|---|---|---|
| 32 | b | | | | | | | | | | e | | | | | | | | | | |
| 19 | b | | | | | | | | | | e | w | | | | | | | | | |
| 16 | b | | | | | | | | | | e | | | | | | | | | | |
| 12 | b | | | | | | | | | | | w | | w | | | | | | | |
| 10 | b | | | | | | | | | | | | | w | | | | | | | |
| 5 | sb | | | | | | | | | | w | | e | | | | | | | | |
| 5b | nb | | | | | | | | | | | | e | | | | | | | | |
| 5a | nb | | | | | | | | | | w | | | | | | | | | | |

Florida's Turnpike is a system of 443 miles of limited-access toll highways. The chart below covers 312 miles of the system from I-75 in northern Florida to Homestead in southern Florida. Northbound travelers should read up the chart. Southbound travelers read down the chart.

| Exit(mm) | ↗ | ★ | ↰ | 👪 | 🚹 | 📞 | ⛽ | 🛏 | 🍴 | 🐾 | W | S | K | T | C | Am | FJ | Lo | Pe | Pi | TA |
|---|---|---|---|---|---|---|---|---|---|---|---|---|---|---|---|---|---|---|---|---|---|
| (299) | b | 1 | S | • | • | • | | | | | | | | | | | | | | | |
| (263) | b | 1 | S | • | • | • | | | | | | | | | | | | | | | |
| (229) | b | 1 | S | • | • | • | | | | | | | | | | | | | | | |
| 193 | b | | | | | | | | | | | | | | | | | | | | • |
| (184) | b | 1 | S | • | • | • | | | | | | | | | | | | | | | |
| 152 | b | | | | | | | | | | e+ | | | e | | | | | | | • |
| (144) | b | 1 | S | • | • | • | | | | | | | | | | | | | | | |
| 116 | b | | | | | | | | | | e | | | | | | | | | | |
| (94) | b | 1 | S | • | • | • | | | | | | | | | | | | | | | |
| (65) | b | 1 | S | • | • | • | | | | | | | | | | | | | | | |
| (19) | b | 1 | S | • | • | • | | | | | | | | | | | | | | | |

N ↑↓ S

*1) Gas, Food.*

# Georgia

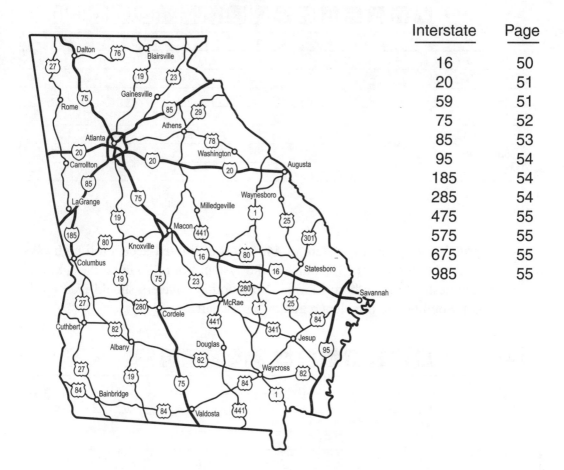

| Interstate | Page |
|:---:|:---:|
| 16 | 50 |
| 20 | 51 |
| 59 | 51 |
| 75 | 52 |
| 85 | 53 |
| 95 | 54 |
| 185 | 54 |
| 285 | 54 |
| 475 | 55 |
| 575 | 55 |
| 675 | 55 |
| 985 | 55 |

**16** Interstate 16 runs east to west for 167 miles from Savannah to I-75 in Macon. Eastbound travelers should read up the chart. Westbound travelers read down the chart.

| Exit(mm) | ⤴ | ★ | ↗ | 🚻 | 🚪 | ⛽ | 🏠 | 🏨 | ✈ | W | S | K | T | C | Am | FJ | Lo | Pe | Pi | TA |
|:---:|:---:|:---:|:---:|:---:|:---:|:---:|:---:|:---:|:---:|:---:|:---:|:---:|:---:|:---:|:---:|:---:|:---:|:---:|:---:|:---:|
| 160 | b | | | | | | | | | | | | | | | | | | | • |
| 51 | b | | | | | | | | | | | | s | | | | | | | • |
| 49 | b | | | | | | | | | | | | | | | | • | | | |
| (46) | wb | R | • | • | • | • | • | • | • | | | | | | | | | | | |
| (44) | eb | R | • | • | • | • | • | • | • | | | | | | | | | | | |

E ↕ W

Interstate 20 in Georgia runs east to west for 202 miles from the South Carolina state line to the Alabama state line. Eastbound travelers should read up the chart. Westbound travelers read down the chart.

| Exit(mm) | ↗ | ★ | 🅿 | 🚻 | ☎ | 🍴 | 🛏 | 🗺 | 🐾 | W | S | K | T | C | Am | FJ | Lo | Pe | Pi | TA |
|---|---|---|---|---|---|---|---|---|---|---|---|---|---|---|---|---|---|---|---|---|
| (201) | wb | W | • | • | • | • | • | • | • | | | | | | | | | | | |
| 200 | b | | | | | | | | | | | | | | | | | | • | |
| 196b | b | | | | | | | | | n | n | | | | | | | | | |
| 196a | b | | | | | | | | | | | | s | | | | | | | |
| 194 | b | | | | | | | | | | | | | s | | | | | • | |
| (182) | b | R | • | • | • | • | • | • | • | | | | | | | | | | | |
| 172 | b | | | | | | | | | | | s | | | | | | | | |
| 114 | b | | | | | | | | | n | | | | | | | | | • | • |
| (108) | wb | R | • | • | • | • | • | • | • | | | | | | | | | | | |
| (103) | eb | R | • | • | • | • | • | • | • | | | | | | | | | | | |
| 90 | b | | | | | | | | | | | s | | | | | | | | |
| (83) | wb | T | | • | | | | | | | | | | | | | | | | |
| 82 | b | | | | | | | | | n | | | s | n | | | | | | |
| (79) | eb | T | | • | | | | | | | | | | | | | | | | |
| 68 | b | | | | | | | | | n | | | | | | | | | | |
| 46a | wb | | | | | | | | | | s | | | | | | | | | |
| 46 | eb | | | | | | | | | | s | | | | | | | | | |
| 44 | b | | | | | | | | | | s | | | s | | | | | | |
| 37 | b | | | | | | | | | | | | | n | | | | | | |
| 36 | b | | | | | | | | | | | | s | | | | | | | |
| 34 | b | | | | | | | | | n | n | | | | | | | | | |
| 24 | b | | | | | | | | | | s | | | | | | | | | |
| 19 | b | | | | | | | | | | | | | | | • | | • | | |
| 11 | b | | | | | | | | | n | | | | | | | | | | |
| 9 | b | | | | | | | | | | | | | | | | • | | | |
| 5 | b | | | | | | | | | | | | | | | | | | | • |
| (1) | eb | W | • | • | • | • | | • | • | | | | | | | | | | | |

E ↕ W

E ↕ W

Interstate 59 in Georgia runs north to south for 20 miles from I-24 near the Tennessee state line to the Alabama state line. Northbound travelers should read up the chart. Southbound travelers read down the chart.

| Exit(mm) | ↗ | ★ | 🅿 | 🚻 | ☎ | 🍴 | 🛏 | 🗺 | 🐾 | W | S | K | T | C | Am | FJ | Lo | Pe | Pi | TA |
|---|---|---|---|---|---|---|---|---|---|---|---|---|---|---|---|---|---|---|---|---|
| (11) | b | 1 T | | | | | | | | | | | | | | | | | | |
| 4 | b | | | | | | | | | | | | | | | | | | | • |

*1) Scenic Vista*

**75** Interstate 75 in Georgia runs north to south for 355 miles from the Tennessee state line to the Florida state line. Northbound travelers should read up the chart. Southbound travelers read down the chart.

| Exit(mm) | ↗ | ★ | 🔀 | 👫 | ) | 🍴 | 🛢 | 🏧 | 🐎 | W | S | K | T | C | Am | FJ | Lo | Pe | Pi | TA |
|---|---|---|---|---|---|---|---|---|---|---|---|---|---|---|---|---|---|---|---|---|
| (352) | sb | | W | • | • | • | • | | | • | | | | | | | | | | | |
| 350 | b | | | | | | | | | | w+ | | | | | | | | | | |
| 348 | b | | | | | | | | | | | | | | e | | | | | | |
| 345 | b | | | | | | | | | | | | | | | • | | | | | |
| 336 | b | | | | | | | | | | e | | | | | | | | | | |
| 333 | b | | | | | | | | | | | | e | | e | | | | | | |
| 328 | b | | | | | | | | | | | | | | | | | | | • | |
| 326 | b | | | | | | | | | | | | | | | | | | | • | |
| 320 | b | | | | | | | | | | | | | | | | • | | | | |
| (319) | sb | | R | • | • | • | • | • | • | • | | | | | | | | | | | |
| 312 | b | | | | | | | | | | w | | | | e | | | | | | |
| (308) | nb | | R | • | • | • | • | • | • | • | | | | | | | | | | | |
| 296 | b | | | | | | | | | | | | | | | | | | | • | • |
| 290 | b | | | | | | | | | | | | | | w | | | | | | |
| 278 | b | | | | | | | | | | | | w | | | | | | | | |
| 271 | b | | | | | | | | | | e | | | | e | | | | | | |
| 269 | b | | | | | | | | | | | | | w | | | | | | | |
| 261 | b | | | | | | | | | | | | | | w | | | | | | |
| 260 | b | | | | | | | | | | | | | w | | | | | | | |
| 233 | b | | | | | | | | | | | | | | e | | | | | | |
| 231 | b | | | | | | | | | | | | | w | | | | | | | |
| 228 | b | | | | | | | | | | | | e | | | | | | | | |
| 218 | b | | | | | | | | | | e | | | | e | | | | | | |
| 201 | b | | | | | | | | | | | | | | | | • | • | | | • |
| 187 | b | | | | | | | | | | w | | | | | | | | | | |
| (179) | sb | | R | • | • | • | • | | • | • | | | | | | | | | | | |
| 171 | b | | | | | | | | | | | | | | e | | | | | | |
| 169 | b | | | | | | | | | | | | w | | | | | | | | |
| 146 | b | | | | | | | | | | | | | | | | | | | • | |
| 136 | b | | | | | | | | | | e | | | | | | | | | | |
| 135 | b | | | | | | | | | | | | | | e | | | | | | |
| (118) | sb | | R | • | • | • | • | • | • | • | | | | | | | | | | | |
| 109 | b | | | | | | | | | | | | | | | | | | | • | |
| (108) | nb | | R | • | • | • | • | • | • | • | | | | | | | | | | | |
| 101 | b | | | | | | | | | | w | | | w | | | | | | • | |
| 97 | b | | | | | | | | | | | | | | | | | | | | • |
| (85) | nb | | R | • | • | • | • | • | • | • | | | | | | | | | | | |
| (76) | sb | | R | • | • | • | • | • | • | • | | | | | | | | | | | |

| Exit(mm) | ⤢ | ★ | ↗ | 👫 | ☎ | ⛱ | 🛏 | 🖥 | 🐾 | W | S | K | T | C | Am | FJ | Lo | Pe | Pi | TA |
|---|---|---|---|---|---|---|---|---|---|---|---|---|---|---|---|---|---|---|---|---|
| 62 | b | | | | | | | | | w | | | | e | | | | | | |
| 60 | b | | | | | | | | | | | | | | | | | | • | |
| 59 | b | | | | | | | | | | | | | | | | | • | | |
| (48) | sb | | R | • | • | • | • | • | • | | | | | | | | | | | |
| (47) | nb | | R | • | • | • | • | • | • | | | | | | | | | | | |
| 18 | b | | | | | | | | | e | e | | e | e | | | | | | |
| 11 | b | | | | | | | | | | | | | | | | | | • | |
| 5 | b | | | | | | | | | | | | | w | | | | | | |
| (3) | nb | | W | • | • | • | • | | • | | | | | | | | | | | |
| 2 | b | | | | | | | | | | | | | | • | | | | | • |

Direction: N ↕ S (left margin).

---

**85**

Interstate 85 in Georgia runs north to south for 179 miles from the South Carolina state line to the Alabama state line. Northbound travelers should read up the chart. Southbound travelers read down the chart.

| Exit(mm) | ⤢ | ★ | ↗ | 👫 | ☎ | ⛱ | 🛏 | 🖥 | 🐾 | W | S | K | T | C | Am | FJ | Lo | Pe | Pi | TA |
|---|---|---|---|---|---|---|---|---|---|---|---|---|---|---|---|---|---|---|---|---|
| (176) | sb | | W | • | • | • | • | • | • | | | | | | | | | | | |
| (160) | nb | | R | • | • | • | • | | • | | | | | | | | | | | |
| 160 | b | | | | | | | | | | | | | | • | | • | | | |
| 149 | b | | | | | | | | | e | | | | w | | | | | | • |
| 129 | b | | | | | | | | | | | | | | | | | • | | |
| 115 | b | | | | | | | | | w+ | | | w | | | | | | | |
| (114) | sb | | R | • | • | • | • | • | • | | | | | | | | | | | |
| (112) | nb | | R | • | • | • | • | | • | | | | | | | | | | | |
| 111 | b | | | | | | | | | w | | | | e | | | | | | |
| 104 | b | | | | | | | | | | | e | | | | | | | | |
| 103 | b | | | | | | | | | | | w | | | | | | | | |
| 99 | b | | | | | | | | | | | e+ | | e | | | | | | |
| 91 | b | | | | | | | | | | | w | | | | | | | | |
| 89 | b | | | | | | | | | | | | e | | | | | | | |
| 69 | b | | | | | | | | | | | w | | | | | | | | |
| 64 | b | | | | | | | | | w | | | | w | | | | | | |
| 47 | b | | | | | | | | | e | | | w | w | | | | | | |
| 41 | b | | | | | | | | | | | | | | | | | | • | |
| 13 | b | | | | | | | | | | | | | | | | | | • | |
| (0.5) | nb | | W | • | • | • | • | • | • | | | | | | | | | | | |

Direction: N ↕ S (left margin).

Interstate 95 in Georgia runs north to south for 113 miles from the South Carolina state line to the Florida state line. Northbound travelers should read up the chart. Southbound travelers read down the chart.

N ↑↓ S

| Exit(mm) | ↗ | ★ | ◧ | 🚻 | ☎ | ⛱ | 🔧 | 🥤 | 🐾 | ⚑ | W | S | K | T | C | Am | FJ | Lo | Pe | Pi | TA |
|---|---|---|---|---|---|---|---|---|---|---|---|---|---|---|---|---|---|---|---|---|---|
| (111) | sb | | W | • | • | • | • | • | | • | | | | | | | | | | | |
| 109 | b | | | | | | | | | | | | | | | | | | | • | |
| 104 | b | | | | | | | | | | w | | | | | | | | | | |
| 102 | b | | | | | | | | | | | | | | e | | | | | | |
| 94 | b | | | | | | | | | | | e | | | e | | | | | | |
| 87 | b | | | | | | | | | | | | | | | | | | | | • |
| (41) | sb | | R | • | • | • | • | • | • | • | | | | | | | | | | | |
| 36a | b | | | | | | | | | | | | | | e | | | | | | |
| 29 | b | | | | | | | | | | | | | | | | | • | | • | • |
| 6 | b | | | | | | | | | | | | | | | | • | | | | |
| 3 | b | | | | | | | | | | | e | w | | | | | | | | |
| 1 | b | 1 | W | • | • | • | • | • | • | • | | | | | | | | • | | | |

*1) Welcome Center accessible to northbound travelers only*

 Interstate 185 is about 48 miles long. It runs north to south between I-85 near La Grange and US 27 south of Columbus. Northbound travelers should read up the chart. Southbound travelers read down the chart.

| Exit(mm) | ↗ | ★ | ◧ | 🚻 | ☎ | ⛱ | 🔧 | 🥤 | 🐾 | ⚑ | W | S | K | T | C | Am | FJ | Lo | Pe | Pi | TA |
|---|---|---|---|---|---|---|---|---|---|---|---|---|---|---|---|---|---|---|---|---|---|
| 12 | b | | W | • | • | • | • | • | • | • | | | | | | | | | | | |
| 8 | b | | | | | | | | | | | e | e | w | | | | | | | |

 Interstate 285 is a 62-mile loop around Atlanta. Exit numbering begins at Washington Road and increases in a clockwise direction.

| Exit(mm) | ↗ | ★ | ◧ | 🚻 | ☎ | ⛱ | 🔧 | 🥤 | 🐾 | ⚑ | W | S | K | T | C | Am | FJ | Lo | Pe | Pi | TA |
|---|---|---|---|---|---|---|---|---|---|---|---|---|---|---|---|---|---|---|---|---|---|
| 53 | b | | | | | | | | | | | | | | | | | | | | | • |
| 51 | b | | | | | | | | | | | | | | | | | | | | • | |
| 37 | b | | | | | | | | | | | | | | e | | | | | | | |
| 32 | b | | | | | | | | | | | | | e | e | | | | | | | |
| 25 | b | | | | | | | | | | | | | | n | | | | | | | |

| Exit(mm) | ↗ | ★ | | | | | | | | W | S | K | T | C | Am | FJ | Lo | Pe | Pi | TA |
|---|---|---|---|---|---|---|---|---|---|---|---|---|---|---|---|---|---|---|---|---|
| 19 | b | | | | | | | | | | | n | | | | | | | | |
| 16 | b | | | | | | | | | | | | | | | | | • | | |
| 12 | b | | | | | | | | | | | | | | | | • | | | |
| 5a | b | | | | | | | | | | e | | | | | | | | | |

Interstate 475 runs north to south for 16 miles. It begins on I-75 at exit 177 and ends at I-75 exit 156, bypassing Macon. Northbound travelers should read up the chart. Southbound travelers read down the chart.

| Exit(mm) | ↗ | ★ | | | | | | | | W | S | K | T | C | Am | FJ | Lo | Pe | Pi | TA |
|---|---|---|---|---|---|---|---|---|---|---|---|---|---|---|---|---|---|---|---|---|
| (8) | nb | R | • | • | • | • | • | • | | | | | | | | | | | | |
| 3 | b | | | | | | | | | e | e+ | e+ | e | | | | | | | |

Interstate 575 is 27 miles long. It runs north to south from GA 5 near Nelson to I-75 exit 268, north of Atlanta.

| Exit(mm) | ↗ | ★ | | | | | | | | W | S | K | T | C | Am | FJ | Lo | Pe | Pi | TA |
|---|---|---|---|---|---|---|---|---|---|---|---|---|---|---|---|---|---|---|---|---|
| 20 | b | | | | | | | | | e | | | w | | | | | | | |

Interstate 675 runs north to south for 10 miles between I-285 and I-75 near Atlanta.

| Exit(mm) | ↗ | ★ | | | | | | | | W | S | K | T | C | Am | FJ | Lo | Pe | Pi | TA |
|---|---|---|---|---|---|---|---|---|---|---|---|---|---|---|---|---|---|---|---|---|
| 1 | b | | | | | | | | | e | | | | | | | | | | |

Interstate 985 is 25 miles long. It runs north to south from US 23 near Gainesville to I-85 exit 113.

| Exit(mm) | ↗ | ★ | | | | | | | | W | S | K | T | C | Am | FJ | Lo | Pe | Pi | TA |
|---|---|---|---|---|---|---|---|---|---|---|---|---|---|---|---|---|---|---|---|---|
| 16 | b | | | | | | | | | n | | | | | | | | | | |
| 4 | b | | | | | | | | | s | | | | | | | | | | |

# Idaho

| Interstate | Page |
|:---:|:---:|
| 15 | 57 |
| 84 | 57 |
| 86 | 58 |
| 90 | 58 |
| 184 | 58 |

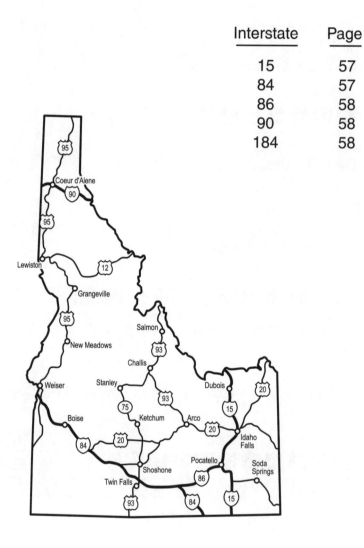

Interstate 15 in Idaho runs north to south for 196 miles from the Montana state line to the Utah state line. Northbound travelers should read up the chart. Southbound travelers read down the chart.

| Exit(mm) | ↗ | ★ | | | | | | | | W | S | K | T | C | Am | FJ | Lo | Pe | Pi | TA |
|---|---|---|---|---|---|---|---|---|---|---|---|---|---|---|---|---|---|---|---|---|
| 167 | b | | R | • | • | • | | | • | | | | | | | | | | | |
| (142) | b | 1 | T | | | | | | | | | | | | | | | | | |
| (101) | b | | R | • | • | • | | | • | | | | | | | | | | | |
| 93 | b | | | | | | | | | | | | e | | | | • | | | |
| (59) | b | | R | • | • | • | • | | • | | | | | | | | | | | |
| 47 | b | | | | | | | | | | | | | | | | • | | | |
| (25) | sb | | R | • | • | • | • | | • | | | | | | | | | | | |
| (7) | nb | | W | • | • | • | • | | • | | | | | | | | | | | |

*1) No Facilities*

Interstate 84 in Idaho runs east to west for approximately 276 miles from the Utah state line to the Oregon state line. Eastbound travelers should read up the chart. Westbound travelers read down the chart.

| Exit(mm) | ↗ | ★ | | | | | | | | W | S | K | T | C | Am | FJ | Lo | Pe | Pi | TA |
|---|---|---|---|---|---|---|---|---|---|---|---|---|---|---|---|---|---|---|---|---|
| (269) | b | | R | • | • | • | | | • | | | | | | | | | | | |
| (229) | b | | R | • | • | • | • | | • | | | | | | | | | | | |
| 208 | b | | | | | | | | | | | | s | | | | | | | |
| 182 | b | | | | | | | | | | | | | | | • | | | | |
| 173 | b | 1 | | | | | | | | | | | | s+ | | • | | | | |
| (171) | eb | | R | • | • | • | • | | • | | | | | | | | | | | |
| 168 | b | | | | | | | | | | | | n | | | | | | | |
| (133) | b | 2 | R | • | • | • | • | | • | | | | | | | | | | | |
| 95 | b | | | | | | | | | | | | s | | | | | • | | |
| (62) | b | | R | • | • | • | • | | • | | | | | | | | | | | |
| 54 | b | | | | | | | | | | | | | | | • | | | | • |
| 50a | b | | | | | | | | | | | | s | s | | | | | | |
| 29 | b | | | | | | | | | | | | s+ | | | • | | | | |
| (1) | eb | | W | • | • | • | • | | • | | | | | | | | | | | |

*1) Target is located 5 miles south of exit. 2) Phones (westbound)*

Interstate 86 runs east to west for about 63 miles from I-15 in Pocatello to I-84 exit 222, east of Heyburn. Eastbound travelers should read up the chart. Westbound travelers read down the chart.

| Exit(mm) | | ★ | | | | | | | | W | S | K | T | C | Am | FJ | Lo | Pe | Pi | TA |
|---|---|---|---|---|---|---|---|---|---|---|---|---|---|---|---|---|---|---|---|---|
| **E** 61 | b | | | | | | | | | s | s | | | | | | | | | |
| (31) wb | | R | • | • | • | • | | • | | | | | | | | | | | | |
| **W** (19) eb | | R | • | • | • | • | | • | | | | | | | | | | | | |

Interstate 90 in Idaho runs east to west for 74 miles from the Montana state line to the Washington state line. Eastbound travelers should read up the chart. Westbound travelers read down the chart.

| Exit(mm) | | ★ | | | | | | | | W | S | K | T | C | Am | FJ | Lo | Pe | Pi | TA |
|---|---|---|---|---|---|---|---|---|---|---|---|---|---|---|---|---|---|---|---|---|
| (73) wb | 1 | T | | | | | | | | | | | | | | | | | | |
| (72) eb | 1 | T | | | | | | | | | | | | | | | | | | |
| **E** (28) b | 2 | T | | | | | | | | | | | | | | | | | | |
| 12 b | | | | | | | | | | | | n | | | | | | | | |
| **W** (8) b | 3 | W | • | • | • | • | | • | | | | | | | | | | | | |
| 7 b | | | | | | | | | | | | | n | | | | | | | |
| 2 b | | | | | | | | | | | | | | | | | | | • | |

*1) Scenic Vista. 2) No Facilities. 3) Welcome Center (eastbound), Rest Area (westbound)*

Interstate 184 is a 6-mile spur off I-84 that ends at 13th Street in downtown Boise.

| Exit(mm) | | ★ | | | | | | | | W | S | K | T | C | Am | FJ | Lo | Pe | Pi | TA |
|---|---|---|---|---|---|---|---|---|---|---|---|---|---|---|---|---|---|---|---|---|
| 1 b | | | | | | | | | | | | | | w | | | | | | |

# Illinois

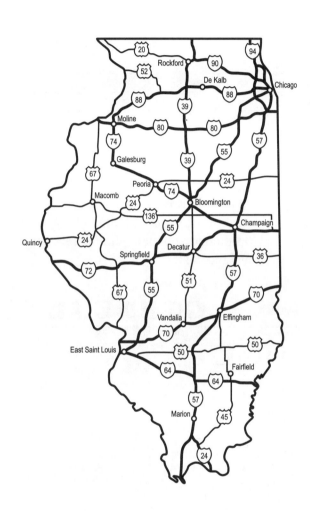

| Interstate | Page |
|:---:|:---:|
| 24 | 59 |
| 39 | 60 |
| 55 | 60 |
| 57 | 61 |
| 64 | 61 |
| 70 | 62 |
| 72 | 62 |
| 74 | 63 |
| 80 | 63 |
| 88 | 64 |
| 90 | 64 |
| 94 | 65 |
| 255 | 65 |
| 270 | 65 |
| 294 | 66 |

Interstate 24 in Illinois runs east to west for 38 miles from the Kentucky state line to Interstate 57 exit 44. Eastbound travelers should read up the chart. Westbound travelers read down the chart.

| Exit(mm) | ↗ | ★ | 🡭 | 🚻 | 🛗 | ⛽ | 🏪 | 🏢 | 🐾 | W | S | K | T | C | Am | FJ | Lo | Pe | Pi | TA |
|:---:|:---:|:---:|:---:|:---:|:---:|:---:|:---:|:---:|:---:|:---:|:---:|:---:|:---:|:---:|:---:|:---:|:---:|:---:|:---:|:---:|
| 37 | b | | W | • | • | • | • | | • | | | | | | | | | | | |

Interstate 39 in Illinois runs north to south for about 140 miles from the Wisconsin state line to I-55 exit 164. From Rockford to the Wisconsin state line, the Interstate is also I-90. Northbound travelers should read up the chart. Southbound travelers read down the chart.

| Exit(mm) | ↗ | ★ | | | | | | | | | W | S | K | T | C | Am | FJ | Lo | Pe | Pi | TA |
|---|---|---|---|---|---|---|---|---|---|---|---|---|---|---|---|---|---|---|---|---|---|
| **N** 1 | b | | | | | | | | | | | | | | | | • | | | | |
| (2) | sb | W | | • | • | • | • | | • | | | | | | | | | | | | |
| 90 | b | | | | | | | | | | | | | | | | | | | • | |
| **S** (85) | b | R | | • | • | • | • | | • | | | | | | | | | | | | |

I-55 in Illinois runs north to south for 295 miles from Chicago to the Missouri state line. Portions of the Interstate are shared with I-70, I-72, and I-74. Northbound travelers should read up the chart. Southbound travelers read down the chart.

| Exit(mm) | ↗ | ★ | | | | | | | | | W | S | K | T | C | Am | FJ | Lo | Pe | Pi | TA |
|---|---|---|---|---|---|---|---|---|---|---|---|---|---|---|---|---|---|---|---|---|---|
| 279b | b | | | | | | | | | | W+ | W+ | | W+ | | | | | | | |
| 263 | b | | | | | | | | | | | | | w | | | | | | | |
| 257 | b | | | | | | | | | | | | e | e | | | | | | | |
| 197 | b | | | | | | | | | | e | | | | | | | | | | |
| **N** (194) | b | R | | • | • | • | • | | • | | | | | | | | | | | | |
| 160b | b | | | | | | | | | | w | | | | | | | | | | |
| **S** 160a | b | | | | | | | | | | | | | e | | | | | | • | • |
| (149) | b | R | | • | • | • | • | | • | | | | | | | | | | | | |
| 126 | b | | | | | | | | | | e+ | | | e | | | | | | | |
| 109 | b | | | | | | | | | | | | | | | | | • | | | |
| (103) | sb | R | | • | • | • | • | | • | | | | | | | | | | | | |
| (102) | nb | R | | • | • | • | • | | • | | | | | | | | | | | | |
| 100b | b | | | | | | | | | | w | | | | | | | | | | |
| **N** 98b | b | | | | | | | | | | | w | | | | | | | | | |
| 90 | b | | | | | | | | | | | | | e | | | | | | | |
| **S** (64) | b | R | | • | • | • | • | | • | | | | | | | | | | | | |
| 52 | b | | | | | | | | | | e | | | | | | | | | | |
| (27) | b | 1 | W | • | • | • | • | | | | | | | | | | | | | | |
| 18 | b | | | | | | | | | | | | | w | | | | | | | |
| 4 | b | | | | | | | | | | | | | | • | | | | | | |

*1) Welcome Center (northbound), Rest Area (southbound)*

Interstate 57 in Illinois runs north to south for 358 miles from Chicago to the Missouri state line. Portions of the Interstate are shared with I-64 and I-70. Northbound travelers should read up the chart. Southbound travelers read down the chart.

| Exit(mm) | ↗ | ★ | ▣ | 🚻 | 📞 | 🍴 | 🛢 | 🏪 | 🐾 | W | S | K | T | C | Am | FJ | Lo | Pe | Pi | TA |
|---|---|---|---|---|---|---|---|---|---|---|---|---|---|---|---|---|---|---|---|---|
| 340a | sb | | | | | | | | | | e | e | e | e | | | | | |
| 340 | nb | | | | | | | | | | | | | e | | | | | |
| 335 | b | | | | | | | | | | | | | | | | | • | • | |
| (332) | b | W | | • | • | • | • | • | • | | | | | | | | | | |
| 315 | b | | | | | | | | | w | | w | e | e | | | | | | |
| (268) | b | R | | • | • | • | • | | • | | | | | | | | | | |
| (222) | b | R | | • | • | • | • | | • | | | | | | | | | | |
| 190b | b | | | | | | | | | w | | | w | | | | | | | |
| (165) | b | R | | • | • | • | • | | • | | | | | | | | | | |
| 162 | b | | | | | | | | | | | | | | | | | | • | |
| 160 | b | | | | | | | | | w | | e | | w | • | | | | | • |
| 159 | b | | | | | | | | | | | | | | | | | • | | |
| 116 | b | | | | | | | | | w | | | | | | | | | | |
| (114) | b | R | | • | • | • | • | | • | | | | | | | | | | |
| 95 | b | | | | | | | | | w | | e | | w | | | | | | • |
| 83 | b | | | | | | | | | | | | | | | • | | | | |
| (79) | sb | R | | • | • | • | • | | • | | | | | | | | | | |
| (74) | nb | R | | • | • | • | • | | • | | | | | | | | | | |
| 71 | b | | | | | | | | | w | | | | | | | | | | |
| 65 | b | | | | | | | | | | | w | | | | | | | | |
| 54b | b | | | | | | | | | w | w | | | | | | | | | |
| 53 | b | | | | | | | | | | | | w | | | | | | | |
| (40) | b | 1 | T | | | | | | | | | | | | | | | | |
| (32) | b | W | | • | • | • | • | | • | | | | | | | | | | |

*1) Scenic Vista*

I-64 in Illinois runs east to west for approximately 132 miles from the Indiana state line to the Missouri state line. A portion of the Interstate is also I-57. Eastbound travelers should read up the chart. Westbound travelers read down the chart.

| Exit(mm) | ↗ | ★ | ▣ | 🚻 | 📞 | 🍴 | 🛢 | 🏪 | 🐾 | W | S | K | T | C | Am | FJ | Lo | Pe | Pi | TA |
|---|---|---|---|---|---|---|---|---|---|---|---|---|---|---|---|---|---|---|---|---|
| (130) | wb | R | | • | • | • | • | | • | | | | | | | | | | |
| (86) | wb | R | | • | • | • | • | | • | | | | | | | | | | |

E ↕ W

| Exit(mm) | ↗ | * | | | | | | | | W | S | K | T | C | Am | FJ | Lo | Pe | Pi | TA |
|---|---|---|---|---|---|---|---|---|---|---|---|---|---|---|---|---|---|---|---|---|
| (82) | eb | | R | • | • | • | • | | • | | | | | | | | | | | |
| 95 | b | | | | | | | | | s | | n | | s | | | | | | • |
| (25) | b | 1 | W | • | • | • | • | | • | | | | | | | | | | | |
| 16 | b | | | | | | | | | | | | s | | | | | | | |
| 14 | b | | | | | | | | | s | s | | | | | | | | | |
| 12 | b | | | | | | | | | | | s | s | | | | | | | |
| 9 | b | | | | | | | | | | | | | s | | | | | | |

*1) Welcome Center (eastbound), Rest Area (westbound)*

Interstate 70 in Illinois runs east to west for 156 miles from the Indiana state line to the Missouri state line. Portions of the Interstate are also I-55 and I-57. Eastbound travelers should read up the chart. Westbound travelers read down the chart.

E ↕ W

| Exit(mm) | ↗ | * | | | | | | | | W | S | K | T | C | Am | FJ | Lo | Pe | Pi | TA |
|---|---|---|---|---|---|---|---|---|---|---|---|---|---|---|---|---|---|---|---|---|
| (149) | wb | | W | • | • | • | • | | • | | | | | | | | | | | |
| 162 | b | | | | | | | | | | | | | | | | | | • | |
| 160 | b | | | | | | | | | n | | s | | n | • | | | | | • |
| 159 | b | | | | | | | | | | | | | | | | | • | | |
| (86) | b | | R | • | • | • | • | | • | | | | | | | | | | | |
| 61 | b | | | | | | | | | s | | | | | | | | | | |
| (27) | b | 1 | W | • | • | • | • | | • | | | | | | | | | | | |
| 18 | b | | | | | | | | | | | | | n | | | | | • | |
| 4 | b | | | | | | | | | | | | | • | | | | | | |

*1) Welcome Center (eastbound), Rest Area (westbound)*

Interstate 72 in Illinois runs east to west for about 182 miles from I-57 in Champaign to US 36 near the Missouri state line. A portion of the Interstate is shared with Interstate 55. Eastbound travelers should read up the chart. Westbound travelers read down the chart.

E ↕ W

| Exit(mm) | ↗ | * | | | | | | | | W | S | K | T | C | Am | FJ | Lo | Pe | Pi | TA |
|---|---|---|---|---|---|---|---|---|---|---|---|---|---|---|---|---|---|---|---|---|
| (152) | b | | R | • | • | • | • | | • | | | | | | | | | | | |
| 141b | b | | | | | | | | | | | | n | | | | | | | |
| 141a | b | | | | | | | | | s | s | | | | | | | | | |
| 98b | eb | | | | | | | | | | | n | | | | | | | | |
| 93 | b | | | | | | | | | n | n | n | n | | | | | | | |

Interstate 74 in Illinois runs east to west for 221 miles from the Indiana state line to the Iowa state line. Portions of the Interstate are also I-55. Eastbound travelers should read up the chart. Westbound travelers read down the chart.

| Exit(mm) | dir | ★ | ↗ | 🚻 | ☎ | ⛱ | 🔲 | 🏪 | 🐾 | W | S | K | T | C | Am | FJ | Lo | Pe | Pi | TA |
|---|---|---|---|---|---|---|---|---|---|---|---|---|---|---|---|---|---|---|---|---|---|
| (208) | wb | | W | • | • | • | • | | • | | | | | | | | | | | |
| 184 | b | | | | | | | | | | | | | s | | | | | | |
| 181 | b | | | | | | | | | n | n | n | | | | | | | | |
| (156) | b | | R | • | • | • | • | | • | | | | | | | | | | | |
| 160b | b | | | | | | | | | n | | | | | | | | | | |
| 160a | b | | | | | | | | | | s | | | | | | | • | • | |
| (114) | b | | R | • | • | • | • | • | • | | | | | | | | | | | |
| 102 | wb | | | | | | | | | | s | | n | | | | | | | |
| 102b | eb | | | | | | | | | | s | | n | | | | | | | |
| 94 | b | | | | | | | | | s | | | | | | | | | | |
| 91b | wb | | | | | | | | | n+ | | | | | | | | | | |
| 91 | eb | | | | | | | | | n+ | | | | | | | | | | |
| 89 | b | | | | | | | | | | | | n | | | | | | | |
| (62) | b | | R | • | • | • | • | | • | | | | | | | | | | | |
| (30) | wb | | R | • | • | • | • | • | • | | | | | | | | | | | |
| (28) | eb | | R | • | • | • | • | • | • | | | | | | | | | | | |
| 4b | b | | | | | | | | | n | | | | | | | | | | |
| 2 | b | 1 | | | | | | | | | s | | | | | | | | | |
| 1 | b | 1 | | | | | | | | s | | s | | | | | | | | |

*1) This exit is in Iowa*

Interstate 80 in Illinois runs east to west for 163 miles from the Indiana state line to the Iowa state line. A small segment is shared with I-94 and I-294. Eastbound travelers should read up the chart. Westbound travelers read down the chart.

| Exit(mm) | dir | ★ | ↗ | 🚻 | ☎ | ⛱ | 🔲 | 🏪 | 🐾 | W | S | K | T | C | Am | FJ | Lo | Pe | Pi | TA |
|---|---|---|---|---|---|---|---|---|---|---|---|---|---|---|---|---|---|---|---|---|---|
| 161 | b | | | | | | | | | | s | n | | | | | | | | |
| (159) | b | 1 | S | • | • | • | | | | | | | | | | | | | | |
| 3b | b | | | | | | | | | | | s | s | | | | | | | |
| 137 | b | | | | | | | | | | | n | | | | | | | | |
| 130b | b | | | | | | | | | n | n | n | | | | | | | | |
| 127 | b | | | | | | | | | | | | n | | | | | | | |
| 122 | b | | | | | | | | | | | | | | | | | | • | |
| (119) | wb | | R | • | • | • | • | | • | | | | | | | | | | | |
| (117) | eb | | R | • | • | • | • | | • | | | | | | | | | | | |

| Exit(mm) | ↗ | * | ↗ | 👫 | ☎ | ⛺ | 🛖 | 🥤 | 🐕 | W | S | K | T | C | Am | FJ | Lo | Pe | Pi | TA |
|---|---|---|---|---|---|---|---|---|---|---|---|---|---|---|---|---|---|---|---|---|
| 112 | b | | | | | | | | | s | | | | | • | | | | | |
| 90 | b | | | | | | | | | s | | s | | n | | | | | | |
| 77 | b | | | | | | | | | | | | | | | | • | | | |
| 75 | b | | | | | | | | | s | s | s | | | | | | | | |
| 56 | b | | | | | | | | | s | | | | | | | | | | |
| (51) | b | | R | • | • | • | • | | • | | | | | | | | | | | |
| 19 | b | | | | | | | | | n | | | | | | | | | | |
| (1) | eb | 2 | W | • | • | • | | | • | | | | | | | | | | | |

*E ↕ W*

*1) Gas, Food. 2) Scenic Vista*

I-88 in Illinois runs east to west for 156 miles from I-290 in Chicago to I-80 near Moline. A portion of the Interstate is also the East-West Tollway. Eastbound travelers should read up the chart. Westbound travelers read down the chart.

| Exit(mm) | ↗ | * | ↗ | 👫 | ☎ | ⛺ | 🛖 | 🥤 | 🐕 | W | S | K | T | C | Am | FJ | Lo | Pe | Pi | TA |
|---|---|---|---|---|---|---|---|---|---|---|---|---|---|---|---|---|---|---|---|---|
| 123 | b | | | | | | | | | | | | | s | | | | | | |
| (93) | b | 1 | S | • | • | • | | | | | | | | | | | | | | |
| 41 | b | | | | | | | | | | | n+ | | | | | | | | |

*E ↕ W*

*1) Gas, Food*

Interstate 90 in Illinois runs east to west for 108 miles from the Indiana state line to the Wisconsin state line. Portions of the Interstate are also I-39, I-94, and the Northwest Tollway. Mile markers on the Northwest Tollway *decrease* from west to east, the opposite of the normal numbering system. Eastbound travelers should read up the chart. Westbound travelers read down the chart.

| Exit(mm) | ↗ | * | ↗ | 👫 | ☎ | ⛺ | 🛖 | 🥤 | 🐕 | W | S | K | T | C | Am | FJ | Lo | Pe | Pi | TA |
|---|---|---|---|---|---|---|---|---|---|---|---|---|---|---|---|---|---|---|---|---|
| 47a | b | | | | | | | | | | | | | n | | | | | | |
| (5) | b | 1 | S | • | • | • | | | | | | | | | | | | | | |
| 7 | b | | | | | | | | | | n+ | | | | | | | | | |
| 23b | b | | | | | | | | | | | | | n | | | | | | |
| 36 | b | | | | | | | | | | | | | | | | | • | | • |
| (55) | b | 1 | S | • | • | • | | | | | | | | | | | | | | |
| 63 | b | | | | | | | | | s | s | s | s | n | | | | | | |
| (2) | eb | | W | • | • | • | • | | • | | | | | | | | | | | |
| 1 | b | | | | | | | | | | | | | | | | | • | | |

*E ↕ W*

*1) Gas, Food*

Interstate 94 runs east to west for 77 miles from the Indiana state line to the Wisconsin state line. Portions are also I-80, I-90 and the Tri-State Tollway. Mile markers on the Tri-State Tollway *decrease* from west to east, the opposite of the usual numbering system. Eastbound travelers should read up the chart. Westbound travelers read down the chart.

| Exit(mm) | ↗ | ✶ | | | | | | | | W | S | K | T | C | Am | FJ | Lo | Pe | Pi | TA |
|---|---|---|---|---|---|---|---|---|---|---|---|---|---|---|---|---|---|---|---|---|
| 161 | b | | | | | | | | | | s | n | | | | | | | | |
| 47a | b | | | | | | | | | | | | n | | | | | | | |
| (60) | b | 1 | S | • | • | • | | | | | | | | | | | | | | |
| 70 | b | | | | | | | | | s | s | | s | n | | | | | | |
| 1a | eb | | | | | | | | | | | | | | | | | | | • |
| 1 | wb | | | | | | | | | | | | | | | | | | | • |

*E ↕ W*

1) Gas, Food

Interstate 255 is a 30-mile route that primarily runs north to south between I-270 near Granite City, Illinois and I-55 in Missouri. Northbound travelers should read up the chart. Southbound travelers read down the chart.

| Exit(mm) | ↗ | ✶ | | | | | | | | W | S | K | T | C | Am | FJ | Lo | Pe | Pi | TA |
|---|---|---|---|---|---|---|---|---|---|---|---|---|---|---|---|---|---|---|---|---|
| 13 | b | | | | | | | | | w | | | | | | | | | | |
| 2 | b | 1 | | | | | | | | n | | | | | | | | | | |
| 1d | wb | 1 | | | | | | | | | s | | | | | | | | | |
| 1c | eb | 1 | | | | | | | | | s | | | | | | | | | |

*N ↕ S*

1) This exit is in Missouri

I-270 forms an open loop around Saint Louis about 50 miles long. This portion in Illinois runs east to west from I-70/I-55 to the Missouri state line. See Missouri for that portion of the Interstate.

| Exit(mm) | ↗ | ✶ | | | | | | | | W | S | K | T | C | Am | FJ | Lo | Pe | Pi | TA |
|---|---|---|---|---|---|---|---|---|---|---|---|---|---|---|---|---|---|---|---|---|
| 6b | b | | | | | | | | | | | | | • | | | | | | |

Interstate 294 in the Chicago area is 53 miles long. It connects I-94 in southern Chicago with I-94 in northern Chicago. Portions are also I-80 and the Tri-State Tollway. Mile markers on the Tri-State Tollway *decrease* from west to east, the opposite of the usual numbering system. Eastbound travelers should read up the chart. Westbound travelers read down the chart.

| Exit(mm) | ⚡ | ★ | ↗ | 👫 | 🚹 | 🍴 | 🛢 | 🏪 | ✸ | W | S | K | T | C | Am | FJ | Lo | Pe | Pi | TA |
|---|---|---|---|---|---|---|---|---|---|---|---|---|---|---|---|---|---|---|---|---|
| (159) | b | 1 | S | • | • | • | | | | | | | | | | | | | | |
| 3b | b | | | | | | | | | | s | s | | | | | | | | |
| (25) | b | 1 | S | • | • | • | | | | | | | | | | | | | | |
| (38) | b | 1 | S | • | • | • | | | | | | | | | | | | | | |

*1) Gas, Food*

# Indiana

| Interstate | Page |
|:---:|:---:|
| 64 | 68 |
| 65 | 68 |
| 69 | 69 |
| 70 | 69 |
| 74 | 70 |
| 80 | 71 |
| 90 | 71 |
| 94 | 72 |
| 164 | 72 |
| 465 | 72 |
| 469 | 72 |

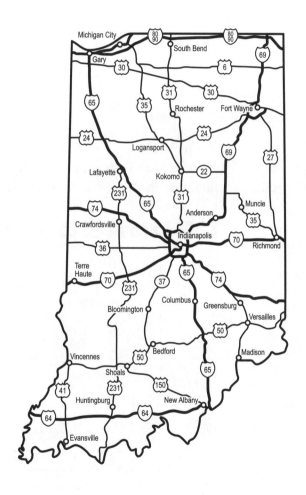

Interstate 64 in Indiana runs east to west for 124 miles from the Kentucky state line to the Illinois state line. Eastbound travelers should read up the chart. Westbound travelers read down the chart.

E ↑↓ W

| Exit(mm) | ⤴ | ★ | 🏞 | 🚻 | ☎ | ⛱ | 🛏 | 🏪 | 🐾 | W | S | K | T | C | Am | FJ | Lo | Pe | Pi | TA |
|---|---|---|---|---|---|---|---|---|---|---|---|---|---|---|---|---|---|---|---|---|
| (115) | wb | | W | • | • | • | • | | | | | | | | | | | | | |
| 105 | b | | | | | | | | | | | s | | | s | | | | | | |
| (97) | b | 1 | T | | | | | | | | | | | | | | | | | | |
| (81) | wb | 1 | T | | | | | | | | | | | | | | | | | | |
| (80) | eb | 1 | T | | | | | | | | | | | | | | | | | | |
| (58) | b | | R | • | • | • | • | | | • | | | | | | | | | | | |
| 57 | b | | | | | | | | | | | | | | | | | • | | | |
| 25b | b | | | | | | | | | | | | | | | | | • | | • | |
| (7) | eb | | W | • | • | • | | | • | • | | | | | | | | | | | |

1) No Facilities

Interstate 65 in Indiana runs north to south for 262 miles from US 12/20 in Gary to the Kentucky state line. Northbound travelers should read up the chart. Southbound travelers read down the chart.

N ↑↓ S

N ↑↓ S

| Exit(mm) | ⤴ | ★ | 🏞 | 🚻 | ☎ | ⛱ | 🛏 | 🏪 | 🐾 | W | S | K | T | C | Am | FJ | Lo | Pe | Pi | TA |
|---|---|---|---|---|---|---|---|---|---|---|---|---|---|---|---|---|---|---|---|---|
| 255 | b | | | | | | | | | | | | | | e | | | | | | |
| 253b | b | | | | | | | | | | | | w | | | | | | | | |
| 253a | b | | | | | | | | | | e | e | | e | | | | | | | |
| 240 | b | | | | | | | | | | | | | | | | | • | | • | |
| (231) | b | | R | • | • | • | • | | | • | | | | | | | | | | | |
| 201 | b | | | | | | | | | | | | | | | | | • | | • | |
| (196) | b | | R | • | • | • | • | | | • | | | | | | | | | | | |
| 172 | b | | | | | | | | | | w | w | | w | e | | | | | | |
| (150) | sb | | R | • | • | • | • | | | • | | | | | | | | | | | |
| (148) | nb | | R | • | • | • | • | | | • | | | | | | | | | | | |
| 139 | b | | | | | | | | | | | | | | | | | • | | | |
| 130 | b | | | | | | | | | | | | | | | | | | | | • |
| 119 | b | | | | | | | | | | | | | w | | | | | | | |
| 103 | b | | | | | | | | | | | | | e | w | | | | | | |
| 99 | b | | | | | | | | | | | | | w | | | | | | | |
| 95 | b | | | | | | | | | | | | | | | | | • | | • | |
| 76b | b | | | | | | | | | | | | | | w | | | | | | |
| (73) | b | | R | • | • | • | • | | | • | | | | | | | | | | | |
| 50b | b | | | | | | | | | | w | | | | w | | | | | | |
| 50a | b | | | | | | | | | | | | | | | | | | | | • |

| Exit(mm) | ↗ | ★ | ◪ | 👫 | ☎ | 🍴 | 🛏 | 💳 | 🐕 | W | S | K | T | C | Am | FJ | Lo | Pe | Pi | TA |
|---|---|---|---|---|---|---|---|---|---|---|---|---|---|---|---|---|---|---|---|---|
| 34 | b | | | | | | | | | | | | | | • | | | | | |
| 29b | sb | | | | | | | | | w | | | | | | | | | | |
| 29a | sb | | | | | | | | | | | | | e | | | | | | |
| 29 | nb | | | | | | | | | | | | | e | | | | | | |
| (22) | b | | R | • | • | • | • | | • | | | | | | | | | | | |
| 16 | b | | | | | | | | | | | | | | | | | | • | |
| 9 | b | | | | | | | | | | | | | e | | | | | | |
| 4 | b | | | | | | | | | w | | w | | | | | | | | |

N ↕ S

Interstate 69 in Indiana runs north to south for 158 miles from the Michigan state line to I-465 exit 37 in Indianapolis. Northbound travelers should read up the chart. Southbound travelers read down the chart.

| Exit(mm) | ↗ | ★ | ◪ | 👫 | ☎ | 🍴 | 🛏 | 💳 | 🐕 | W | S | K | T | C | Am | FJ | Lo | Pe | Pi | TA |
|---|---|---|---|---|---|---|---|---|---|---|---|---|---|---|---|---|---|---|---|---|
| 157 | b | | | | | | | | | | | | | | | | | • | • | |
| (144) | sb | | R | • | • | • | • | | • | | | | | | | | | | | |
| 129 | b | | | | | | | | | e | | | | w | | | | | | |
| 112a | b | | | | | | | | | e | | | | | | | | | | |
| 111b | b | | | | | | | | | | w | | w | | | | | | | |
| 105a | b | | | | | | | | | e | | | | | | | | | | |
| (93) | sb | | R | • | • | • | • | | • | | | | | | | | | | | |
| (89) | nb | | R | • | • | • | • | | • | | | | | | | | | | | |
| 59 | b | | | | | | | | | | | | | e | | | | | | |
| (50) | b | | R | • | • | • | • | | • | | | | | | | | | | | |
| 45 | b | | | | | | | | | | | | | | | | | • | | |
| 34 | b | | | | | | | | | | | | | | | | | | • | |
| 26 | b | | | | | | | | | w | | | w | w | | | | | | |
| 14 | b | | | | | | | | | | | | | | | | | | • | |
| 5 | b | | | | | | | | | | | | w | | | | | | | |
| 3 | b | | | | | | | | | w | w | | | e | | | | | | |

N ↕ S

Interstate 70 in Indiana runs east to west for 157 miles from the Ohio state line to the Illinois state line. Eastbound travelers should read up the chart. Westbound travelers read down the chart.

| Exit(mm) | ↗ | ★ | ◪ | 👫 | ☎ | 🍴 | 🛏 | 💳 | 🐕 | W | S | K | T | C | Am | FJ | Lo | Pe | Pi | TA |
|---|---|---|---|---|---|---|---|---|---|---|---|---|---|---|---|---|---|---|---|---|
| 156b | b | | | | | | | | | | | | | | | | | | • | |
| 156a | b | | | | | | | | | | s | | s | s | | | | | | |

| Exit(mm) | ↗ | * | | | | | | | | W | S | K | T | C | Am | FJ | Lo | Pe | Pi | TA |
|---|---|---|---|---|---|---|---|---|---|---|---|---|---|---|---|---|---|---|---|---|
| 149b | b | | | | | | | | | | | | | | | | | | • | |
| (144) | b | R | • | • | • | • | | • | | | | | | | | | | | | |
| 131 | b | | | | | | | | | | | | | | • | | | | | |
| (107) | b | R | • | • | • | • | | • | | | | | | | | | | | | |
| 104 | b | | | | | | | | | s | | | | | | | | | | |
| 96 | b | | | | | | | | | | | | | | | | | | • | |
| 91 | b | | | | | | | | | | | | | n | | | | | | |
| 66 | b | | | | | | | | | | | | | n | | | | | | |
| (65) | b | R | • | • | • | • | | • | | | | | | | | | | | | |
| 59 | b | | | | | | | | | | | | | | | | | | | • |
| 23 | b | | | | | | | | | | | | | | | | • | • | • | |
| 11 | b | | | | | | | | | | | | | | | | | | • | |
| 7 | b | | | | | | | | | s | s | | n | | | | | | | |
| (1) | eb | W | • | • | • | • | | • | | | | | | | | | | | | |

Interstate 74 in Indiana runs east to west for 172 miles from the Ohio state line to the Illinois state line. A portion is also shared with I-465. Eastbound travelers should read up the chart. Westbound travelers read down the chart.

| Exit(mm) | ↗ | * | | | | | | | | W | S | K | T | C | Am | FJ | Lo | Pe | Pi | TA |
|---|---|---|---|---|---|---|---|---|---|---|---|---|---|---|---|---|---|---|---|---|
| (152) | b | R | • | • | • | • | | • | | | | | | | | | | | | |
| 143 | b | | | | | | | | | | | | | | | | | | • | |
| 134a | b | | | | | | | | | s | | | | | | | | | | |
| 116 | b | | | | | | | | | s | | | | | | | | | | |
| 113 | b | | | | | | | | | | | | n | | | | | | | |
| 52 | b | | | | | | | | | | | s | | | | | | | | |
| 2a | b | | | | | | | | | | | | n | | | | | | | |
| 4 | b | | | | | | | | | | | | | | | | • | | • | |
| 12b | b | | | | | | | | | | | s | s | | | | | | | |
| 13a | b | | | | | | | | | | n | | | | | | | | | |
| 66 | b | | | | | | | | | s | | s | | | | | | | | |
| 61 | b | | | | | | | | | | | | | | | | • | | | |
| (57) | b | R | • | • | • | • | | • | | | | | | | | | | | | |
| (23) | b | R | • | • | • | • | | • | | | | | | | | | | | | |
| 4 | b | | | | | | | | | | | | | | | | | | • | |
| (1) | eb | W | • | • | • | • | • | • | | | | | | | | | | | | |

Interstate 80 in Indiana runs east to west for 152 miles from the Ohio state line to the Illinois state line. Portions are also I-90, I-94, and the Indiana Toll Road. Eastbound travelers should read up the chart. Westbound travelers read down the chart.

| Exit(mm) | ↗ | ★ | 🏞 | 🚻 | ☎ | ⛱ | 🛢 | 🍴 | 🐾 | W | S | K | T | C | Am | FJ | Lo | Pe | Pi | TA |
|---|---|---|---|---|---|---|---|---|---|---|---|---|---|---|---|---|---|---|---|---|
| (146) | b | 1 | S | • | • | • | | | | • | | | | | | | | | | | |
| (126) | b | 1 | S | • | • | • | | • | • | | | | | | | | | | | |
| 92 | b | | | | | | | | | | s | | n | | n | | | | | | |
| (90) | b | 1 | S | • | • | • | | • | • | | | | | | | | | | | |
| 83 | b | | | | | | | | | | | | n+ | | | | | | | | |
| 72 | b | 2 | | | | | | | | | | | | | | | | | • | | |
| (56) | b | 1 | S | • | • | • | | • | • | | | | | | | | | | | |
| (22) | b | 1 | S | • | • | • | | | • | | | | | | | | | | | |
| 15b | b | | | | | | | | | | | | | | | | | • | | | • |
| 9a | b | | | | | | | | | | | | | | | | | | • | • | |
| 6 | b | | | | | | | | | | | | | | | | | | | • | • |
| 5a | b | | | | | | | | | | | | s | | | | | | | | |
| 3 | wb | | | | | | | | | | | | | s | | | | | | | |
| 3a | eb | | | | | | | | | | | | | s | | | | | | | |
| 2 | wb | | | | | | | | | | | | s | | | | | | • | | |
| 2a | eb | | | | | | | | | | | | s | | | | | | • | | |

*1) Gas, Food. 2) Off US 31, north of I-80.*

Interstate 90 in Indiana runs east to west for about 157 miles from the Ohio state line to the Illinois state line. Portions are also I-80 and the Indiana Toll Road. Eastbound travelers should read up the chart. Westbound travelers read down the chart.

| Exit(mm) | ↗ | ★ | 🏞 | 🚻 | ☎ | ⛱ | 🛢 | 🍴 | 🐾 | W | S | K | T | C | Am | FJ | Lo | Pe | Pi | TA |
|---|---|---|---|---|---|---|---|---|---|---|---|---|---|---|---|---|---|---|---|---|
| (146) | b | 1 | S | • | • | • | | | | • | | | | | | | | | | | |
| (126) | b | 1 | S | • | • | • | | • | • | | | | | | | | | | | |
| 92 | b | | | | | | | | | | s | | n | | n | | | | | | |
| (90) | b | 1 | S | • | • | • | | • | • | | | | | | | | | | | |
| 83 | b | | | | | | | | | | | | n+ | | | | | | | | |
| 72 | b | 2 | | | | | | | | | | | | | | | | | • | | |
| (56) | b | 1 | S | • | • | • | | • | • | | | | | | | | | | | |
| (22) | b | 1 | S | • | • | • | | | • | | | | | | | | | | | |
| 21 | b | 3 | | | | | | | | | | | | | | | | | • | | | • |

*1) Gas, Food. 2) Off US 31, north of I-90. 3) Services located on IN 51 (Ripley St).*

Interstate 94 in Indiana runs east to west for 46 miles from the Michigan state line to the Illinois state line. A portion is also shared with I-80. Eastbound travelers should read up the chart. Westbound travelers read down the chart.

E ↕ W

| Exit(mm) | ↗ | ★ | 🏙 | 🚻 | ♿ | 🍽 | ⛽ | 🏨 | 🐾 | W | S | K | T | C | Am | FJ | Lo | Pe | Pi | TA |
|---|---|---|---|---|---|---|---|---|---|---|---|---|---|---|---|---|---|---|---|---|
| (43) | wb | | W | • | • | • | • | • | • | | | | | | | | | | | |
| 34b | b | | | | | | | | | n | | | | | | | | | | |
| 26a | b | | | | | | | | | | s | | | | | | | | | |
| 22b | b | | | | | | | | | | | | | | • | | | | • | |
| 22a | b | | | | | | | | | | | | | | | | | • | | |
| 15b | b | | | | | | | | | | | | | | | • | | | • | |
| 9a | b | | | | | | | | | | | | | | • | • | | | | |
| 6 | b | | | | | | | | | | | | | | | | | • | • | |
| 5a | b | | | | | | | | | | s | | | | | | | | | |
| 3 | wb | | | | | | | | | | | | s | | | | | | | |
| 3a | eb | | | | | | | | | | | | s | | | | | | | |
| 2 | wb | | | | | | | | | | s | | | | | | | | • | |
| 2a | eb | | | | | | | | | | s | | | | | | | | • | |

Interstate 164 runs north to south for 21 miles from I-64 near Elberfeld to US 41 in southern Evansville. Northbound travelers should read up the chart. Southbound travelers read down the chart.

| Exit(mm) | ↗ | ★ | 🏙 | 🚻 | ♿ | 🍽 | ⛽ | 🏨 | 🐾 | W | S | K | T | C | Am | FJ | Lo | Pe | Pi | TA |
|---|---|---|---|---|---|---|---|---|---|---|---|---|---|---|---|---|---|---|---|---|
| 7b | b | | | | | | | | | | | | | | w | | | | | |

Interstate 465 forms a 54-mile loop around Indianapolis. Exit numbering begins at US 31 and increases in a clockwise direction.

| Exit(mm) | ↗ | ★ | 🏙 | 🚻 | ♿ | 🍽 | ⛽ | 🏨 | 🐾 | W | S | K | T | C | Am | FJ | Lo | Pe | Pi | TA |
|---|---|---|---|---|---|---|---|---|---|---|---|---|---|---|---|---|---|---|---|---|
| 52 | b | | | | | | | | | | | s | | | | | | | | |
| 46 | b | | | | | | | | | | | w | e | | | | | | | |
| 42 | b | | | | | | | | | | | w | | | | | | | | |
| 27 | b | | | | | | | | | | s | | | | | | | | | |
| 17 | b | | | | | | | | | | | | | w | w | | | | | |
| 13a | b | | | | | | | | | | e | | | | | | | | | |

| Exit(mm) | ↗ | ★ | ◹ | ♿ | ☎ | ⛱ | 🛏 | 🏧 | 🐾 | W | S | K | T | C | Am | FJ | Lo | Pe | Pi | TA |
|---|---|---|---|---|---|---|---|---|---|---|---|---|---|---|---|---|---|---|---|---|
| 12b | b | | | | | | | | | | | w | w | | | | | | | |
| 4 | b | | | | | | | | | | | | | | | | • | | • | |
| 2a | b | | | | | | | | | | | | n | | | | | | | |

 Interstate 469 forms a partial loop around Fort Wayne. The Interstate is about 31 miles long. Exit numbering increases in a counter-clockwise direction.

| Exit(mm) | ↗ | ★ | ◹ | ♿ | ☎ | ⛱ | 🛏 | 🏧 | 🐾 | W | S | K | T | C | Am | FJ | Lo | Pe | Pi | TA |
|---|---|---|---|---|---|---|---|---|---|---|---|---|---|---|---|---|---|---|---|---|
| 25 | b | | | | | | | | | | w | | | w | | | | | | | |

# Iowa

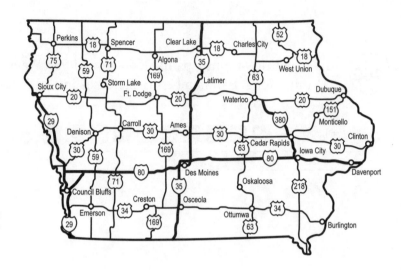

| Interstate | Page |
|:---:|:---:|
| 29 | 74 |
| 35 | 75 |
| 80 | 76 |
| 235 | 77 |
| 380 | 77 |
| 680 | 77 |

Interstate 29 in Iowa runs north to south for 152 miles from the South Dakota state line to the Missouri state line. A 4-mile section in Council Bluffs is also I-80. Northbound travelers should read up the chart. Southbound travelers read down the chart.

| Exit(mm) | ↗ | ★ | ⬈ | 👫 | 🚹 | ⛱ | 🛢 | 🏤 | 🐾 | W | S | K | T | C | Am | FJ | Lo | Pe | Pi | TA |
|:---:|:---:|:---:|:---:|:---:|:---:|:---:|:---:|:---:|:---:|:---:|:---:|:---:|:---:|:---:|:---:|:---:|:---:|:---:|:---:|:---:|
| 149 | b | | W | • | • | • | • | | | | | | | | | | | | | |
| 144a | b | | | | | | | | | | | | e+ | | | | | | | |
| 143 | b | | | | | | | | | e | e | | | | | | | | | |
| (139) | b | 1 | W | • | • | • | • | • | • | | | | | | | | | | | |
| (110) | b | | R | • | • | • | | • | • | | | | | | | | | | | |
| (91) | b | 2 | T | | | | | | | | | | | | | | | | | |
| (80) | sb | | R | • | • | • | | • | | | | | | | | | | | | |

N ↕ S

| Exit(mm) | ↗ | ★ | ↱ | 🚻 | ☎ | ⛱ | ⛽ | 🚮 | 🐾 | W | S | K | T | C | Am | FJ | Lo | Pe | Pi | TA |
|---|---|---|---|---|---|---|---|---|---|---|---|---|---|---|---|---|---|---|---|---|
| (78) | nb | | R | • | • | • | | • | | | | | | | | | | | | |
| 3 | b | | | | | | | | | w | w | | | w | | | | | | • |
| 1b | b | | | | | | | | | | | | | | | | | | • | |
| (38) | b | | R | • | • | • | • | • | • | | | | | | | | | | | |

*(N ↕ S)*

1) Welcome Center (southbound), Rest Area (northbound)
2) No Facilities.

Interstate 35 in Iowa runs north to south for 219 miles from the Minnesota state line to the Missouri state line. Part of the Interstate is also I-80. Northbound travelers should read up the chart. Southbound travelers read down the chart.

| Exit(mm) | ↗ | ★ | ↱ | 🚻 | ☎ | ⛱ | ⛽ | 🚮 | 🐾 | W | S | K | T | C | Am | FJ | Lo | Pe | Pi | TA |
|---|---|---|---|---|---|---|---|---|---|---|---|---|---|---|---|---|---|---|---|---|
| 214 | b | | W | • | • | • | • | • | • | | | | | | | | | | | |
| (196) | b | 1 | T | | | | | | | | | | | | | | | | | |
| (159) | b | | R | • | • | • | • | • | | | | | | | | | | | | |
| 144 | b | | | | | | | | | | | | | | | | | • | | | |
| (120) | nb | | R | • | • | • | • | • | • | | | | | | | | | | | |
| (119) | sb | | R | • | • | • | • | • | • | | | | | | | | | | | |
| (94) | b | | R | • | • | • | • | | | • | | | | | | | | | | | |
| 90 | b | | | | | | | | | | w | | | w | | | | | | | |
| 127 | b | | | | | | | | | | | | | e | | | | | | | |
| 126 | b | | | | | | | | | | | | | | | | | | | • | |
| 125 | b | | W | • | • | • | | | | | | | | | | | | • | | | |
| 124 | sb | | | | | | | | | | | | e | w | | | | | | | |
| 72c | nb | | | | | | | | | | | | e | w | | | | | | | |
| (53) | nb | 1 | T | | | | | | | | | | | | | | | | | | |
| (51) | sb | 1 | T | | | | | | | | | | | | | | | | | | |
| (33) | b | 2 | R | • | • | • | • | • | • | | | | | | | | | | | |
| (7) | b | 3 | W | • | • | • | • | • | • | | | | | | | | | | | |
| 4 | b | | W | • | • | • | | | | | | | | | | | | | | | |

*(N ↕ S)*

1) No Facilities
2) Wi-Fi Access
3) Welcome Center (northbound), Rest Area (southbound).

Interstate 80 in Iowa runs east to west for 307 miles from the Illinois state line to the Nebraska state line. A portion of the Interstate is also I-35. Eastbound travelers should read up the chart. Westbound travelers read down the chart.

| Exit(mm) | ➤ | ★ | type | 🚻 | 📞 | ⛱ | ⛽ | 🏪 | ✈ | W | S | K | T | C | Am | FJ | Lo | Pe | Pi | TA |
|---|---|---|---|---|---|---|---|---|---|---|---|---|---|---|---|---|---|---|---|---|
| 306 | b | 1 | W | • | • | • | | | • | | | | | | | | | | | |
| (300) | b | 2 | R | • | • | • | • | | • | | | | | | | | | | | |
| 295a | b | | | | | | | | | | | | | s | | | | | | |
| 292 | b | | | | | | | | | | | | | | • | | | | | |
| 284 | b | | | | | | | | | | | | | | | | | | • | • |
| (270) | b | 3 | W | • | • | • | • | • | • | | | | | | | | | | | |
| 265 | b | | | | | | | | | | | | | | | • | | | | |
| 240 | b | | | | | | | | | | | n | | s | | | | | | |
| (237) | b | | R | • | • | • | • | • | • | | | | | | | | | | | |
| 225 | b | | W | • | • | • | • | | | | | | | | | | | | | |
| (208) | b | | R | • | • | • | • | • | • | | | | | | | | | | | |
| 201 | b | | | | | | | | | | | | | | | • | | | | |
| (180) | b | 4 | R | • | • | • | • | • | • | | | | | | | | | | | |
| 168 | b | | | | | | | | | | | n+ | | | | | | | | |
| (147) | b | 2 | R | • | • | • | • | | • | | | | | | | | | | | |
| 142 | b | | | | | | | | | | | | | | | | | | | • |
| 127 | b | | | | | | | | | | | | | s | | | | | | |
| 126 | b | | | | | | | | | | | | | | | | | | | • |
| 125 | b | | W | • | • | • | | | | | | | | | | | • | | | |
| 124 | wb | | | | | | | | | | | | s | | | | | | n | |
| 121 | b | | | | | | | | | | | | n | | | | | | | |
| (119) | b | | R | • | • | • | • | • | • | | | | | | | | | | | |
| (81) | eb | 2 | R | • | • | • | • | • | • | | | | | | | | | | | |
| (80) | wb | 2 | R | • | • | • | • | • | • | | | | | | | | | | | |
| (32) | b | 5 | T | | | | | | | | | | | | | | | | | |
| (19) | b | 6 | W | • | • | • | • | • | • | | | | | | | | | | | |
| 3 | b | | | | | | | | | | s | s | | s | | | | | | • |
| 1b | b | | | | | | | | | | | | | | | | | | • | |

1) *Scenic Vista*
2) *Wi-Fi Access*
3) *Welcome Center (westbound), Rest Area (eastbound)*
4) *RV Dump Station eastbound only*
5) *No Facilities*
6) *Welcome Center (eastbound), Rest Area (westbound)*

I-235 is a 14-mile route in Des Moines that runs through the downtown area. It begins at I-35 exit 72 and ends at I-35/80 exit 137.

| Exit(mm) | ↗ | ★ | ⬛ | 👥 | 🚻 | ⛽ | 🛏 | 🧺 | 🐾 | W | S | K | T | C | Am | FJ | Lo | Pe | Pi | TA |
|---|---|---|---|---|---|---|---|---|---|---|---|---|---|---|---|---|---|---|---|---|
| 3 | b | | | | | | | n | n | | | | | | | | | | | |
| 1 | b | | | | | | | | | | n | | | | | | | | | |

Interstate 380 in Iowa is a 72-mile spur route off I-80 that connects Iowa City with Waterloo. It is a north/south route. Northbound travelers should read up the chart. Southbound travelers read down the chart.

| | Exit(mm) | ↗ | ★ | ⬛ | 👥 | 🚻 | ⛽ | 🛏 | 🧺 | 🐾 | W | S | K | T | C | Am | FJ | Lo | Pe | Pi | TA |
|---|---|---|---|---|---|---|---|---|---|---|---|---|---|---|---|---|---|---|---|---|---|
| N | 68 | b | | | | | | | | | | | | | | • | | | | | |
| ↕ | 24 | b | | | | | | | | | w | w | | w | | | | | | | |
| S | (13) | b | R | • | • | • | • | • | | | | | | | | | | | | | |

Interstate 680 is a 42-mile route connecting I-80 exit 27 in Iowa with I-80 exit 446 in Nebraska, west of Omaha. A portion of the Interstate is shared with I-29. It provides an alternate route around Omaha and Council Bluffs for I-80 travelers. Eastbound travelers should read up the chart. Westbound travelers read down the chart.

| | Exit(mm) | ↗ | ★ | ⬛ | 👥 | 🚻 | ⛽ | 🛏 | 🧺 | 🐾 | W | S | K | T | C | Am | FJ | Lo | Pe | Pi | TA |
|---|---|---|---|---|---|---|---|---|---|---|---|---|---|---|---|---|---|---|---|---|---|
| E | (18) | wb | R | • | • | • | | | | | | | | | | | | | | | |
| ↕ | (16) | eb | R | • | • | • | | | | | | | | | | | | | | | |
| W | (15) | wb | R | • | | • | | | | | | | | | | | | | | | |

# Kansas

| Interstate | Page |
|---|---|
| 35 | 78 |
| 70 | 79 |
| 135 | 80 |
| 470 | 80 |

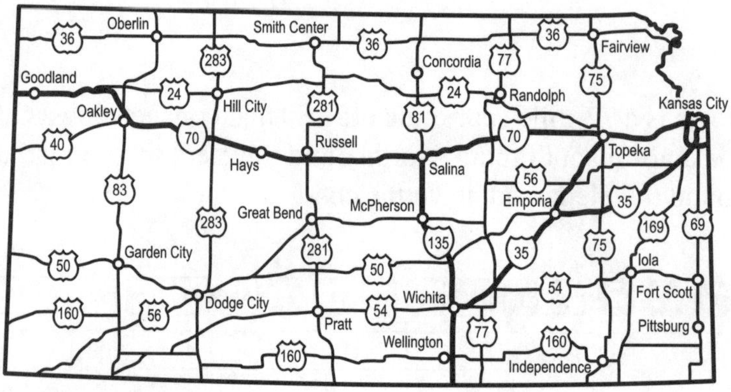

**35**   Interstate 35 in Kansas runs north to south for 235 miles from the Missouri state line to the Oklahoma state line. A portion of the Interstate is also the Kansas Turnpike. Northbound travelers should read up the chart. Southbound travelers read down the chart.

| Exit(mm) | ↗ | * | icons | W | S | K | T | C | Am | FJ | Lo | Pe | Pi | TA |
|---|---|---|---|---|---|---|---|---|---|---|---|---|---|---|
| 228b | b | | | | | | e | | | | | | | |
| 227 | b | | | e | | | | | | | | | | |
| 224 | b | | | | e | | | | | | | | | |
| 220 | b | | | | | | e | e | | | | | | |
| 218 | b | | | | | e | | | | | | | | |
| 215 | b | | | | | | e | | | | | | | |
| 183b | b | | | w | | | | | | | | | | |
| (175) | b | | R • • • • • • • | | | | | | | | | | | |
| 155 | b | | | | | | | | | | | | • | |
| 128 | b | | | w | | | | | | | | | | |
| 127 | b | | | | | | | | | | • | | | |
| (98) | b | 1 | S • • • • • | | | | | | | | | | | |
| 71 | b | | | e | | | | | | | | | | |

(Left margin direction indicator: N ↕ S)

| Exit(mm) | ↗ | ✱ | 🡥 | 👫 | ☎ | ⛱ | 🏪 | 🥤 | 🐾 | W | S | K | T | C | Am | FJ | Lo | Pe | Pi | TA |
|---|---|---|---|---|---|---|---|---|---|---|---|---|---|---|---|---|---|---|---|---|
| (65) | b | 1 | S | • | • | • | | | • | | | | | | | | | | | |
| 53 | b | | | | | | | | | w+ | | | | | | | | | | |
| 50 | b | | | | | | | | | e | | w | w | | | | | | | |
| 42 | b | | | | | | | | | | | | w | | | | | | | |
| (26) | b | 1 | S | • | • | • | | | • | | | | | | | | | | | |

N ↕ S

1) Gas, Food

 Interstate 70 in Kansas runs east to west for 423 miles from the Missouri state line to the Colorado state line. A segment is also the Kansas Turnpike. Eastbound travelers should read up the chart. Westbound travelers read down the chart.

| Exit(mm) | ↗ | ✱ | 🡥 | 👫 | ☎ | ⛱ | 🏪 | 🥤 | 🐾 | W | S | K | T | C | Am | FJ | Lo | Pe | Pi | TA |
|---|---|---|---|---|---|---|---|---|---|---|---|---|---|---|---|---|---|---|---|---|
| (414) | b | | T | • | | | | | | | | | | | | | | | | |
| 414 | b | | | | | | | | | | | | | | | | | n | | |
| 224 | b | | | | | | | | | s | | | | | | | | | | |
| (209) | b | 1 | S | • | • | • | | | • | | | | | | | | | | | |
| (188) | b | 1 | S | • | • | • | | | • | | | | | | | | | | | |
| 356 | b | | | | | | | | | s | s | | s | s | | | | | | |
| (336) | b | | R | • | • | • | | • | • | | | | | | | | | | | |
| (310) | b | | R | • | • | • | | • | • | | | | | | | | | | | |
| 298 | b | | | | | | | | | n | | | n | | | | | | | |
| (294) | b | | R | • | • | • | | • | • | | | | | | | | | | | |
| (265) | b | | R | • | • | • | | • | • | | | | | | | | | | | |
| 253 | b | | | | | | | | | | | | | | | | • | | | |
| 252 | b | | | | | | | | | | | | | | | | | | • | • |
| (224) | b | | R | • | • | • | | • | • | | | | | | | | | | | |
| (187) | b | | R | • | • | • | | • | • | | | | | | | | | | | |
| 159 | b | | | | | | | | | n | | | | | | | | | | |
| (132) | b | | R | • | • | • | • | • | • | | | | | | | | | | | |
| (97) | b | | R | • | • | • | • | • | • | | | | | | | | | | | |
| 76 | b | | | | | | | | | | | | | | | | • | | | |
| 53 | b | | | | | | | | | n | | | | | | | | | | |
| (48) | b | | R | • | • | • | • | • | • | | | | | | | | | | | |
| 17 | b | | | | | | | | | n | | | | | | | | | | |
| (7) | b | 2 | W | • | • | • | • | • | • | | | | | | | | | | | |

E ↕ W (upper)
E ↕ W (lower)

1) Gas, Food. 2) Welcome Center (eastbound), Rest Area (westbound).

Interstate 135 in Kansas runs north to south for 95 miles between Salina and Wichita. Northbound travelers should read up the chart. Southbound travelers read down the chart.

| Exit(mm) | 🡖 | ★ | 🢒 | 🚻 | ☎ | ⛱ | ▯ | 🚽 | 🐾 | W | S | K | T | C | Am | FJ | Lo | Pe | Pi | TA |
|---|---|---|---|---|---|---|---|---|---|---|---|---|---|---|---|---|---|---|---|---|
| 89 | b | | | | | | | | | e | e | | e | | | | | | | |
| (68) | b | R | • | • | • | | | • | • | | | | | | | | | | | |
| 60 | b | | | | | | | | | w | | | | | | | | | | |
| 31 | b | | | | | | | | | | | | | | • | | | | | |
| 30 | b | | | | | | | | | w | | | | | | | | | | |
| (23) | b | R | • | • | • | • | • | • | • | | | | | | | | | | | |
| 14 | b | | | | | | | | | | | | | e | | | | | | |
| 1b | b | | | | | | | | | | | w | | | | | | | | |

N ↕ S

Interstate 135 in Kansas runs north to south for 95 miles between Salina and Wichita. Northbound travelers should read up the chart. Southbound travelers read down the chart.

| Exit(mm) | 🡖 | ★ | 🢒 | 🚻 | ☎ | ⛱ | ▯ | 🚽 | 🐾 | W | S | K | T | C | Am | FJ | Lo | Pe | Pi | TA |
|---|---|---|---|---|---|---|---|---|---|---|---|---|---|---|---|---|---|---|---|---|
| 1b | b | | | | | | | | | | | | | n | | | | | | |

# Kentucky

| Interstate | Page |
|---|---|
| 24 | 81 |
| 64 | 82 |
| 65 | 82 |
| 71 | 83 |
| 75 | 84 |
| 265 | 84 |

Interstate 24 in Kentucky runs east to west for 94 miles from the Tennessee state line to the Illinois state line. Eastbound travelers should read up the chart. Westbound travelers read down the chart.

| Exit(mm) | ⤴ | ★ | 🅿 | 🚻 | 📞 | ⛱ | ⛽ | 🏪 | 🐾 | W | S | K | T | C | Am | FJ | Lo | Pe | Pi | TA |
|---|---|---|---|---|---|---|---|---|---|---|---|---|---|---|---|---|---|---|---|---|
| (93) | wb | | W | • | • | • | • | | • | | | | | | | | | | | |
| 89 | b | | | | | | | | | | | | | | | | | | | • |
| 86 | b | | | | | | | | | | | | | | | | | | • | • |
| 65 | b | | | | | | | | | | | | | | s | | | | | |
| 27 | b | | | | | | | | | | | | | | n | | | | | |
| 7 | b | 1 | W | • | • | • | • | | • | | | s | | | | | | | | |
| 4 | b | | | | | | | | | | s | s | | | s | | | | | |
| 3 | b | | | | | | | | | | | | | | | | | | | • |

E ↕ W

*1) Welcome Center (eastbound)*

Interstate 64 in Kentucky runs east to west for 192 miles from the West Virginia state line to the Indiana state line. Eastbound travelers should read up the chart. Westbound travelers read down the chart.

| Exit(mm) | ↗ | * | ↗ | 🚻 | ☎ | ⛱ | 🛈 | 🏪 | 🐾 | W | S | K | T | C | Am | FJ | Lo | Pe | Pi | TA |
|---|---|---|---|---|---|---|---|---|---|---|---|---|---|---|---|---|---|---|---|---|
| 185 | b | | | | | | | | | | | | | | | | • | | | |
| (174) | eb | | R | • | • | • | • | | • | | | | | | | | | | | |
| (173) | wb | | W | • | • | • | • | | • | | | | | | | | | | | |
| 172 | b | | | | | | | | | | | n | | | | | | • | | |
| (141) | b | | R | • | • | • | • | | • | | | | | | | | | | | |
| 137 | b | | | | | | | | | s | | | | | | | | | | |
| 110 | b | | | | | | | | | s | | | n | | | | | | | |
| (108) | wb | | R | • | • | • | • | | • | | | | | | | | | | | |
| (98) | eb | | R | • | • | • | • | | • | | | | | | | | | | | |
| 94 | b | | | | | | | | | s | s | | | | | | | | | |
| 115 | b | | | | | | | | | | | | n | | | | | | | |
| (60) | b | | R | • | • | • | • | | • | | | | | | | | | | | |
| 53b | b | | | | | | | | | n | | n | | | | | | | | |
| 43 | b | | | | | | | | | | | | | | | | • | | | |
| 35 | b | | | | | | | | | | | | n | | | | | | | |
| 32 | wb | | | | | | | | | n+ | | | | | | | | | | |
| 32b | eb | | | | | | | | | n+ | | | | | | | | | | |
| (29) | b | 1 | W | • | • | • | • | | • | | | | | | | | | | | |
| 28 | b | | | | | | | | | | | | | | | | | • | | |
| 17 | b | | | | | | | | | | s | | s | | | | | | | |
| 15 | b | | | | | | | | | s | s | | | | | | | | | |

1) *Welcome Center (eastbound), Rest Area (westbound)*

Interstate 65 in Kentucky runs north to south for 138 miles from the Indiana state line to the Tennessee state line. Northbound travelers should read up the chart. Southbound travelers read down the chart.

| Exit(mm) | ↗ | * | ↗ | 🚻 | ☎ | ⛱ | 🛈 | 🏪 | 🐾 | W | S | K | T | C | Am | FJ | Lo | Pe | Pi | TA |
|---|---|---|---|---|---|---|---|---|---|---|---|---|---|---|---|---|---|---|---|---|
| 133a | nb | | | | | | | | | | | | | e | | | | | | |
| 132 | sb | · | | | | | | | | | | | | w | | | | | | |
| 128 | b | | | | | | | | | | | e | | | | | | | | |
| 121 | b | | | | | | | | | | | | | e | | | | | • | |
| 116 | b | | | | | | | | | | | | | | | • | | | | |

| Exit(mm) | ⤤ | ★ | ➚ | 👫 | ) | 🏕 | ⛽ | 🏪 | 🐾 | W | S | K | T | C | Am | FJ | Lo | Pe | Pi | TA |
|---|---|---|---|---|---|---|---|---|---|---|---|---|---|---|---|---|---|---|---|---|
| (114) | sb |  | W | • | • | • | • |  | • |  |  |  |  |  |  |  |  |  |  |  |
| 105 | b |  |  |  |  |  |  |  |  |  |  |  |  |  |  |  |  |  | • |  |
| 94 | b |  |  |  |  |  |  |  |  |  |  |  | w |  |  |  |  |  |  |  |
| 86 | b |  |  |  |  |  |  |  |  |  |  |  |  |  |  |  |  | • | • |  |
| (82) | sb |  | R | • | • | • | • | • | • |  |  |  |  |  |  |  |  |  |  |  |
| (81) | nb |  | R | • | • | • | • | • | • |  |  |  |  |  |  |  |  |  |  |  |
| 81 | b |  |  |  |  |  |  |  |  |  |  |  |  |  |  |  |  |  | • |  |
| (55) | sb |  | R | • | • | • | • | • | • |  |  |  |  |  |  |  |  |  |  |  |
| 53 | b |  |  |  |  |  |  |  |  |  |  |  |  | e |  |  |  |  |  |  |
| (39) | nb |  | R | • | • | • | • | • | • |  |  |  |  |  |  |  |  |  |  |  |
| (30) | sb |  | R | • | • | • | • | • | • |  |  |  |  |  |  |  |  |  |  |  |
| 22 | b |  |  |  |  |  |  |  |  |  |  | w |  | e |  |  |  |  |  |  |  |
| 6 | b |  |  |  |  |  |  |  |  |  |  |  |  |  |  |  |  |  | • |  |
| 2 | b |  |  |  |  |  |  |  |  |  |  |  | w |  |  | • |  |  |  |  |  |
| (1) | nb |  | W | • | • | • | • |  | • |  |  |  |  |  |  |  |  |  |  |  |

N ↕ S

Interstate 71 in Kentucky runs north to south for 96 miles from the Ohio state line to I-64 exit 6 in Louisville. A portion of the Interstate is also I-75. Northbound travelers should read up the chart. Southbound travelers read down the chart.

| Exit(mm) | ⤤ | ★ | ➚ | 👫 | ) | 🏕 | ⛽ | 🏪 | 🐾 | W | S | K | T | C | Am | FJ | Lo | Pe | Pi | TA |
|---|---|---|---|---|---|---|---|---|---|---|---|---|---|---|---|---|---|---|---|---|
| 182 | b |  |  |  |  |  |  |  |  |  | w | w |  | w |  |  |  |  |  |  |  |
| 181 | b |  |  |  |  |  |  |  |  |  |  | w |  |  |  |  |  |  |  |  | • |
| (177) | b | 1 | W | • | • | • | • |  |  |  |  |  |  |  |  |  |  |  |  |  |  |
| 175 | b |  |  |  |  |  |  |  |  |  |  |  |  |  |  |  |  |  | • | • |  |
| 44 | b |  |  |  |  |  |  |  |  |  | w |  |  |  |  |  |  |  |  |  |  |
| 28 | b |  |  |  |  |  |  |  |  |  |  |  |  |  |  |  |  |  |  | • |  |
| 22 | b |  |  |  |  |  |  |  |  |  | e |  |  | w |  |  |  |  |  |  |  |
| (13) | b |  | R | • | • | • | • |  | • |  |  |  |  |  |  |  |  |  |  |  |  |

N ↕ S

1) Welcome Center (southbound), Rest Area (northbound)

Interstate 75 in Kentucky runs north to south for 192 miles from the Ohio state line to the Tennessee state line. A portion of it is shared with I-71. Northbound travelers should read up the chart. Southbound travelers read down the chart.

| Exit(mm) | ↗ | * | ↗ | 👫 | ☎ | 🍴 | ⛽ | 🛒 | 🐾 | W | S | K | T | C | Am | FJ | Lo | Pe | Pi | TA |
|---|---|---|---|---|---|---|---|---|---|---|---|---|---|---|---|---|---|---|---|---|
| 182 | b | | | | | | | | | w | w | | | w | | | | | | |
| 181 | b | | | | | | | | | | | w | | | | | | | | • |
| (177) | b | 1 | W | • | • | • | • | | | | | | | | | | | | | |
| 175 | b | | | | | | | | | | | | | | | | | | • | • |
| 171 | b | | | | | | | | | | | | | | | • | | | | |
| 159 | b | | | | | | | | | e | | | | w | | | | | | |
| 129 | b | | | | | | | | | | | | | | | | | • | | |
| (127) | b | | R | • | • | • | • | | • | | | | | | | | | | | |
| 126 | b | | | | | | | | | e | | w | | e | | | | | | |
| 120 | b | | | | | | | | | | | | | | • | | | | | |
| 115 | b | | | | | | | | | | | | | e | | | | | | |
| 110 | b | | | | | | | | | | | | | w | | | | | | |
| 108 | b | | | | | | | | | | | | w | | | | | | | |
| 95 | b | | | | | | | | | | | | | | | | • | | | |
| 90a | sb | | | | | | | | | | | | | e | | | | | | |
| 90 | nb | | | | | | | | | | | | | e | | | | | | |
| (82) | b | | R | • | • | • | • | | • | | | | | | | | | | | |
| 76 | b | | | | | | | | | e | | | | | | | | | | |
| 38 | b | | | | | | | | | e | | | | | | | | | | |
| 29 | b | | | | | | | | | | | | | w | | | • | | • | |
| 11 | b | | | | | | | | | w | | | | | | | | | • | |
| (1) | nb | | W | • | • | • | • | | • | | | | | | | | | | | |

*1) Welcome Center (southbound), Rest Area (northbound)*

Interstate 265 forms a partial loop around Louisville and is about 37 miles long. Exit numbering begins at US 31 and increases in a counter-clockwise direction.

| Exit(mm) | ↗ | * | ↗ | 👫 | ☎ | 🍴 | ⛽ | 🛒 | 🐾 | W | S | K | T | C | Am | FJ | Lo | Pe | Pi | TA |
|---|---|---|---|---|---|---|---|---|---|---|---|---|---|---|---|---|---|---|---|---|
| 265  32 | b | | | | | | | | | e | | w | | | | | | | | |
| 17 | b | | | | | | | | | | | | w | | | | | | | |

# Louisiana

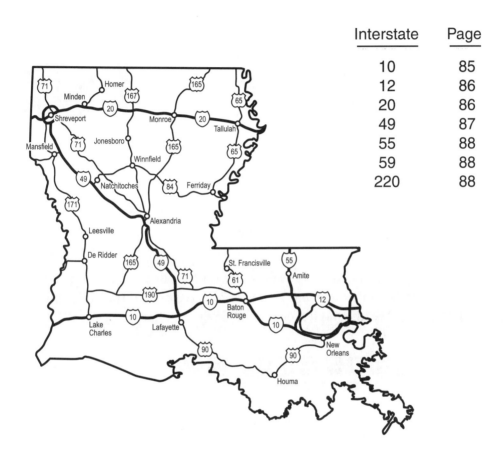

| Interstate | Page |
|:---:|:---:|
| 10 | 85 |
| 12 | 86 |
| 20 | 86 |
| 49 | 87 |
| 55 | 88 |
| 59 | 88 |
| 220 | 88 |

Interstate 10 in Louisiana runs east to west for 274 miles from the Mississippi state line to the Texas state line. Eastbound travelers should read up the chart. Westbound travelers read down the chart.

| Exit(mm) | ↗ | ★ | ◩ | 👫 | 🚻 | ⛺ | 🛏 | 🏢 | 🐾 | W | S | K | T | C | Am | FJ | Lo | Pe | Pi | TA |
|:---:|:---:|:---:|:---:|:---:|:---:|:---:|:---:|:---:|:---:|:---:|:---:|:---:|:---:|:---:|:---:|:---:|:---:|:---:|:---:|:---:|
| (270) | wb | | W | • | • | • | | • | • | | | | | | | | | | | |
| 266 | b | | | | | | | | | | | | | s | | | | | | • |
| 221 | b | | | | | | | | | | | n | | | | | | | | |
| 209 | b | | | | | | | | | | | | | | | | | | • | |
| 177 | b | | | | | | | | | | | | | s | | | | | | |
| 163 | b | | | | | | | | | | s | s | | n | | | | | | |

E ↑↓ W

| Exit(mm) | ↗ | * | i1 | i2 | i3 | i4 | i5 | i6 | i7 | i8 | W | S | K | T | C | Am | FJ | Lo | Pe | Pi | TA |
|---|---|---|---|---|---|---|---|---|---|---|---|---|---|---|---|---|---|---|---|---|---|
| 157b | b | | | | | | | | | | s | | | | | | | | | | |
| 151 | b | | | | | | | | | | | | | | | | | | • | • | |
| (121) | b | | R | • | • | • | | • | • | | | | | | | | | | | | |
| 112 | b | | | | | | | | | | | | | | | | | | | | • | |
| 109 | b | | | | | | | | | | | | | | | | | | | | • | |
| 103a | b | | | | | | | | | | | s | | | | | | | | | | |
| 101 | b | | | | | | | | | | | | | | s | | | | | | | • |
| 87 | b | | | | | | | | | | | | | | | | | | • | | | |
| 82 | b | | | | | | | | | | | s | | | | | | | | | | |
| 64 | b | | | | | | | | | | | s | | | | | | | | | | |
| 43 | b | | | | | | | | | | | | | | | | | | • | | | |
| 23 | b | | | | | | | | | | | n | | | s | | | | | | | |
| 20 | b | | | | | | | | | | | | | | | | | | | | • | |
| (1) | eb | | W | • | • | • | | • | | | | | | | | | | | | | |

---

**12** Interstate 12 in Louisiana runs east to west for about 85 miles between I-10 exit 159 in Baton Rouge and I-10 exit 267. Eastbound travelers should read up the chart. Westbound travelers read down the chart.

| Exit(mm) | ↗ | * | i1 | i2 | i3 | i4 | i5 | i6 | i7 | i8 | W | S | K | T | C | Am | FJ | Lo | Pe | Pi | TA |
|---|---|---|---|---|---|---|---|---|---|---|---|---|---|---|---|---|---|---|---|---|---|---|
| 80 | b | | | | | | | | | | | s | s | | n | | | | | | | |
| 63b | wb | | | | | | | | | | | n | | | | | | | | | | |
| 63 | eb | | | | | | | | | | | n | | | | | | | | | | |
| (60) | b | | R | • | • | • | | • | | | | | | | | | | | | | | |
| 40 | b | | | | | | | | | | | | | | | | | | | • | • | |
| 15 | b | | | | | | | | | | | n | | | | | | | | | | |
| 10 | b | | | | | | | | | | | | | | | | | | | | • | |
| 7 | b | | | | | | | | | | | s | | | | | | | | | | |
| 2b | b | | | | | | | | | | | | | | | n | | | | | | |

---

**20** Interstate 20 in Louisiana runs east to west for 189 miles from the Mississippi state line to the Texas state line. Eastbound travelers should read up the chart. Westbound travelers read down the chart.

| Exit(mm) | ↗ | * | i1 | i2 | i3 | i4 | i5 | i6 | i7 | i8 | W | S | K | T | C | Am | FJ | Lo | Pe | Pi | TA |
|---|---|---|---|---|---|---|---|---|---|---|---|---|---|---|---|---|---|---|---|---|---|---|
| (184) | b | 1 | W | • | • | • | | • | • | | | | | | | | | | | | | |

| Exit(mm) | ↗ | ★ | ⬈ | 🚻 | ☎ | ⛺ | ◨ | 🛒 | 🐾 | W | S | K | T | C | Am | FJ | Lo | Pe | Pi | TA |
|---|---|---|---|---|---|---|---|---|---|---|---|---|---|---|---|---|---|---|---|---|
| 171 | b | | | | | | | | | | | | | | | | | | • | • |
| (150) | b | | R | • | • | • | | • | • | | | | | | | | | | | |
| 138 | b | | | | | | | | | n | | | | | | | | | • | |
| 120 | b | | | | | | | | | | s | | | | | | | | | |
| 118b | wb | | | | | | | | | | | | n | | | | | | | |
| 118 | eb | | | | | | | | | | | | n | | | | | | | |
| 114 | b | | | | | | | | | n | | | s | | | | | | | |
| (97) | wb | | R | • | • | • | | • | • | | | | | | | | | | | |
| (95) | eb | | R | • | • | • | | • | • | | | | | | | | | | | |
| 86 | b | | | | | | | | | n | | | | | | | | | | |
| (58) | b | | R | • | • | • | | • | • | | | | | | | | | | | |
| 33 | b | | | | | | | | | | | | | | | | | | • | |
| 22 | b | | | | | | | | | | | n | | | | | | | | |
| 10 | b | | | | | | | | | s | | | s | | | | | | | |
| 8 | b | | | | | | | | | | | | | | | | | | • | • |
| 5 | b | | | | | | | | | | | | | | • | | | | | |
| 3 | b | | | | | | | | | | | | | | | • | • | | | |
| (2) | eb | | W | • | • | • | | • | • | | | | | | | | | | | |

1) Welcome Center (westbound), Rest Area (eastbound)

**49**  Interstate 49 in Louisiana runs north to south for 206 miles from I-20 exit 17 in Shreveport to I-10 exit 103 in Lafayette. Northbound travelers should read up the chart. Southbound travelers read down the chart.

| Exit(mm) | ↗ | ★ | ⬈ | 🚻 | ☎ | ⛺ | ◨ | 🛒 | 🐾 | W | S | K | T | C | Am | FJ | Lo | Pe | Pi | TA |
|---|---|---|---|---|---|---|---|---|---|---|---|---|---|---|---|---|---|---|---|---|
| 138 | b | 1 | | | | | | | | e+ | | | | | | | | | | |
| 90 | b | | | | | | | | | | | w | | | | | | | | |
| 83 | b | | | | | | | | | w+ | | w+ | | | | | | | | |
| 80 | b | | | | | | | | | | w+ | | | | | | | | | |
| (35) | b | | R | • | | • | | • | • | | | | | | | | | | | |
| 18 | b | | | | | | | | | e | | | | | | | | | | |
| 0 | b | 2 | | | | | | | | s | | | | | | | | | | |

1) Wal-Mart is 5 miles east of exit
2) Wal-Mart is on US 167

Interstate 55 in Louisiana runs north to south for 66 miles from the Mississippi state line to I-10 exit 209. Northbound travelers should read up the chart. Southbound travelers read down the chart.

| Exit(mm) | ⤴ | ★ | | | | | | | | W | S | K | T | C | Am | FJ | Lo | Pe | Pi | TA |
|---|---|---|---|---|---|---|---|---|---|---|---|---|---|---|---|---|---|---|---|---|
| N (65) | sb | W | • | • | • | | | • | • | | | | | | | | | | | |
| 31 | b | | | | | | | | | | e | | | | e | | | | | |
| S 1 | sb | | | | | | | | | | | | | | | | | | | • |

 Interstate 59 in Louisiana runs north to south for 11 miles from the Mississippi state line to I-10/12 in Slidell. Northbound travelers should read up the chart. Southbound travelers read down the chart.

| Exit(mm) | ⤴ | ★ | | | | | | | | W | S | K | T | C | Am | FJ | Lo | Pe | Pi | TA |
|---|---|---|---|---|---|---|---|---|---|---|---|---|---|---|---|---|---|---|---|---|
| (1) | sb | W | • | • | • | | | • | • | | | | | | | | | | | |

 Interstate 220 in Shreveport is 17 miles long. It begins on I-20 at exit 11 and ends at I-20 exit 26.

| Exit(mm) | ⤴ | ★ | | | | | | | | W | S | K | T | C | Am | FJ | Lo | Pe | Pi | TA |
|---|---|---|---|---|---|---|---|---|---|---|---|---|---|---|---|---|---|---|---|---|
| 12 | b | | | | | | | | | | | s | | | | | | | | |

# Maine

| Interstate | Page |
|:---:|:---:|
| 95 | 89 |
| 295 | 90 |

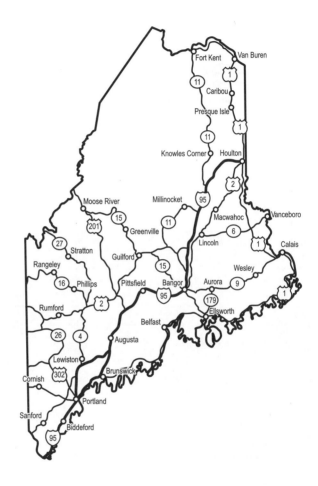

 Interstate 95 in Maine runs north to south for 305 miles from the United States/ Canada border to New Hampshire. A segment is also the Maine Turnpike. Northbound travelers should read up the chart. Southbound travelers read down the chart.

| Exit(mm) | ↗ | ⋆ | 🚻 | 🚹 | 🚾 | ⛽ | 🏕 | 🏧 | 🛏 | ✈ | W | S | K | T | C | Am | FJ | Lo | Pe | Pi | TA |
|---|---|---|---|---|---|---|---|---|---|---|---|---|---|---|---|---|---|---|---|---|---|
| 305 | b | | R | • | • | • | | | • | | | | | | | | | | | | |
| 302 | b | | | | | | | | | | w | | | | | | | | | | |
| (249) | nb | 1 | T | | | | | | | | | | | | | | | | | | |
| (240) | b | | R | • | • | • | | | • | | | | | | | | | | | | |

N ↑↓ S (direction indicator on left of table)

| Exit(mm) | ↗ | * | ⬈ | 🚻 | ☎ | 🍴 | 🛏 | ⛽ | 🐕 | W | S | K | T | C | Am | FJ | Lo | Pe | Pi | TA |
|---|---|---|---|---|---|---|---|---|---|---|---|---|---|---|---|---|---|---|---|---|
| (196) | b | 2 | T | | | | | | | | | | | | | | | | | |
| 187 | b | | | | | | | | | w | e | w | w | | | | | | | |
| (176) | sb | | W | • | • | • | • | | • | | | | | | | | | | | |
| (173) | nb | | W | • | • | • | • | | • | | | | | | | | | | | |
| 157 | b | | | | | | | | | w | | | | | | | | | | |
| (145) | b | | R | • | • | • | | | • | | | | | | | | | | | |
| 130 | b | | | | | | | | | | | | e | | | | | | | |
| 127 | b | | | | | | | | | e | | | | | | | | | | |
| (117) | sb | | R | • | • | • | • | | • | | | | | | | | | | | |
| (113) | nb | | R | • | • | • | • | | • | | | | | | | | | | | |
| 112 | sb | | | | | | | | | e | e | | | | | | | | | |
| 112a | nb | | | | | | | | | e | e | | | | | | | | | |
| 109a | sb | | | | | | | | | | | e | | | | | | | | |
| 109 | nb | | | | | | | | | | | e | | | | | | | | |
| (98) | nb | 3 | S | • | • | • | | | • | | | | | | | | | | | |
| (83) | sb | 3 | S | • | • | • | | | • | | | | | | | | | | | |
| (59) | nb | 3 | S | • | • | • | | | • | | | | | | | | | | | |
| (58) | sb | 3 | S | • | • | • | | | • | | | | | | | | | | | |
| 45 | b | | | | | | | | | | | | w | | | | | | | |
| 44 | nb | | | | | | | | | e | e | | | | | | | | | |
| 32 | b | | | | | | | | | e | | | | | | | | | | | |
| (25) | b | 3 | S | • | • | • | | | • | | | | | | | | | | | |
| (3) | nb | | W | • | • | • | • | | • | | | | | | | | | | | |
| 2 | b | | | | | | | | | | | | | | | | | | • | |

1) Scenic Vista
2) No Facilities
3) Gas, Food

Interstate 295 in Maine runs north to south from I-95 near Gardiner to I-95 near Scarborough. Northbound travelers should read up the chart. Southbound travelers read down the chart.

| Exit(mm) | ↗ | * | ⬈ | 🚻 | ☎ | 🍴 | 🛏 | ⛽ | 🐕 | W | S | K | T | C | Am | FJ | Lo | Pe | Pi | TA |
|---|---|---|---|---|---|---|---|---|---|---|---|---|---|---|---|---|---|---|---|---|
| 17 | b | | W | • | • | • | • | | | | | | | | | | | | | |

# Maryland

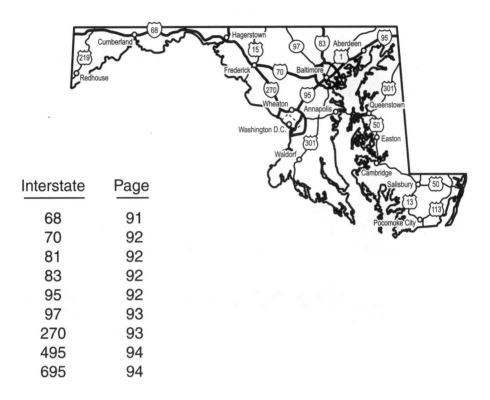

| Interstate | Page |
|---|---|
| 68 | 91 |
| 70 | 92 |
| 81 | 92 |
| 83 | 92 |
| 95 | 92 |
| 97 | 93 |
| 270 | 93 |
| 495 | 94 |
| 695 | 94 |

Interstate 68 in Maryland runs east to west for about 82 miles from I-70 exit 1 near Hancock to the West Virginia state line. Eastbound travelers should read up the chart. Westbound travelers read down the chart.

| Exit(mm) | ↗ | ★ | 🚗 | 🚻 | 🌙 | ⛱ | ⛽ | 🏪 | 🐾 | W | S | K | T | C | Am | FJ | Lo | Pe | Pi | TA |
|---|---|---|---|---|---|---|---|---|---|---|---|---|---|---|---|---|---|---|---|---|
| E (74) | b |  | R | • | • | • | • |  |  |  |  |  |  |  |  |  |  |  |  |  |
| (64) | b | 1 | T |  | • |  |  |  |  |  |  |  |  |  |  |  |  |  |  |  |
| 40 | b |  |  |  |  |  |  |  |  |  | s |  |  |  |  |  |  |  |  |  |
| W (6) | eb |  | W | • | • | • | • |  | • |  |  |  |  |  |  |  |  |  |  |  |

*1) Scenic Vista*

Interstate 70 in Maryland runs east to west for 94 miles from Baltimore at Cooks Lane to the Pennsylvania state line. Eastbound travelers should read up the chart. Westbound travelers read down the chart.

| Exit(mm) | ↗ | * | | | | | | | | W | S | K | T | C | Am | FJ | Lo | Pe | Pi | TA |
|---|---|---|---|---|---|---|---|---|---|---|---|---|---|---|---|---|---|---|---|---|
| 87a | b | 1 | | | | | | | | s+ | | | | | | | | | | |
| 68 | b | | | | | | | | | n | | | | | | | | | | |
| 54 | b | | | | | | | | | s | s | | | | | | | | | |
| (39) | b | | W | • | • | • | • | • | • | | | | | | | | | | | |
| 29 | b | | | | | | | | | | | | s | | | | | | | |
| 24 | b | | | | | | | | | | | | | | | | | | • | |

*E ↕ W*

1) Wal-Mart is two miles south of exit on US 40

Interstate 81 runs north to south for 12 miles between the Pennsylvania state line and the West Virginia state line. Northbound travelers should read up the chart. Southbound travelers read down the chart.

| Exit(mm) | ↗ | * | | | | | | | | W | S | K | T | C | Am | FJ | Lo | Pe | Pi | TA |
|---|---|---|---|---|---|---|---|---|---|---|---|---|---|---|---|---|---|---|---|---|
| 6b | b | | | | | | | | | w | | | | | | | | | | |
| 5 | b | | | | | | | | | | e | e | e | | | | | | | |

Interstate 83 runs north to south for 38 miles from the Pennsylvania state line to Fayette Street in downtown Baltimore. Northbound travelers should read up the chart. Southbound travelers read down the chart.

| Exit(mm) | ↗ | * | | | | | | | | W | S | K | T | C | Am | FJ | Lo | Pe | Pi | TA |
|---|---|---|---|---|---|---|---|---|---|---|---|---|---|---|---|---|---|---|---|---|
| 20 | b | | | | | | | | | e | | | | | | | | | | |

Interstate 95 in Maryland runs north to south for 110 miles from the Delaware state line to the Virginia state line. A portion of it is shared with I-495. Northbound travelers should read up the chart. Southbound travelers read down the chart.

| Exit(mm) | ↗ | * | | | | | | | | W | S | K | T | C | Am | FJ | Lo | Pe | Pi | TA |
|---|---|---|---|---|---|---|---|---|---|---|---|---|---|---|---|---|---|---|---|---|
| 109b | b | | | | | | | | | | | | | | | | | | • | |

| Exit(mm) | | * | | | | | | | | W | S | K | T | C | Am | FJ | Lo | Pe | Pi | TA |
|---|---|---|---|---|---|---|---|---|---|---|---|---|---|---|---|---|---|---|---|---|
| 109a | b | | | | | | | | | | | | | e | | | | | • | |
| 100 | b | | | | | | | | | | | | | | | | • | | | |
| (96) | b | 1 | S | • | • | • | • | | • | | | | | | | | | | | |
| 93 | b | | | | | | | | | | | | | | | | | | | • |
| 85 | b | | | | | | | | | | e | | e | | | | | | | |
| (81) | b | 1 | S | • | • | • | • | | • | | | | | | | | | | | |
| 80 | b | | | | | | | | | | | | | e | | | | | | |
| 77b | b | | | | | | | | | w | | | w | | | | | | | |
| 67a | b | | | | | | | | | | | | | e | | | | | | |
| 57 | b | | | | | | | | | | | | | | | | | | | • |
| 41a | b | | | | | | | | | | | | | | | | | | | • |
| (37) | b | | W | • | • | • | • | • | • | | | | | | | | | | | |
| 23 | b | | | | | | | | | | | | w+ | | | | | | | |
| 17 | b | | | | | | | | | w | | | | | | | | | | |

*N ↕ S*

1) Gas, Food

Interstate 97 runs north to south for 17 miles between I-695 in Ferndale and US 50 near Annapolis. Northbound travelers should read up the chart. Southbound travelers read down the chart.

| Exit(mm) | | * | | | | | | | | W | S | K | T | C | Am | FJ | Lo | Pe | Pi | TA |
|---|---|---|---|---|---|---|---|---|---|---|---|---|---|---|---|---|---|---|---|---|
| 12 | b | | | | | | | | | e | | e | | | | | | | | |

Interstate 270 in Maryland is 32 miles long. It connects I-70 exit 53 in Frederick with I-495 near Bethesda. Northbound travelers should read up the chart. Southbound travelers read down the chart.

| Exit(mm) | | * | | | | | | | | W | S | K | T | C | Am | FJ | Lo | Pe | Pi | TA |
|---|---|---|---|---|---|---|---|---|---|---|---|---|---|---|---|---|---|---|---|---|
| 31b | b | | | | | | | | | | | | | s | | | | | | |
| 31a | b | | | | | | | | | n | n | | | | | | | | | |
| (28) | wb | 1 | T | | | | | | | | | | | | | | | | | |
| 16 | b | | | | | | | | | n | | n | | | | | | | | |
| 11a | b | | | | | | | | | | n | | | | | | | | | |
| 8 | b | | | | | | | | | | | | | s | | | | | | |

*N ↕ S*

1) Scenic Vista

Interstate 495 forms a 64-mile loop around Washington, D.C. Portions of it are shared with I-95.

| Exit(mm) | ↗ | ★ | | | | | | | | | W | S | K | T | C | Am | FJ | Lo | Pe | Pi | TA |
|---|---|---|---|---|---|---|---|---|---|---|---|---|---|---|---|---|---|---|---|---|---|
| 23 | b | | | | | | | | | | | | | w+ | | | | | | | |
| 17 | b | | | | | | | | | | | w | | | | | | | | | |

 Interstate 695 forms a 48-mile loop around Baltimore. Exit numbering begins at MD 173 and increases in a clockwise direction. Exit numbers are based on the consecutive numbering system.

| Exit(mm) | ↗ | ★ | | | | | | | | | W | S | K | T | C | Am | FJ | Lo | Pe | Pi | TA |
|---|---|---|---|---|---|---|---|---|---|---|---|---|---|---|---|---|---|---|---|---|---|
| 35b | b | | | | | | | | | | n | n | | | | | | | | | |
| 32b | b | | | | | | | | | | | | n | | | | | | | | |
| 20 | b | | | | | | | | | | | | | s | | | | | | | |
| 15a | b | | | | | | | | | | | e | | | | | | | | | |
| 3a | b | | | | | | | | | | | | | s | | | | | | | |

# Massachusetts

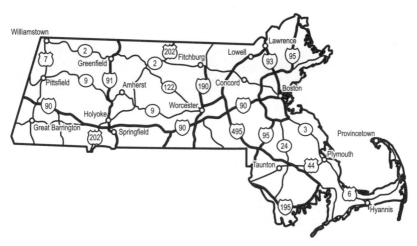

| Interstate | Page |
|------------|------|
| 84 | 95 |
| 90 | 96 |
| 91 | 96 |
| 93 | 96 |
| 95 | 97 |
| 195 | 97 |
| 290 | 98 |
| 495 | 98 |

Interstate 84 in Massachusetts runs east to west for approximately 8 miles from I-90 exit 9 to the Connecticut state line. Exit numbers are based on the consecutive numbering system. Eastbound travelers should read up the chart. Westbound travelers read down the chart.

| Exit(mm) | ↗ | ★ | 🔀 | 🚻 | 🛢 | ⛱ | 🛗 | 🏧 | ⛽ | W | S | K | T | C | Am | FJ | Lo | Pe | Pi | TA |
|----------|---|---|---|---|---|---|---|---|---|---|---|---|---|---|----|----|----|----|----|-----|
| 3a | b | | | | | | | | | | | | | s | | | | | | |
| (5) | wb | | T | | | • | | | | | | | | | | | | | | |
| (1) | eb | | T | | • | • | | | | | | | | | | | | | | |

E ↕ W

Interstate 90 in Massachusetts runs east to west for 136 miles from I-93 exit 20 in Boston to the New York state line. I-90 is also the Massachusetts Turnpike. Exit numbers are based on the consecutive numbering system. Eastbound travelers should read up the chart. Westbound travelers read down the chart.

| Exit(mm) | ⤴ | ★ | 🅿 | 🚻 | ☎ | ⛽ | 🍴 | 🏪 | 🐾 | W | S | K | T | C | Am | FJ | Lo | Pe | Pi | TA |
|---|---|---|---|---|---|---|---|---|---|---|---|---|---|---|---|---|---|---|---|---|
| (117) | eb | 1 | S | • | • | • | • | | | | | | | | | | | | | |
| 13 | b | | | | | | | | | | | | s | | | | | | | |
| (114) | wb | 1 | S | • | • | • | • | | | | | | | | | | | | | |
| (105) | wb | 1 | S | • | • | • | • | | | | | | | | | | | | | |
| (84) | wb | 1 | S | • | • | • | • | | | | | | | | | | | | | |
| (80) | eb | 1 | S | • | • | • | • | | | | | | | | | | | | | |
| (56) | wb | 1 | S | • | • | • | • | | | | | | | | | | | | | |
| (55) | eb | 1 | S | • | • | • | • | | | | | | | | | | | | | |
| 6 | b | | | | | | | | | | | | | | | • | | | | |
| (29) | b | 1 | S | • | • | • | • | | | | | | | | | | | | | |
| (12) | b | 2 | T | | | | | | | | | | | | | | | | | |
| (8) | b | 1 | S | • | • | • | • | | | | | | | | | | | | | |

E ↕ W

1) Gas, Food. 2)No Facilities.

Interstate 91 in Massachusetts runs north to south for 55 miles from the Vermont state line to the Connecticut state line. Exit numbers are based on the consecutive numbering system. Northbound travelers should read up the chart. Southbound travelers read down the chart.

| Exit(mm) | ⤴ | ★ | 🅿 | 🚻 | ☎ | ⛽ | 🍴 | 🏪 | 🐾 | W | S | K | T | C | Am | FJ | Lo | Pe | Pi | TA |
|---|---|---|---|---|---|---|---|---|---|---|---|---|---|---|---|---|---|---|---|---|
| (54) | b | | T | | • | | | | | | | | | | | | | | | |
| (34) | nb | 1 | T | | | | | | | | | | | | | | | | | |
| (18) | b | 2 | T | | • | | | | | | | | | | | | | | | |
| 15 | b | | | | | | | | | | | | e | e | | | | | | |

N ↕ S

1) No Facilities. 2) Scenic Vista.

Interstate 93 runs north to south for 47 miles from the New Hampshire state line to I-95 exit 12 in Canton. Exit numbers are based on the consecutive numbering system. Northbound travelers should read up the chart. Southbound travelers read down the chart.

| Exit(mm) | ⤴ | ★ | 🅿 | 🚻 | ☎ | ⛽ | 🍴 | 🏪 | 🐾 | W | S | K | T | C | Am | FJ | Lo | Pe | Pi | TA |
|---|---|---|---|---|---|---|---|---|---|---|---|---|---|---|---|---|---|---|---|---|
| 37c | b | | | | | | | | | | | | w | | | | | | | |

| Exit(mm) | | ★ | | | | | | | W | S | K | T | C | Am | FJ | Lo | Pe | Pi | TA |
|---|---|---|---|---|---|---|---|---|---|---|---|---|---|---|---|---|---|---|---|
| 29 | nb | | | | | | | | | | e | | | | | | | | |
| 16 | b | | | | | | | | | | w | | | | | | | | |

Interstate 95 in Massachusetts runs north to south for 90 miles from the New Hampshire state line to the Rhode Island state line. Exit numbers are based on the consecutive numbering system. Northbound travelers should read up the chart. Southbound travelers read down the chart.

| Exit(mm) | Dir | Note | ★ | 1 | 2 | 3 | 4 | 5 | 6 | W | S | K | T | C | Am | FJ | Lo | Pe | Pi | TA |
|---|---|---|---|---|---|---|---|---|---|---|---|---|---|---|---|---|---|---|---|---|
| (89) | sb | | W | • | • | • | • | | | | | | | | | | | | | |
| 57 | b | | | | | | | | | | | e | | | | | | | | |
| 47a | nb | | | | | | | | | e | | | | | | | | | | |
| (46) | nb | 1 | S | • | • | | | | | | | | | | | | | | | |
| (38) | sb | 1 | S | • | • | | | | | | | | | | | | | | | |
| (33) | sb | | T | | • | • | | | | | | | | | | | | | | |
| (27) | sb | | R | • | • | • | • | | | | | | | | | | | | | |
| 9 | b | | | | | | | | | w | | | | | | | | | | |
| (10) | b | 2 | W | • | • | • | • | | • | | | | | | | | | | | |
| (2) | nb | 3 | T | | | | | | | | | | | | | | | | | |
| 2a | b | | | | | | | | | | | e | | | | | | | | |

N ↕ S

1) Gas, Food
2) Welcome Center (northbound), Rest Area (southbound)
3) No Facilities

Interstate 195 in Massachusetts runs east to west for 40 miles from I-495 exit 1 to the Rhode Island state line. Exit numbers are based on the consecutive numbering system. Eastbound travelers should read up the chart. Westbound travelers read down the chart.

| Exit(mm) | Dir | Note | ★ | 1 | 2 | 3 | 4 | 5 | 6 | W | S | K | T | C | Am | FJ | Lo | Pe | Pi | TA |
|---|---|---|---|---|---|---|---|---|---|---|---|---|---|---|---|---|---|---|---|---|
| (37) | eb | | R | • | • | • | | | • | | | | | | | | | | | |
| 18 | b | | | | | | | | | s+ | | s+ | | | | | | | | |
| (6) | eb | | R | • | • | • | | | • | | | | | | | | | | | |
| (5) | wb | 1 | T | | | | | | | | | | | | | | | | | |
| 1 | b | | | | | | | | | s | s | | s | | | | | | | |

E ↕ W

1) No Facilities

Interstate 290 in Massachusetts is a 20-mile route between I-90 and I-495 in the Worcester area. Exit numbers are based on the consecutive numbering system. Eastbound travelers should read up the chart. Westbound travelers read down the chart.

| Exit(mm) | ↗ | * | | | | | | | | | W | S | K | T | C | Am | FJ | Lo | Pe | Pi | TA |
|---|---|---|---|---|---|---|---|---|---|---|---|---|---|---|---|---|---|---|---|---|---|
| 25a | b | | | | | | | | | | | | | | n | | | | | | |
| 21 | eb | | | | | | | | | | | | | | n | | | | | | . |

Interstate 495 in Massachusetts runs north to south for 120 miles from I-95 exit 59 near Amesbury to I-195 and MA 25 near Wareham. Exit numbers are based on the consecutive numbering system. Northbound travelers should read up the chart. Southbound travelers read down the chart.

| Exit(mm) | ↗ | * | | | | | | | | | W | S | K | T | C | Am | FJ | Lo | Pe | Pi | TA |
|---|---|---|---|---|---|---|---|---|---|---|---|---|---|---|---|---|---|---|---|---|---|
| (114) | sb | R | • | • | • | • | | | | | | | | | | | | | | | |
| (110) | nb | T | | • | • | | | | | | | | | | | | | | | | |
| 47 | b | | | | | | | | | | w+ | | | | | | | | | | |
| 39 | b | | | | | | | | | | | | | | w | | | | | | |
| 38 | b | | | | | | | | | | | w | | | | | | | | | |
| (87) | b | R | • | • | • | • | | • | | | | | | | | | | | | | |
| 19 | b | | | | | | | | | | | w | | | | | | | | | |
| 18 | b | | | | | | | | | | e | | | | | | | | | | |
| 15 | b | | | | | | | | | | | | | | e | | | | | | |
| (11) | b | T | | • | | | | | | | | | | | | | | | | | |

N ↕ S

# Michigan

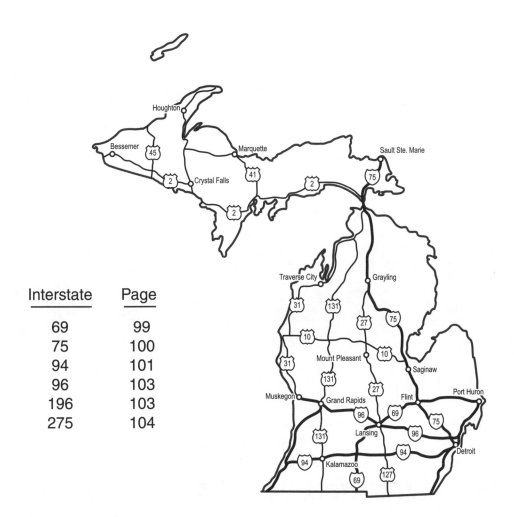

| Interstate | Page |
|---|---|
| 69 | 99 |
| 75 | 100 |
| 94 | 101 |
| 96 | 103 |
| 196 | 103 |
| 275 | 104 |

**69** Interstate 69 in Michigan runs north to south for 203 miles from Port Huron to the Indiana state line. Portions are shared with I-94 and I-96. Northbound travelers should read up the chart. Southbound travelers read down the chart.

| Exit(mm) | | ★ | | | | | | | | W | S | K | T | C | Am | FJ | Lo | Pe | Pi | TA |
|---|---|---|---|---|---|---|---|---|---|---|---|---|---|---|---|---|---|---|---|---|
| N 274 | b | | W | • | • | • | | | • | | | | | | | | w | | | |
| 199 | nb | | | | | | | | | | e | | e | | | | | | | |
| S (174) | sb | | R | • | • | • | • | | | • | | | | | | | | | | | |

| Exit(mm) | ↗ | * | ⛟ | 🚻 | ☎ | ⛱ | ◈ | 🥤 | 🐕 | W | S | K | T | C | Am | FJ | Lo | Pe | Pi | TA |
|---|---|---|---|---|---|---|---|---|---|---|---|---|---|---|---|---|---|---|---|---|
| (160) | nb | | R | • | • | • | • | | • | | | | | | | | | | | |
| 155 | b | | | | | | | | | | | w+ | | | | | | | | |
| 141 | b | | | | | | | | | | w | | w | | | | | | | |
| 139 | b | | | | | | | | | | | | | e | | | | | | |
| 138 | b | | | | | | | | | | | e | | | | | | | | |
| 131 | b | | | | | | | | | | | | | w | | | | | | |
| (126) | nb | | R | • | • | • | | | • | | | | | | | | | | | |
| (101) | sb | | R | • | • | • | | | • | | | | | | | | | | | |
| 81 | sb | | | | | | | | | | | | | | • | | | | | |
| 93a | b | | | | | | | | | | w | | | w | | | | | | |
| 70 | b | | | | | | | | | | | | | | • | | | | | |
| (68) | nb | | R | • | • | • | • | | • | | | | | | | | | | | |
| 61 | b | | | | | | | | | | e | | | | | | | | | |
| (41) | sb | | R | • | • | • | | | • | | | | | | | | | | | |
| 36 | b | | | | | | | | | | | e | | | | | | | | |
| (28) | nb | | R | • | • | • | | | • | | | | | | | | | | | |
| 25 | b | | | | | | | | | | | | | | • | | | | | |
| 13 | b | | | | | | | | | | e | | | | | | | | | |
| (6) | nb | | W | • | • | • | • | | • | | | | | | | | | | | |

N ↕ S

Interstate 75 in Michigan runs north to south for 395 miles from the United States/Canada border to the Ohio state line. Northbound travelers should read up the chart. Southbound travelers read down the chart.

| Exit(mm) | ↗ | * | ⛟ | 🚻 | ☎ | ⛱ | ◈ | 🥤 | 🐕 | W | S | K | T | C | Am | FJ | Lo | Pe | Pi | TA |
|---|---|---|---|---|---|---|---|---|---|---|---|---|---|---|---|---|---|---|---|---|
| 394 | b | | W | • | • | • | | | | | | | | | | | | | | |
| 392 | b | | | | | | | | | | | e | e | | | | | | | |
| (389) | nb | | R | • | • | • | | | • | | | | | | | | | | | |
| (346) | sb | 1 | R | • | • | • | | | • | | | | | | | | | | | |
| (343) | b | | W | • | • | • | | | | | | | | | | | | | | |
| 338 | b | | W | • | • | • | • | | | | | | | | | | | | | |
| (328) | sb | | R | • | • | • | | | • | | | | | | | | | | | |
| (317) | nb | 1 | R | • | • | • | | | • | | | | | | | | | | | |
| (287) | sb | | R | • | • | • | • | | • | | | | | | | | | | | |
| 282 | b | | | | | | | | | | w | | w | | | | | | | |
| (277) | nb | | R | • | • | • | • | | • | | | | | | | | | | | |
| (262) | sb | | R | • | • | • | • | | • | | | | | | | | | | | |
| 254 | nb | | | | | | | | | | | w+ | | | | | | | | |

N ↕ S

| Exit(mm) | ↗ | ★ |  |  |  |  |  |  |  | W | S | K | T | C | Am | FJ | Lo | Pe | Pi | TA |
|---|---|---|---|---|---|---|---|---|---|---|---|---|---|---|---|---|---|---|---|---|
| (251) | nb |  | R | • | • | • | • |  | • |  |  |  |  |  |  |  |  |  |  |  |
| (235) | sb |  | R | • | • | • | • |  | • |  |  |  |  |  |  |  |  |  |  |  |
| (210) | nb |  | R | • | • | • | • |  | • |  |  |  |  |  |  |  |  |  |  |  |
| (201) | sb |  | R | • | • | • | • |  | • |  |  |  |  |  |  |  |  |  |  |  |
| (175) | nb |  | R | • | • | • | • |  | • |  |  |  |  |  |  |  |  |  |  |  |
| 164 | b |  |  |  |  |  |  |  |  |  |  |  |  | e |  |  |  |  |  |  |
| (158) | sb |  | R | • | • | • | • |  | • |  |  |  |  |  |  |  |  |  |  |  |
| 151 | b |  |  |  |  |  |  |  |  |  |  |  |  |  |  |  |  |  | • |  |
| 149b | b |  |  |  |  |  |  |  |  |  |  | w |  |  |  |  |  |  |  |  |
| 144 | sb |  |  |  |  |  |  |  |  |  |  |  | w |  |  |  |  |  |  | • |
| 144b | nb |  |  |  |  |  |  |  |  |  |  |  | w |  |  |  |  |  |  | • |
| 131 | b |  |  |  |  |  |  |  |  |  |  | e |  |  |  |  |  |  |  |  |
| (129) | b |  | R | • | • | • | • |  | • |  |  |  |  |  |  |  |  |  |  |  |
| 122 | b |  |  |  |  |  |  |  |  |  |  |  | w |  |  |  |  |  |  |  |
| 118 | b |  |  |  |  |  |  |  |  | w | w |  |  |  |  |  |  |  |  |  |
| 117 | sb |  |  |  |  |  |  |  |  |  |  | e | w |  |  |  |  |  |  |  |
| 117b | nb |  |  |  |  |  |  |  |  |  |  | e | w |  |  |  |  |  |  |  |
| (95) | b |  | R | • | • | • | • |  | • |  |  |  |  |  |  |  |  |  |  |  |
| (86) | nb | 2 | T |  |  |  |  |  |  |  |  |  |  |  |  |  |  |  |  |  |
| 83b | sb |  |  |  |  |  |  |  |  |  |  |  | e |  |  |  |  |  |  |  |
| 83a | sb |  |  |  |  |  |  |  |  |  |  | w |  |  |  |  |  |  |  |  |
| 83 | nb |  |  |  |  |  |  |  |  |  |  | w | e |  |  |  |  |  |  |  |
| 77b | b |  |  |  |  |  |  |  |  | w+ |  |  |  |  |  |  |  |  |  |  |
| 65a | b |  |  |  |  |  |  |  |  |  | e |  |  |  |  |  |  |  |  |  |
| 63 | b |  |  |  |  |  |  |  |  |  |  | e |  |  |  |  |  |  |  |  |
| 42 | b |  |  |  |  |  |  |  |  |  |  | w |  |  |  |  |  |  |  |  |
| 32 | b |  |  |  |  |  |  |  |  |  |  | e | e | • |  |  |  |  |  |  |
| 18 | b |  |  |  |  |  |  |  |  |  |  |  |  |  |  |  |  |  | • |  |
| 15 | b |  |  |  |  |  |  |  |  |  |  |  | w |  |  |  |  |  | • | • |
| (10) | nb |  | W | • | • | • | • |  | • |  |  |  |  |  |  |  |  |  |  |  |

*1) Scenic Vista. 2) No Facilities*

**94** Interstate 94 in Michigan runs east to west for 275 miles from Port Huron to the Indiana state line. A portion of it is shared with I-69. Eastbound travelers should read up the chart. Westbound travelers read down the chart.

| Exit(mm) | ↗ | ★ |  |  |  |  |  |  |  | W | S | K | T | C | Am | FJ | Lo | Pe | Pi | TA |
|---|---|---|---|---|---|---|---|---|---|---|---|---|---|---|---|---|---|---|---|---|
| 274 | b |  | W | • | • | • |  |  | • |  |  |  |  | n |  |  |  |  |  |  |
| (255) | eb |  | R | • | • | • |  |  | • |  |  |  |  |  |  |  |  |  |  |  |

| Exit(mm) | ↗ | * | (R/W) |  |  |  |  |  |  | W | S | K | T | C | Am | FJ | Lo | Pe | Pi | TA |
|---|---|---|---|---|---|---|---|---|---|---|---|---|---|---|---|---|---|---|---|---|
| (251) | wb |  | R | • | • | • |  |  | • |  |  |  |  |  |  |  |  |  |  |  |
| 243 | b |  |  |  |  |  |  |  |  |  |  | n | n |  |  |  |  |  |  |  |
| 240 | wb |  |  |  |  |  |  |  |  | n |  |  |  |  |  |  |  |  |  |  |
| 240b | eb |  |  |  |  |  |  |  |  | n |  |  |  |  |  |  |  |  |  |  |
| 232 | b |  |  |  |  |  |  |  |  |  | s |  | s |  |  |  |  |  |  |  |
| 231 | eb |  |  |  |  |  |  |  |  |  | n | n |  |  |  |  |  |  |  |  |
| 230 | b |  |  |  |  |  |  |  |  | n |  |  |  |  |  |  |  |  |  |  |
| 202b | b |  |  |  |  |  |  |  |  | s |  |  |  |  |  |  |  |  |  |  |
| 190 | b |  |  |  |  |  |  |  |  | n |  |  |  | n |  |  |  |  |  |  |
| 187 | b |  |  |  |  |  |  |  |  |  | s |  |  |  |  |  |  |  |  |  |
| 181b | wb |  |  |  |  |  |  |  |  | n |  |  |  |  |  |  |  |  |  |  |
| 181 | eb |  |  |  |  |  |  |  |  | n |  |  |  |  |  |  |  |  |  |  |
| 175 | b |  |  |  |  |  |  |  |  |  |  |  | s |  |  |  |  |  |  |  |
| 172 | b |  |  |  |  |  |  |  |  |  | n |  |  |  |  |  |  |  |  |  |
| (168) | eb |  | R | • | • | • | • | • | • |  |  |  |  |  |  |  |  |  |  |  |
| 167 | b |  |  |  |  |  |  |  |  |  |  |  |  |  |  |  |  |  | • | • |
| (150) | wb |  | R | • | • | • | • | • | • |  |  |  |  |  |  |  |  |  |  |  |
| 138 | b |  |  |  |  |  |  |  |  |  |  |  | s |  |  |  |  |  |  |  |
| 137 | b |  |  |  |  |  |  |  |  |  | s | s | s |  |  |  |  |  |  |  |
| (135) | eb |  | R | • | • | • | • | • | • |  |  |  |  |  |  |  |  |  |  |  |
| (113) | wb |  | R | • | • | • | • | • | • |  |  |  |  |  |  |  |  |  |  |  |
| 104 | b |  |  |  |  |  |  |  |  |  |  |  |  |  | • |  |  | • |  |  |  |
| 98a | b |  |  |  |  |  |  |  |  | s | s |  |  |  |  |  |  |  |  |  |  |
| 97 | b |  |  |  |  |  |  |  |  |  | s | s | s |  |  |  |  |  |  |  |
| (96) | eb |  | R | • | • | • | • | • | • |  |  |  |  |  |  |  |  |  |  |  |
| (85) | wb |  | R | • | • | • | • | • | • |  |  |  |  |  |  |  |  |  |  |  |
| 76a | b |  |  |  |  |  |  |  |  |  |  | s | s |  |  |  |  |  |  |  |
| 72 | b |  |  |  |  |  |  |  |  |  |  |  |  | s |  |  |  |  |  |  |
| (42) | wb |  | R | • | • | • | • | • | • |  |  |  |  |  |  |  |  |  |  |  |
| (36) | eb |  | R | • | • | • | • | • | • |  |  |  |  |  |  |  |  |  |  |  |
| 30 | b |  |  |  |  |  |  |  |  |  |  |  |  |  |  | • |  |  |  |  |
| 29 | b |  |  |  |  |  |  |  |  | n |  |  |  |  |  |  |  |  |  |  |
| 28 | b |  |  |  |  |  |  |  |  |  |  |  | n |  |  |  |  |  |  |  |
| 23 | b |  |  |  |  |  |  |  |  |  |  |  |  | n |  |  |  |  |  |  |
| 12 | b |  |  |  |  |  |  |  |  |  |  |  |  |  |  |  |  |  |  | • |
| (0.5) | eb |  | W | • | • | • | • | • | • |  |  |  |  |  |  |  |  |  |  |  |

Left margin direction markers: E ↕ W (near exits 190–181b) and E ↕ W (near exits 97–85).

Interstate 96 in Michigan is 191 miles long. It runs east to west from I-75 in Detroit to US 31 near Muskegon. A portion is shared with I-69 and I-275. Eastbound travelers should read up the chart. Westbound travelers read down the chart.

| Exit(mm) | | ★ | ↗ | 🚻 | 📞 | 🍽 | 🛖 | 🏪 | 🚐 | 🐕 | W | S | K | T | C | Am | FJ | Lo | Pe | Pi | TA |
|---|---|---|---|---|---|---|---|---|---|---|---|---|---|---|---|---|---|---|---|---|---|
| 176 | b | | | | | | | | | | s | | | | | | | | | | |
| 167 | b | | | | | | | | | | | | | s | | | | | | | |
| (161) | eb | | R | • | • | • | • | | | • | | | | | | | | | | | |
| 145 | b | | | | | | | | | | | s | s | n | | | | | | | |
| (141) | wb | | R | • | • | • | • | | | • | | | | | | | | | | | |
| (135) | eb | | R | • | • | • | • | | | • | | | | | | | | | | | |
| (111) | wb | | R | • | • | • | • | | | • | | | | | | | | | | | |
| 110 | b | | | | | | | | | | | | | | n | | | | | | |
| 104 | b | | | | | | | | | | | n | | n | | | | | | | |
| 98a | b | | | | | | | | | | | | | | | • | | | | | |
| 93a | b | | | | | | | | | | s | | | s | | | | | | | |
| 91 | b | | | | | | | | | | | | | | | | • | | | | |
| (87) | eb | | R | • | • | • | • | | | • | | | | | | | | | | | |
| (79) | wb | | R | • | • | • | • | | | • | | | | | | | | | | | |
| 67 | b | | | | | | | | | | | | | | | | | | • | | |
| (63) | eb | | R | • | • | • | • | | | • | | | | | | | | | | | |
| (45) | wb | | R | • | • | • | • | | | | | | | | | | | | | | |
| 43b | b | | | | | | | | | | n | | | | | | | | | | |
| 43a | b | | | | | | | | | | | s | | s | | | | | | | |
| 30a | wb | | | | | | | | | | n | n | | n | n | | | | | | |
| 30 | eb | | | | | | | | | | | | | n | | | | | | | |
| (25) | eb | | R | • | • | • | | | | • | | | | | | | | | | | |
| (8) | wb | | R | • | • | • | • | | | • | | | | | | | | | | | |

Interstate 196 in Michigan is 81 miles long. It runs east to west from I-96 in Grand Rapids to I-94 at Benton Harbor. Eastbound travelers should read up the chart. Westbound travelers read down the chart.

| Exit(mm) | | ★ | ↗ | 🚻 | 📞 | 🍽 | 🛖 | 🏪 | 🚐 | 🐕 | W | S | K | T | C | Am | FJ | Lo | Pe | Pi | TA |
|---|---|---|---|---|---|---|---|---|---|---|---|---|---|---|---|---|---|---|---|---|---|---|
| 69b | wb | | | | | | | | | | | | | n | | | | | | | |
| 69 | eb | | | | | | | | | | | | | n | | | | | | | |
| 67 | b | | | | | | | | | | n | | | n | | | | | | | |
| (58) | eb | | R | • | • | • | • | | | • | | | | | | | | | | | |

| Exit(mm) | | ★ | | | | | | | | W | S | K | T | C | Am | FJ | Lo | Pe | Pi | TA |
|---|---|---|---|---|---|---|---|---|---|---|---|---|---|---|---|---|---|---|---|---|
| (43) wb | | R | • | • | • | • | | • | | | | | | | | | | | | |
| (25) eb | | R | • | • | • | • | | • | | | | | | | | | | | | |
| 20 b | | | | | | | | | | | s | | | | | | | | | |

E ↑ W (left axis for above table)

Interstate 275 is a 36-mile spur route. It runs north to south connecting I-96 with I-75. Northbound travelers should read up the chart. Southbound travelers read down the chart.

| Exit(mm) | | ★ | | | | | | | | W | S | K | T | C | Am | FJ | Lo | Pe | Pi | TA |
|---|---|---|---|---|---|---|---|---|---|---|---|---|---|---|---|---|---|---|---|---|
| 167 b | | | | | | | | | | | | | w | | | | | | | |
| 28 b | | | | | | | | | | | w | | | | | | | | | |
| 25 b | | | | | | | | | | | w | | w | | | | | | | |
| (23) nb | | R | • | • | • | | | | | | | | | | | | | | | |
| (4) sb | | R | • | • | • | | | | | | | | | | | | | | | |

N ↑ S (left axis for above table)

# Minnesota

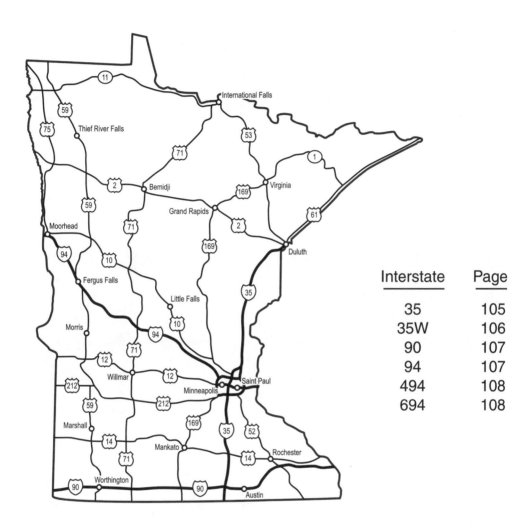

| Interstate | Page |
|------------|------|
| 35 | 105 |
| 35W | 106 |
| 90 | 107 |
| 94 | 107 |
| 494 | 108 |
| 694 | 108 |

**35**

Interstate 35 in Minnesota runs north to south for 260 miles from Duluth to the Iowa state line. I-35 splits south of Minneapolis into I-35E and I-35W. It comes together again north of Minneapolis. Northbound travelers should read up the chart. Southbound travelers read down the chart.

| Exit(mm) | | ★ | | | | | | | | | W | S | K | T | C | Am | FJ | Lo | Pe | Pi | TA |
|----------|---|---|---|---|---|---|---|---|---|---|---|---|---|---|---|---|----|----|----|----|----|----|
| 252 | b | | | | | | | | | | | | w | | | | | | | | | |

| Exit(mm) | ↗ | ★ | ▣ | ▣ | ▣ | ▣ | ▣ | ▣ | ▣ | W | S | K | T | C | Am | FJ | Lo | Pe | Pi | TA |
|---|---|---|---|---|---|---|---|---|---|---|---|---|---|---|---|---|---|---|---|---|
| 249 | b | 1 | W | • | • | • | • |  | • |  |  |  |  |  |  |  |  |  |  |  |
| 237 | b |  |  |  |  |  |  |  |  | w+ |  |  |  |  |  |  |  |  |  |  |
| (226) | nb |  | R | • | • | • | • |  | • |  |  |  |  |  |  |  |  |  |  |  |
| (208) | sb |  | R | • | • | • | • |  | • |  |  |  |  |  |  |  |  |  |  |  |
| (198) | nb |  | R | • | • | • | • |  | • |  |  |  |  |  |  |  |  |  |  |  |
| 169 | b |  |  |  |  |  |  |  |  | e |  |  |  |  |  |  |  |  |  |  |
| (154) | nb |  | R | • | • | • | • |  | • |  |  |  |  |  |  |  |  |  |  |  |
| 131 | b |  |  |  |  |  |  |  |  | e |  |  | e |  |  |  |  |  |  |  |
| (131) | sb |  | R | • | • | • | • |  | • |  |  |  |  |  |  |  |  |  |  |  |
| 115 | b |  |  |  |  |  |  |  |  | w |  |  | w |  |  |  |  |  |  |  |
| 109 | b |  |  |  |  |  |  |  |  |  | w |  |  |  |  |  |  |  |  |  |
| 98 | b |  |  |  |  |  |  |  |  |  | e |  |  |  |  |  |  |  |  |  |
| 97a | b |  |  |  |  |  |  |  |  | e |  |  |  |  |  |  |  |  |  |  |
| 93 | b |  |  |  |  |  |  |  |  |  |  |  | w |  |  |  |  |  |  |  |
| 88b | b |  |  |  |  |  |  |  |  |  |  | w | w |  |  |  |  |  |  |  |
| 85 | b |  |  |  |  |  |  |  |  |  |  |  |  | w |  |  |  |  |  |  |
| (75) | sb |  | R | • | • | • | • |  | • |  |  |  |  |  |  |  |  |  |  |  |
| (68) | nb |  | R | • | • | • | • |  | • |  |  |  |  |  |  |  |  |  |  |  |
| 56 | b |  |  |  |  |  |  |  |  | e |  |  |  |  |  |  |  |  |  |  |
| 42b | b |  |  |  |  |  |  |  |  | w |  |  |  |  | • |  |  |  |  |  |
| 41 | b |  |  |  |  |  |  |  |  |  |  |  | w |  |  |  |  |  |  |  |
| (35) | b |  | R | • | • | • | • |  | • |  |  |  |  |  |  |  |  |  |  |  |
| 11 | b |  |  |  |  |  |  |  |  |  |  |  |  |  |  |  |  |  |  | • |
| (1) | nb |  | W | • | • | • | • |  | • |  |  |  |  |  |  |  |  |  |  |  |

*1) Scenic Vista*

Interstate 35W is a 41-mile route that separates from I-35 at exit 88 and rejoins I-35 at exit 127. Northbound travelers should read up the chart. Southbound travelers read down the chart.

| Exit(mm) | ↗ | ★ | ▣ | ▣ | ▣ | ▣ | ▣ | ▣ | ▣ | W | S | K | T | C | Am | FJ | Lo | Pe | Pi | TA |
|---|---|---|---|---|---|---|---|---|---|---|---|---|---|---|---|---|---|---|---|---|---|
| 36 | b |  |  |  |  |  |  |  |  |  |  |  | w |  |  |  |  |  |  |  |
| 33 | b |  |  |  |  |  |  |  |  | e |  |  |  |  |  |  |  |  |  |  |
| 1 | sb |  |  |  |  |  |  |  |  |  |  | w | w |  |  |  |  |  |  |  |

Interstate 90 in Minnesota runs east to west for 277 miles from the Wisconsin state line to the South Dakota state line. Eastbound travelers should read up the chart. Westbound travelers read down the chart.

| Exit(mm) | ↗ | ★ | 🛣 | 🚻 | 📞 | 🧺 | 🛢 | 💳 | 🐾 | W | S | K | T | C | Am | FJ | Lo | Pe | Pi | TA |
|---|---|---|---|---|---|---|---|---|---|---|---|---|---|---|---|---|---|---|---|---|
| 275 | wb | 1 | W | • | • | • | • |  | • | | | | | | | | | | | |
| (244) | eb | 1 | R | • | • | • | • |  | • | | | | | | | | | | | |
| (222) | wb | | R | • | • | • | • |  | • | | | | | | | | | | | |
| (202) | eb | | R | • | • | • | • |  | • | | | | | | | | | | | |
| 177 | b | | | | | | | | | | | n | n | | | | | | | |
| (171) | wb | | R | • | • | • | • |  | • | | | | | | | | | | | |
| (162) | eb | | R | • | • | • | • |  | • | | | | | | | | | | | |
| 146 | b | | | | | | | | | | | | | | • | | | | | |
| 119 | b | | | | | | | | | | s | | | | | | | | | |
| (118) | b | 1 | R | • | • | • | • |  | • | | | | | | | | | | | |
| 102 | b | | | | | | | | | | | s | | | | | | | | |
| (72) | wb | 1 | R | • | • | • | • |  | • | | | | | | | | | | | |
| (69) | eb | 1 | R | • | • | • | • |  | • | | | | | | | | | | | |
| 43 | b | | | | | | | | | | s | | | | | | | | | |
| (25) | wb | | R | • | • | • | • |  | • | | | | | | | | | | | |
| (24) | eb | | R | • | • | • | • |  | • | | | | | | | | | | | |
| (0) | eb | | W | • | • | • | • |  | • | | | | | | | | | | | |

*1) Scenic Vista*

Interstate 94 in Minnesota runs east to west for 259 miles from the Wisconsin state line to the North Dakota state line. A portion of it is shared with I-694. Eastbound travelers should read up the chart. Westbound travelers read down the chart.

| Exit(mm) | ↗ | ★ | 🛣 | 🚻 | 📞 | 🧺 | 🛢 | 💳 | 🐾 | W | S | K | T | C | Am | FJ | Lo | Pe | Pi | TA |
|---|---|---|---|---|---|---|---|---|---|---|---|---|---|---|---|---|---|---|---|---|
| (256) | wb | | W | • | • | • | • |  | • | | | | | | | | | | | |
| 245 | b | | | | | | | | | | | | s | | | | | | | |
| 239b | b | | | | | | | | | | | n | n | | | | | | | |
| 238 | b | | | | | | | | | | | n | n | | | | | | | |
| 229 | b | | | | | | | | | | | | s | | | | | | | |
| 34 | b | | | | | | | | | | | | s | n | | | | | | |
| 215 | b | | | | | | | | | | | n | | | | | | | | |
| (215) | eb | | R | • | • | • | • | | | | | | | | | | | | | |
| 213 | b | | | | | | | | | s | s | | s | | | | | | | |

| Exit(mm) | dir | ★ | ↗ | 🚻 | ☎ | ⛱ | 🏢 | 🗺 | 🐎 | W | S | K | T | C | Am | FJ | Lo | Pe | Pi | TA |
|---|---|---|---|---|---|---|---|---|---|---|---|---|---|---|---|---|---|---|---|---|
| 207 | b | | | | | | | | | | | | n | | | | | | | • |
| 193 | b | | | | | | | | | | | n | | | | | | | | |
| (187) | eb | | R | • | • | • | • | | • | | | | | | | | | | | |
| 183 | b | | | | | | | | | | | | | | | • | | | | |
| (177) | wb | | R | • | • | • | • | | • | | | | | | | | | | | |
| 171 | b | | | | | | | | | | | | | | | | | | • | |
| 167b | b | | | | | | | | | | n+ | | | | | | | | | |
| (152) | b | | R | • | • | • | • | • | • | | | | | | | | | | | |
| (105) | wb | | R | • | • | • | • | • | • | | | | | | | | | | | |
| 103 | b | | | | | | | | | n | | n | | | | | | | | |
| (100) | eb | | R | • | • | • | • | • | • | | | | | | | | | | | |
| (69) | wb | | R | • | • | • | • | • | • | | | | | | | | | | | |
| (60) | eb | | R | • | • | • | • | • | • | | | | | | | | | | | |
| 54 | b | | | | | | | | | s | | n | n | | | | | | | |
| 2 | b | | | | | | | | | | | | n+ | | | | | | | |
| (2) | eb | | W | • | • | • | • | | • | | | | | | | | | | | |

E ↕ W

Interstates 494 and 694 form a 74-mile loop around Minneapolis/ Saint Paul. Part of I-694 is shared with I-94. Exit numbering begins at MN 5 near the airport and increases in a clockwise direction.

| Exit(mm) | dir | ★ | ↗ | 🚻 | ☎ | ⛱ | 🏢 | 🗺 | 🐎 | W | S | K | T | C | Am | FJ | Lo | Pe | Pi | TA |
|---|---|---|---|---|---|---|---|---|---|---|---|---|---|---|---|---|---|---|---|---|
| 67 | b | | | | | | | | | n+ | n+ | n+ | | | | | | | | |
| 60 | b | | | | | | | | | | | s | | | | | | | | |
| 57 | b | | | | | | | | | | | w | | | | | | | | |
| 50 | b | | | | | | | | | | | n | | | | | | | | |
| 43a | b | | | | | | | | | | | s | | | | | | | | |
| 34 | b | | | | | | | | | | | s | n | | | | | | | | |
| 23 | b | | | | | | | | | | | e | | | | | | | | |
| 6a | b | | | | | | | | | | | s | | | | | | | | |
| 3 | b | | | | | | | | | s | | | | | | | | | | |

# Mississippi

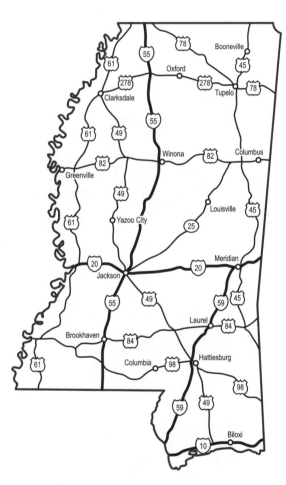

Interstate 10 in Mississippi runs east to west for 77 miles from the Alabama state line to the Louisiana state line. Eastbound travelers should read up the chart. Westbound travelers read down the chart.

| Exit(mm) | ↗ | ★ | Type | 👫 | ☎ | 🍴 | ⛽ | 🏪 | 🐕 | W | S | K | T | C | Am | FJ | Lo | Pe | Pi | TA |
|---|---|---|---|---|---|---|---|---|---|---|---|---|---|---|---|---|---|---|---|---|
| (74) | wb | 1 | W | • | • | • |  | • | • |  |  |  |  |  |  |  |  |  |  |  |
| 69 | b |  |  |  |  |  |  |  |  |  |  |  |  | s |  |  |  |  |  |  |
| (63) | b | 1 | R | • | • | • | • | • | • |  |  |  |  |  |  |  |  |  |  |  |
| 46b | b |  |  |  |  |  |  |  |  |  |  |  | n |  |  |  |  |  |  |  |
| 44 | b |  |  |  |  |  |  |  |  |  |  |  |  |  |  |  |  |  | • |  |
| 34b | b |  |  |  |  |  |  |  |  |  |  |  | n |  |  |  |  |  |  |  |
| 34a | b |  |  |  |  |  |  |  |  |  | s | s |  |  |  |  |  |  |  |  |
| 31 | b |  |  |  |  |  |  |  |  |  |  |  |  |  |  |  | • | • |  |  |
| (10) | eb | 2 | T |  |  |  |  |  |  |  |  |  |  |  |  |  |  |  |  |  |
| 2 | b | 1 | W | • | • | • |  | • | • |  |  |  |  |  |  |  |  |  |  |  |

*1) 24hr Security. 2) No Facilities*

Interstate 20 in Mississippi runs east to west for 154 miles from the Alabama state line to the Louisiana state line. Portions are shared with I-59 and I-55. Eastbound travelers should read up the chart. Westbound travelers read down the chart.

| Exit(mm) | ↗ | ★ | Type | 👫 | ☎ | 🍴 | ⛽ | 🏪 | 🐕 | W | S | K | T | C | Am | FJ | Lo | Pe | Pi | TA |
|---|---|---|---|---|---|---|---|---|---|---|---|---|---|---|---|---|---|---|---|---|
| (164) | wb |  | W | • | • | • |  | • | • |  |  |  |  |  |  |  |  |  |  |  |
| 160 | b |  |  |  |  |  |  |  |  |  |  |  |  |  |  |  |  |  |  | • |
| 154 | b |  |  |  |  |  |  |  |  |  |  |  | n |  |  |  |  |  |  |  |
| 153 | b |  |  |  |  |  |  |  |  |  | s |  |  |  |  |  |  |  |  |  |
| 109 | b |  |  |  |  |  |  |  |  |  | s |  |  |  |  |  |  |  |  |  |
| (90) | eb | 1 | R | • | • | • | • | • | • |  |  |  |  |  |  |  |  |  |  |  |
| 88 | b |  |  |  |  |  |  |  |  |  | n |  |  |  |  |  |  |  |  |  |
| (75) | wb | 1 | R | • | • | • | • | • | • |  |  |  |  |  |  |  |  |  |  |  |
| 54 | b |  |  |  |  |  |  |  |  |  | n |  |  |  |  |  |  |  |  |  |
| 48 | b |  |  |  |  |  |  |  |  |  |  |  | n |  |  |  |  |  |  |  |
| 47 | wb |  |  |  |  |  |  |  |  |  | s+ |  |  |  |  |  | • | • |  |  |
| 47a | eb |  |  |  |  |  |  |  |  |  | s+ |  |  |  |  |  |  |  |  |  |
| 47b | eb |  |  |  |  |  |  |  |  |  |  |  |  |  |  |  | • |  | • |  |
| 45a | wb |  |  |  |  |  |  |  |  |  |  |  |  |  |  |  |  |  | • | • |
| 40 | wb |  |  |  |  |  |  |  |  |  | s |  |  |  |  |  |  |  |  |  |
| 40a | eb |  |  |  |  |  |  |  |  |  | s |  |  |  |  |  |  |  |  |  |
| 36 | b |  |  |  |  |  |  |  |  |  | s+ |  |  |  |  |  |  |  |  |  |

| Exit(mm) | ↗ | * | ↗ | 🚻 | ☎ | 🏕 | ⛽ | 🏧 | 🐕 | W | S | K | T | C | Am | FJ | Lo | Pe | Pi | TA |
|---|---|---|---|---|---|---|---|---|---|---|---|---|---|---|---|---|---|---|---|---|
| (6) | eb | 2 | T | | | | | | | | | | | | | | | | | |
| 5b | wb | | | | | | | | | | | | s | | | | | | | |
| 4a | eb | | | | | | | | | | | | s | | | | | | | |
| 1b | b | | | | | | | | | | s | | | | | | | | | |
| 1a | b | | W | • | • | | | | | | | | | | | | | | | |

*Direction: E ↕ W*

*1) 24hr Security. 2) No Facilities*

Interstate 55 in Mississippi runs north to south for 291 miles from the Tennessee state line to the Louisiana state line. A small portion is shared with I-20. Northbound travelers should read up the chart. Southbound travelers read down the chart.

| Exit(mm) | ↗ | * | ↗ | 🚻 | ☎ | 🏕 | ⛽ | 🏧 | 🐕 | W | S | K | T | C | Am | FJ | Lo | Pe | Pi | TA |
|---|---|---|---|---|---|---|---|---|---|---|---|---|---|---|---|---|---|---|---|---|
| 291 | b | | | | | | | | | | | e | | | | | | | | |
| 289 | b | | | | | | | | | e | | w | w | | | | | | | |
| (279) | sb | 1 | W | • | • | • | | • | • | | | | | | | | | | | |
| (276) | nb | 1 | R | • | • | • | • | • | • | | | | | | | | | | | |
| 243b | b | | | | | | | | | | | | w | | | | | | | |
| 243a | b | | | | | | | | | e | | | | | | | | | | |
| (240) | b | 1 | R | • | • | • | | • | • | | | | | | | | | | | |
| 206 | b | | | | | | | | | e | | | | | | | | | | |
| (204) | sb | | T | • | | | | | | | | | | | | | | | | |
| (202) | nb | | T | • | | | | | | | | | | | | | | | | |
| (173) | sb | 1 | R | • | • | • | | • | • | | | | | | | | | | | |
| (163) | nb | 1 | R | • | • | • | | • | • | | | | | | | | | | | |
| (121) | sb | | T | | • | | | | | | | | | | | | | | | |
| 119 | b | | | | | | | | | | | | | | | | | • | | |
| (117) | nb | | T | | • | | | | | | | | | | | | | | | |
| 108 | b | | | | | | | | | e | | | | | | | | | | |
| 103 | b | | | | | | | | | | | e | w | | | | | | | |
| 102b | b | | | | | | | | | | | w | e | | | | | | | |
| 45a | sb | | | | | | | | | | | | | | | | | | • | • |
| 61 | b | | | | | | | | | e | | | | | | | | | | |
| (54) | b | 1 | R | • | • | • | • | • | • | | | | | | | | | | | |
| 40 | b | | | | | | | | | e | | | e | | | | | | | |
| 18 | b | | | | | | | | | e | | | | | | | | | | |
| (3) | nb | 1 | W | • | • | • | | • | • | | | | | | | | | | | |

*Direction: N ↕ S*

*1) 24hr Security*

Interstate 59 in Mississippi runs north to south for 172 miles from the Alabama state line to the Louisiana state line. A portion of it is shared with I-20. Northbound travelers should read up the chart. Southbound travelers read down the chart.

| Exit(mm) | ↗ | ★ | 🡒 | 👫 | ♿ | 🍴 | ⛽ | 🏪 | 🐾 | W | S | K | T | C | Am | FJ | Lo | Pe | Pi | TA |
|---|---|---|---|---|---|---|---|---|---|---|---|---|---|---|---|---|---|---|---|---|
| (164) | sb |  | W | • | • | • |  | • | • |  |  |  |  |  |  |  |  |  |  |  |
| 160 | b |  |  |  |  |  |  |  |  |  |  |  |  |  |  |  |  |  |  | • |
| 154 | b |  |  |  |  |  |  |  |  |  |  |  |  | w |  |  |  |  |  |  |
| 153 | b |  |  |  |  |  |  |  |  | e |  |  |  |  |  |  |  |  |  |  |
| (109) | sb | 1 | T |  |  |  |  |  |  |  |  |  |  |  |  |  |  |  |  |  |
| (106) | nb | 1 | T |  |  |  |  |  |  |  |  |  |  |  |  |  |  |  |  |  |
| 67a | b |  |  |  |  |  |  |  |  |  |  |  |  | e |  |  |  |  |  |  |
| 65 | b |  |  |  |  |  |  |  |  | w | w |  |  |  |  |  |  |  |  |  |
| (56) | b | 1 | T |  |  |  |  |  |  |  |  |  |  |  |  |  |  |  |  |  |
| (13) | sb | 1 | T |  |  |  |  |  |  |  |  |  |  |  |  |  |  |  |  |  |
| (8) | nb | 1 | T |  |  |  |  |  |  |  |  |  |  |  |  |  |  |  |  |  |
| 4 | b |  |  |  |  |  |  |  |  | e |  |  |  |  |  |  |  |  |  |  |
| (3) | nb |  | W | • | • | • |  | • | • |  |  |  |  |  |  |  |  |  |  |  |

N ↕ S

*1) No Facilities*

# Missouri

| Interstate | Page |
|---|---|
| 29 | 113 |
| 35 | 114 |
| 44 | 114 |
| 55 | 115 |
| 57 | 115 |
| 64 | 116 |
| 70 | 116 |
| 270 | 117 |
| 435 | 117 |

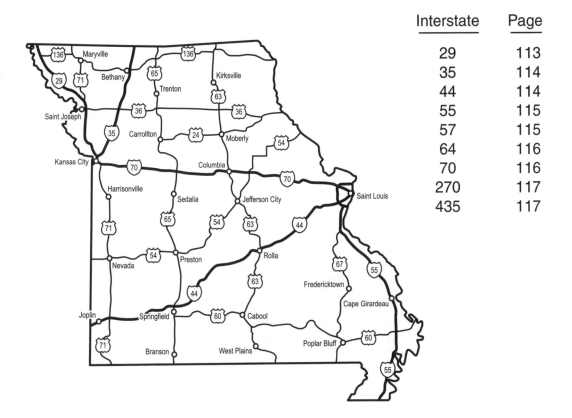

Interstate 29 in Missouri runs north to south for 124 miles from the Iowa state line to I-70 in Kansas City. A small segment is also I-35. Northbound travelers should read up the chart. Southbound travelers read down the chart.

| Exit(mm) | ⤴ | ★ | ↗ | 🚻 | ) | ⛽ | 🔒 | 🏨 | 🐾 | W | S | K | T | C | Am | FJ | Lo | Pe | Pi | TA |
|---|---|---|---|---|---|---|---|---|---|---|---|---|---|---|---|---|---|---|---|---|
| (109) | sb | W | • | • | • | • |  | • |  |  |  |  |  |  |  |  |  |  |  |  |
| (82) | b | R | • | • | • | • |  | • |  |  |  |  |  |  |  |  |  |  |  |  |
| 50 | b |  |  |  |  |  |  |  |  | w+ |  |  |  |  |  |  |  |  |  |  |
| 47 | b |  |  |  |  |  |  |  |  |  |  | w |  |  |  |  |  |  |  |  |
| 44 | b |  |  |  |  |  |  |  |  | w |  |  |  |  | • |  | • |  |  |  |
| (27) | b | R | • | • | • | • |  | • |  |  |  |  |  |  |  |  |  |  |  |  |
| 10 | b |  |  |  |  |  |  |  |  |  |  | w |  |  |  |  |  |  |  |  |
| 8 | b |  |  |  |  |  |  |  |  | e |  |  |  |  |  |  |  |  |  |  |
| 6 | b |  |  |  |  |  |  |  |  |  |  |  | w |  |  |  |  |  |  |  |

N ↕ S

Interstate 35 in Missouri runs north to south for 115 miles from the Iowa state line to the Kansas state line. Portions are also shared with I-29 and I-70. Northbound travelers should read up the chart. Southbound travelers read down the chart.

N ↕ S

| Exit(mm) | ⤴ | ★ | ▨ | 🚻 | ☎ | 🍴 | 🏕 | 🥤 | 🐾 | W | S | K | T | C | Am | FJ | Lo | Pe | Pi | TA |
|---|---|---|---|---|---|---|---|---|---|---|---|---|---|---|---|---|---|---|---|---|
| 92 | b | | | | | | | | | w | | | | | | | | | | |
| (81) | b | | R | • | • | • | • | | • | | | | | | | | | | | |
| 54 | b | | | | | | | | | w | | | | | | | | | | |
| (35) | sb | | R | • | • | • | • | | • | | | | | | | | | | | |
| (34) | nb | | R | • | • | • | • | | • | | | | | | | | | | | |
| 26 | b | | | | | | | | | | | | | | | • | | | | | |
| 16 | b | | | | | | | | | w | | e | w | w | | | | | | |
| 9 | b | | | | | | | | | | | | e | | | | | | | |

Interstate 44 in Missouri runs east to west for 291 miles from I-55 in Saint Louis to the Oklahoma state line. Eastbound travelers should read up the chart. Westbound travelers read down the chart.

| Exit(mm) | ⤴ | ★ | ▨ | 🚻 | ☎ | 🍴 | 🏕 | 🥤 | 🐾 | W | S | K | T | C | Am | FJ | Lo | Pe | Pi | TA |
|---|---|---|---|---|---|---|---|---|---|---|---|---|---|---|---|---|---|---|---|---|
| 278 | b | | | | | | | | | | n | | | | | | | | | |
| 277b | b | | | | | | | | | n | | n | | | | | | | | |
| 274 | b | | | | | | | | | | | | s | | | | | | | |
| 261 | b | | | | | | | | | n | | | | | | | | | | |
| (235) | b | | R | • | • | • | • | | • | | | | | | | | | | | |
| 226 | b | | | | | | | | | s | | | | | | • | | | | |
| 208 | b | | | | | | | | | s | | | | | | | | | | |
| 184 | b | | | | | | | | | s | | | | | | | | | | |
| (178) | b | | R | • | • | • | • | | • | | | | | | | | | | | |
| 161b | wb | | | | | | | | | n | | n | | | | | | | | |
| 161 | eb | | | | | | | | | n | | n | | | | | | | | |
| 129 | b | | | | | | | | | s | | | | | | | | | | |
| (111) | b | | R | • | • | • | • | | • | | | | | | | | | | | |
| 100 | b | | | | | | | | | s | | | | | | | | | | |
| 88 | b | | | | | | | | | | | | | | | | | | • | |
| 80a | b | | | | | | | | | s | | s | | | | | | | | |
| 77 | b | | | | | | | | | s | | | | | | | | | | |
| (52) | b | | R | • | • | • | • | | • | | | | | | | | | | | |
| 46 | b | | | | | | | | | | | | | | | | | | | • |
| 11a | b | | | | | | | | | | | | | | | | • | | | |

Direction (left margin): E ↕ W

| Exit(mm) | ↗ | ★ | 🛈 | 🚻 | ☎ | ⛱ | 🏪 | 🥤 | 🐾 | W | S | K | T | C | Am | FJ | Lo | Pe | Pi | TA |
|---|---|---|---|---|---|---|---|---|---|---|---|---|---|---|---|---|---|---|---|---|
| 8b | b | | | | | | | | | n | n | | | | | | | | | |
| 8a | b | | | | | | | | | | | | s | | | | | | | |
| 4 | b | | | | | | | | | | | | | | • | • | • | | | |
| (2) | b | 1 | W | • | • | • | • | | • | | | | | | | | | | | |

1) Welcome Center (eastbound), Rest Area (westbound)

**55** Interstate 55 in Missouri runs north to south for 210 miles from the Illinois state line to the Arkansas state line. Northbound travelers should read up the chart. Southbound travelers read down the chart.

Direction (left margin): N ↕ S

| Exit(mm) | ↗ | ★ | 🛈 | 🚻 | ☎ | ⛱ | 🏪 | 🥤 | 🐾 | W | S | K | T | C | Am | FJ | Lo | Pe | Pi | TA |
|---|---|---|---|---|---|---|---|---|---|---|---|---|---|---|---|---|---|---|---|---|
| 197 | b | | | | | | | | | | e | | | | | | | | | |
| 193 | b | | | | | | | | | | | | e | | | | | | | |
| 191 | b | | | | | | | | | e | | | | | | | | | | |
| 190 | b | | | | | | | | | | | w | | | | | | | | |
| 175 | b | | | | | | | | | e | | | | | | | | | | |
| (160) | b | | R | • | • | • | • | | • | | | | | | | | | | | |
| 143 | b | | | | | | | | | | | | | | • | | | | | |
| 129 | b | | | | | | | | | w | | | | | | | | | | |
| (110) | b | | R | • | • | • | • | | • | | | | | | | | | | | |
| 99 | b | | | | | | | | | w+ | | | | | | | | | | |
| 96 | b | | | | | | | | | w | w | | w | e | | | | | | |
| 66b | b | | | | | | | | | w+ | | | | | | | | | | |
| 58 | b | | | | | | | | | | | | | | • | • | | | • | |
| (42) | b | 1 | W | • | • | • | • | | • | | | | | | | | | | | |
| 40 | b | | | | | | | | | | | | | | | | | • | | |
| 19 | b | | | | | | | | | | | | | | | | | • | | |
| (3) | b | | R | • | • | • | • | | • | | | | | | | | | | | |

1) Welcome Center (northbound), Rest Area (southbound)

**57** Interstate 57 in Missouri runs north to south for 22 miles from the Illinois state line to Interstate 55 near Sikeston. Northbound travelers should read up the chart. Southbound travelers read down the chart.

| Exit(mm) | ↗ | ★ | 🛈 | 🚻 | ☎ | ⛱ | 🏪 | 🥤 | 🐾 | W | S | K | T | C | Am | FJ | Lo | Pe | Pi | TA |
|---|---|---|---|---|---|---|---|---|---|---|---|---|---|---|---|---|---|---|---|---|
| 10 | b | | | | | | | | | | | | | | | | | • | | |

Interstate 64 in Missouri is about 27 miles long. It runs east to west from the Illinois state line to the Missouri River near Weldon Spring. Eastbound travelers should read up the chart. Westbound travelers read down the chart.

| Exit(mm) | ↗ | ★ | 🡕 | 👫 | ☎ | ⛱ | 🛢 | 🏪 | 🐾 | W | S | K | T | C | Am | FJ | Lo | Pe | Pi | TA |
|---|---|---|---|---|---|---|---|---|---|---|---|---|---|---|---|---|---|---|---|---|
| 31a | b | | | | | | | | | | | | s | | | | | | | |
| 17 | b | | | | | | | | | s | s | | s | | | | | | | |

Interstate 70 in Missouri runs east to west from the Illinois state line to the Kansas state line. It is 252 miles long. Eastbound travelers should read up the chart. Westbound travelers read down the chart.

| Exit(mm) | ↗ | ★ | 🡕 | 👫 | ☎ | ⛱ | 🛢 | 🏪 | 🐾 | W | S | K | T | C | Am | FJ | Lo | Pe | Pi | TA |
|---|---|---|---|---|---|---|---|---|---|---|---|---|---|---|---|---|---|---|---|---|
| 234 | b | | | | | | | | | | | n | n | | | | | | | |
| 229a | wb | | | | | | | | | | | | | s | | | | | | |
| 229 | eb | | | | | | | | | | | | | s | | | | | | |
| 228 | b | | | | | | | | | | | s | | | | | | | | |
| 227 | b | | | | | | | | | s | s | | | | | | | | | |
| 225 | b | | | | | | | | | | | s | s | | | | | | | |
| 203 | b | | | | | | | | | | | | | | | | | | | • |
| (198) | b | R | • | • | • | • | • | | • | | | | | | | | | | | |
| 193 | b | | | | | | | | | n | | | | | | | | | | |
| 188 | b | | | | | | | | | | | | | | | | | • | | |
| (169) | wb | R | • | • | • | • | • | | • | | | | | | | | | | | |
| (167) | eb | R | • | • | • | • | • | | • | | | | | | | | | | | |
| 148 | b | | | | | | | | | | | | | | | | | • | | |
| 128a | b | | | | | | | | | s+ | s | | n | | | | | | | |
| 124 | b | | | | | | | | | s | | s | | | | | | | | |
| (104) | b | R | • | • | • | • | • | | • | | | | | | | | | | | |
| 103 | b | | | | | | | | | n | | | | | | | | | | |
| 101 | b | | | | | | | | | | | | | | | | | | • | |
| 58 | b | | | | | | | | | | | | | | | | | | | • |
| (57) | b | R | • | • | • | • | • | | • | | | | | | | | | | | |
| 49 | b | | | | | | | | | | | | | | | | | | • | |
| 28 | b | | | | | | | | | s | | | | | | | | | • | • |
| 20 | b | | | | | | | | | s+ | | | | | | | | | | |
| 15b | b | | | | | | | | | n | n | n | | | | | | | | |
| 14 | b | | | | | | | | | | | | | s | | | | | | |
| 12 | b | | | | | | | | | | | | n | | | | | | | |

Interstate 270 in Missouri is 36 miles long. It forms a partial loop around Saint Louis. Exit numbering begins at I-55 and increases in a clockwise direction.

| Exit(mm) | ⤢ | ★ | ↗ | 👥 | ☎ | ⛱ | ⛽ | 🏨 | 🐕 | W | S | K | T | C | Am | FJ | Lo | Pe | Pi | TA |
|---|---|---|---|---|---|---|---|---|---|---|---|---|---|---|---|---|---|---|---|---|
| 34 | b | | W | • | • | • | • | | • | | | | | | | | | | | |
| 30 | b | | | | | | | | | | | | n | s | | | | | | |
| 29 | b | | | | | | | | | s | s | n | | | | | | | | |
| 20c | b | | | | | | | | | | e | e | | | | | | | | |

 Interstate 435 is an 83-mile loop around Kansas City. Exit numbering begins at Lackman Road in Kansas and increases in a clockwise direction.

| Exit(mm) | ⤢ | ★ | ↗ | 👥 | ☎ | ⛱ | ⛽ | 🏨 | 🐕 | W | S | K | T | C | Am | FJ | Lo | Pe | Pi | TA |
|---|---|---|---|---|---|---|---|---|---|---|---|---|---|---|---|---|---|---|---|---|
| 70 | b | | | | | | | | | | | e | | | | | | | | |
| 69 | b | | | | | | | | | | e | | | | | | | | | |
| 57 | b | | | | | | | | | | | | | | | | • | | | |
| 3 | b | | | | | | | | | | | e | | | | | | | | |

# Montana

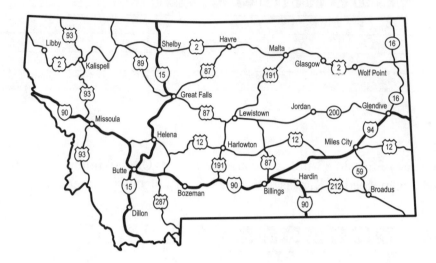

| Interstate | Page |
|:---:|:---:|
| 15 | 118 |
| 90 | 119 |
| 94 | 120 |

**15** Interstate 15 in Montana runs north to south for 398 miles from the US/Canada border to the Idaho state line. A portion of it is also shared with I-90. Northbound travelers should read up the chart. Southbound travelers read down the chart.

| Exit(mm) | ⤴ | ★ | ↗ | 👥 | 🚻 | 🍴 | 🛏 | 🏪 | 🐾 | W | S | K | T | C | Am | FJ | Lo | Pe | Pi | TA |
|:---:|:---:|:---:|:---:|:---:|:---:|:---:|:---:|:---:|:---:|:---:|:---:|:---:|:---:|:---:|:---:|:---:|:---:|:---:|:---:|:---:|
| 397 | b | | R | • | • | • | | | • | | | | | | | | | | | |
| (361) | nb | 1 | T | | | | | | | | | | | | | | | | | |
| (319) | b | | R | • | • | • | | | • | | | | | | | | | | | |
| (288) | b | 1 | T | | | | | | | | | | | | | | | | | |
| 252 | sb | | | | | | | | | e+ | | | | | | | | | | |
| 280 | b | | | | | | | | | | | | | | | | | • | | |
| 278 | b | | | | | | | | | | e+ | e+ | | | | | | | | |
| (245) | sb | 2 | T | | | | | | | | | | | | | | | | | |
| (239) | b | | R | • | • | • | | | • | | | | | | | | | | | |

N ↕ S

| Exit(mm) | ↗ | * | ⬈ | 🚻 | ☎ | ⛱ | 🛏 | 🍴 | 🐾 | W | S | K | T | C | Am | FJ | Lo | Pe | Pi | TA |
|---|---|---|---|---|---|---|---|---|---|---|---|---|---|---|---|---|---|---|---|---|
| (222) | b | 1 | T | | | | | | | | | | | | | | | | | |
| (205) | sb | 1 | T | | | | | | | | | | | | | | | | | |
| 193 | b | | | | | | | | | w | w | | | | | | | | | |
| 192 | sb | | | | | | | | | e | | | | | | | | | | |
| 192a | nb | | | | | | | | | e | | | | | | | | | | |
| (178) | b | | R | • | • | • | | | • | | | | | | | | | | | |
| (161) | nb | 1 | T | | | | | | | | | | | | | | | | | |
| 138 | b | 2 | T | | | • | | | | | | | | | | | | | | |
| (130) | sb | 2 | T | | | | | | | | | | | | | | | | | |
| 127 | b | | | | | | | | | e | | | | | | | | | | |
| 122 | b | | | | | | | | | | | | | | | | | • | | |
| (109) | b | | R | • | • | • | | | • | | | | | | | | | | | |
| (34) | b | 1 | T | | | | | | | | | | | | | | | | | |

1) No Facilities
2) Scenic Vista

Interstate 90 in Montana is about 552 miles long. It runs east to west from the Wyoming state line to the Idaho state line. A portion is shared with I-15. Eastbound travelers should read up the chart. Westbound travelers read down the chart.

| Exit(mm) | ↗ | * | ⬈ | 🚻 | ☎ | ⛱ | 🛏 | 🍴 | 🐾 | W | S | K | T | C | Am | FJ | Lo | Pe | Pi | TA |
|---|---|---|---|---|---|---|---|---|---|---|---|---|---|---|---|---|---|---|---|---|
| 495 | b | | | | | | | | | | | | | | | | | • | | |
| (476) | eb | | R | • | • | • | | | • | | | | | | | | | | | |
| (475) | wb | | R | • | • | • | | | • | | | | | | | | | | | |
| 455 | b | | | | | | | | | | | | | | | | | • | | |
| 452 | b | | | | | | | | | n+ | | n+ | | | | | | | | |
| 446 | b | | | | | | | | | n | | | n | n | | | | | | |
| (419) | b | | R | • | • | • | | | • | | | | | | | | | | | |
| (381) | b | | R | • | • | • | | | • | | | | | | | | | | | |
| (321) | b | 1 | T | | | | | | | | | | | | | | | | | |
| 306 | b | | | | | | | | | s | | s | | | | | | | | |
| 305 | b | | | | | | | | | | | | s | | | | | | | |
| 298 | b | | | | | | | | | | | | | | | | | • | | |
| (237) | eb | 1 | T | | | | | | | | | | | | | | | | | |
| (235) | b | 1 | T | | | | | | | | | | | | | | | | | |
| 127 | b | | | | | | | | | s | | | | | | | | | | |
| 122 | b | | | | | | | | | | | | | | | | | • | | |
| (210) | wb | 1 | T | | | | | | | | | | | | | | | | | |

| Exit(mm) | ↗ | * | 🛈 | 👫 | 📞 | ⛽ | 🏕 | 🍽 | 🐾 | W | S | K | T | C | Am | FJ | Lo | Pe | Pi | TA |
|---|---|---|---|---|---|---|---|---|---|---|---|---|---|---|---|---|---|---|---|---|
| (169) | eb | | R | • | • | • | | | | • | | | | | | | | | | | |
| (167) | wb | | R | • | • | • | | | | • | | | | | | | | | | | |
| (143) | b | | R | • | • | • | | | | • | | | | | | | | | | | |
| (128) | b | 1 | T | | | | | | | | | | | | | | | | | | |
| 101 | b | | | | | | | | | | w+ | | | | n | | | | | | |
| 96 | b | | | | | | | | | | | | | | | | | • | | | |
| (73) | wb | 1 | T | | | | | | | | | | | | | | | | | | |
| (72) | eb | 1 | T | | | | | | | | | | | | | | | | | | |
| (58) | b | | R | • | • | • | | | | • | | | | | | | | | | | |
| (4) | b | | R | • | | • | | | | • | | | | | | | | | | | |

*E ↕ W*

1) No Facilities

Interstate 94 in Montana runs east to west from the North Dakota state line to I-90 near Billings. It is about 250 miles long. Eastbound travelers should read up the chart. Westbound travelers read down the chart.

| Exit(mm) | ↗ | * | 🛈 | 👫 | 📞 | ⛽ | 🏕 | 🍽 | 🐾 | W | S | K | T | C | Am | FJ | Lo | Pe | Pi | TA |
|---|---|---|---|---|---|---|---|---|---|---|---|---|---|---|---|---|---|---|---|---|
| 242 | wb | | R | • | • | • | | | | • | | | | | | | | | | | |
| 241 | eb | | R | • | • | • | | | | • | | | | | | | | | | | |
| 192 | b | | R | • | • | • | | | | • | | | | | | | | | | | |
| 138 | b | | | | | | | | | | n | | n | | | | | | | | |
| (114) | eb | | R | • | • | • | | | | • | | | | | | | | | | | |
| (113) | wb | 1 | R | • | • | • | | | | • | | | | | | | | | | | |
| (65) | b | | R | • | • | • | | | | • | | | | | | | | | | | |
| (41) | eb | | R | • | • | • | | | | • | | | | | | | | | | | |
| (38) | wb | | R | • | • | • | | | | • | | | | | | | | | | | |

*N ↕ S*

1) Scenic Vista

# Nebraska

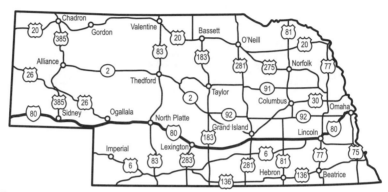

| Interstate | Page |
|---|---|
| 80 | 121 |
| 680 | 122 |

**80**   Interstate 80 in Nebraska runs east to west for 455 miles from the Iowa state line to the Wyoming state line. Eastbound travelers should read up the chart. Westbound travelers read down the chart.

| Exit(mm) | ↗ | ★ | ⤢ | 🚻 | ☎ | 🍴 | ⛽ | 🥤 | 🐾 | W | S | K | T | C | Am | FJ | Lo | Pe | Pi | TA |
|---|---|---|---|---|---|---|---|---|---|---|---|---|---|---|---|---|---|---|---|---|
| 445 b | | | | | | | | | | | | n | | | | | | | | |
| 440 b | | | | | | | | | | | | | | n | | | | | | |
| 432 b | | | | | | | | | | | | | | | | • | | | | |
| (431) wb | R | | • | • | • | • | | | • | | | | | | | | | | | |
| (425) eb | R | | • | • | • | • | | | • | | | | | | | | | | | |
| (405) wb | R | | • | • | • | • | | | • | | | | | | | | | | | |
| 403 b | | | | | | | | | | S+ | S+ | | | s | | | | | | |
| (381) eb | R | | • | • | • | • | | | • | | | | | | | | | | | |
| (375) wb | R | | • | • | • | • | | | • | | | | | | | | | | | |
| (355) wb | R | | • | • | • | • | | | • | | | | | | | | | | | |
| 353 b | | | | | | | | | | | | | | | | | | | • | |
| (350) eb | R | | • | • | • | • | | | • | | | | | | | | | | | |
| 332 b | | | | | | | | | | | | | | | | | | • | | |
| (316) wb | R | | • | • | • | • | | | • | | | | | | | | | | | |

| Exit(mm) | ↗ | * | [dir] | [restroom] | [phone] | [picnic] | [icon5] | [vending] | [pet] | W | S | K | T | C | Am | FJ | Lo | Pe | Pi | TA |
|---|---|---|---|---|---|---|---|---|---|---|---|---|---|---|---|---|---|---|---|---|
| (314) | eb | | R | • | • | • | • | | • | | | | | | | | | | | |
| 312 | b | | | | | | | | | | | | | | | | | | • | |
| 305 | b | | | | | | | | | | | | | | | | | | | • |
| 300 | b | | | | | | | | | | | | | | | | | | • | |
| 272 | b | | | | | | | | | n+ | | | | | | | | | | |
| (270) | wb | | R | • | • | • | • | | • | | | | | | | | | | | |
| (269) | eb | | R | • | • | • | • | | • | | | | | | | | | | | |
| 257 | b | | | | | | | | | | | | | | | | | | • | |
| 237 | b | | | | | | | | | n | | | | | | | | | | |
| (227) | wb | | R | • | • | • | • | | • | | | | | | | | | | | |
| (226) | eb | | R | • | • | • | • | | • | | | | | | | | | | | |
| (194) | b | | R | • | • | • | • | | • | | | | | | | | | | | |
| 179 | b | | | | | | | | | | | | | | | | • | | | |
| 177 | b | | | | | | | | | n | | | | | | | | | | |
| (159) | b | | R | • | • | • | • | | • | | | | | | | | | | | |
| (132) | wb | | R | • | • | • | • | | • | | | | | | | | | | | |
| 126 | b | | | | | | | | | | | | | | | | | | | • |
| (124) | eb | | R | • | • | • | • | | • | | | | | | | | | | | |
| 107 | b | | | | | | | | | | | | | | | | | | • | |
| (99) | eb 1 | | T | | | | | | | | | | | | | | | | | |
| (87) | wb | | R | • | • | • | • | | • | | | | | | | | | | | |
| (82) | eb | | R | • | • | • | • | | • | | | | | | | | | | | |
| (61) | wb | | R | • | • | • | • | | • | | | | | | | | | | | |
| 59 | b | | | | | | | | | n | | | | | | | | | | |
| (51) | eb | | R | • | • | • | • | | • | | | | | | | | | | | |
| (25) | wb | | R | • | • | • | • | | • | | | | | | | | | | | |
| (18) | eb 2 | | T | | | | | | | | | | | | | | | | | |
| (9) | eb | | R | • | • | • | • | | • | | | | | | | | | | | |

1) *Scenic Vista*
2) *No Facilities*

Interstate 680 in Omaha is 13 miles long. It runs between I-80 and the Iowa state line. Northbound travelers should read up the chart. Southbound travelers read down the chart.

| Exit(mm) | ↗ | * | [dir] | [restroom] | [phone] | [picnic] | [icon5] | [vending] | [pet] | W | S | K | T | C | Am | FJ | Lo | Pe | Pi | TA |
|---|---|---|---|---|---|---|---|---|---|---|---|---|---|---|---|---|---|---|---|---|
| 5 | b | | | | | | | | | | w | | | | | | | | | | |

# Nevada

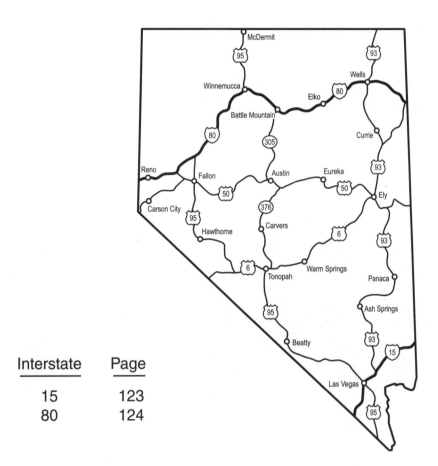

| Interstate | Page |
| --- | --- |
| 15 | 123 |
| 80 | 124 |

Interstate 15 in Nevada runs north to south for 124 miles from the Arizona state line to the California state line. Northbound travelers should read up the chart. Southbound travelers read down the chart.

| Exit(mm) | ↗ | ★ | 🚻 | 🧍 | ⛽ | 🏕 | 🛢 | 🏢 | 🐾 | W | S | K | T | C | Am | FJ | Lo | Pe | Pi | TA |
| --- | --- | --- | --- | --- | --- | --- | --- | --- | --- | --- | --- | --- | --- | --- | --- | --- | --- | --- | --- | --- |
| 122 | b | | W | • | | • | | | | | | | | | | | | | | | |
| (110) | b | 1 | T | | | | | | | | | | | | | | | | | |
| (96) | nb | 1 | T | | | | | | | | | | | | | | | | | |
| (87) | b | 2 | T | | | | | | | | | | | | | | | | | |
| 54 | b | | | | | | | | | | | | | | | | | | • | |
| 48 | b | | | | | | e+ | | | | | | | | | | | | | • | |

N ↑↓ S

| Exit(mm) | ⤴ | ★ | ⬈ | 🚻 | ♿ | ⛺ | ⛽ | 🛏 | 🐾 | W | S | K | T | C | Am | FJ | Lo | Pe | Pi | TA |
|---|---|---|---|---|---|---|---|---|---|---|---|---|---|---|---|---|---|---|---|---|
| N  46 | b |  |  |  |  |  |  |  |  |  |  |  |  |  |  |  |  | • |  |  |
| 33 | b |  |  |  |  |  |  |  |  |  |  |  |  |  |  |  |  |  |  | • |
| S  12 | b |  | W | • |  | • |  |  |  |  |  |  |  |  |  |  |  |  |  |  |

1) Truck Parking, No Facilities
2) No Facilities

 **80**  Interstate 80 in Nevada is 411 miles long. It runs east to west from the Utah state line to the California state line. Eastbound travelers should read up the chart. Westbound travelers read down the chart.

| Exit(mm) | ⤴ | ★ | ⬈ | 🚻 | ♿ | ⛺ | ⛽ | 🛏 | 🐾 | W | S | K | T | C | Am | FJ | Lo | Pe | Pi | TA |
|---|---|---|---|---|---|---|---|---|---|---|---|---|---|---|---|---|---|---|---|---|
| 410 | b |  | W | • |  | • |  |  |  |  |  |  |  |  |  |  |  |  |  | • |
| (373) | b |  | T | • |  | • |  |  |  |  |  |  |  |  |  |  |  |  |  |  |
| (354) | eb | 1 | T |  |  |  |  |  |  |  |  |  |  |  |  |  |  |  |  |  |
| 352 | b |  |  |  |  |  |  |  |  |  |  |  |  |  |  |  |  | • |  |  |  |
| 301 | b |  |  |  |  |  |  |  |  |  |  | n |  |  |  |  |  |  |  |  |
| E  280 | b |  |  |  |  |  |  |  |  |  |  |  |  |  |  |  |  | • |  |  |
| (270) | b | 1 | T |  |  |  |  |  |  |  |  |  |  |  |  |  |  |  |  |  |
| W  (258) | b |  | R | • |  | • |  | • | • |  |  |  |  |  |  |  |  |  |  |
| 231 | b |  |  |  |  |  |  |  |  |  |  |  |  |  |  |  | • |  |  |  |
| 227a | b | 2 |  |  |  |  |  |  |  |  |  |  |  |  |  |  |  |  |  | • |
| 216 | b |  | R | • | • | • |  | • | • |  |  |  |  |  |  |  |  |  |  |
| 187 | b |  | R | • | • | • |  | • | • |  |  |  |  |  |  |  |  |  |  |
| 176 | b |  |  |  |  |  |  |  |  |  | s |  |  |  |  |  | • |  |  |  |
| 158 | b |  | R | • | • | • |  | • | • |  |  |  |  |  |  |  |  |  |  |
| 151 | b |  |  |  |  |  |  |  |  |  |  |  |  |  |  |  |  |  |  | • |
| E  83 | b |  | R | • | • | • |  |  |  |  |  |  |  |  |  |  |  |  |  |
| 46 | b |  |  |  |  |  |  |  |  |  |  |  |  |  |  |  |  | • |  | • |  |
| W  (42) | wb |  | R | • | • | • |  | • | • |  |  |  |  |  |  |  |  |  |  |
| (27) | eb | 3 | T |  |  |  |  |  |  |  |  |  |  |  |  |  |  |  |  |  |
| 21 | b |  |  |  |  |  |  |  |  |  |  |  |  |  |  |  |  | • |  |  |
| 19 | b |  |  |  |  |  |  |  |  |  |  | n+ |  |  |  |  |  |  |  | • |
| 10 | b |  |  |  |  |  |  |  |  |  |  | s |  |  |  |  |  |  |  |  |
| (6) | b | 3 | T |  |  |  |  |  |  |  |  |  |  |  |  |  |  |  |  |  |
| 4 | b |  |  |  |  |  |  |  |  |  |  |  |  |  |  |  |  | • |  |  |  |
| (4) | eb | 3 | T |  |  |  |  |  |  |  |  |  |  |  |  |  |  |  |  |  |

1) No Facilities
2) TA Travel Center on University Blvd
3) Scenic Vista

# New Hampshire

| Interstate | Page |
|---|---|
| 89 | 125 |
| 93 | 126 |
| 95 | 126 |
| 293 | 126 |

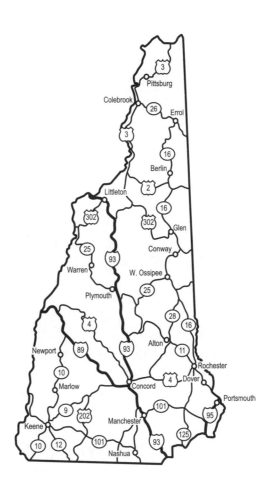

Interstate 89 in New Hampshire runs north to south for 61 miles from the Vermont state line to I-93 in Concord. Exit numbers are based on the consecutive numbering system. Northbound travelers should read up the chart. Southbound travelers read down the chart.

| Exit(mm) | ↗ | ★ | 🚻 | 📞 | 🍽 | ⛽ | 🏨 | 🐾 | W | S | K | T | C | Am | FJ | Lo | Pe | Pi | TA |
|---|---|---|---|---|---|---|---|---|---|---|---|---|---|---|---|---|---|---|---|
| 20 b | | | | | | | | | w | | e | | | | | | | | |
| (57) sb | W | • | • | • | • | | • | | | | | | | | | | | | |
| (40) nb | R | • | • | • | • | | • | | | | | | | | | | | | |
| (26) sb | R | • | • | • | • | | • | | | | | | | | | | | | |

**93**

Interstate 93 in New Hampshire runs north to south for 132 miles from the Vermont state line to the Massachusetts state line. Exit numbers are based on the consecutive numbering system. Northbound travelers should read up the chart. Southbound travelers read down the chart.

N ↕ S

| Exit(mm) | ↗ | ★ | ▪ | 🚻 | ☎ | ⛱ | ▤ | 🥤 | 🐾 | W | S | K | T | C | Am | FJ | Lo | Pe | Pi | TA |
|---|---|---|---|---|---|---|---|---|---|---|---|---|---|---|---|---|---|---|---|---|
| 44 | b | 1 | W | • | • | • | | | • | | | | | | | | | | | |
| 42 | b | | | | | | | | | w | | | | | | | | | | |
| (61) | sb | | R | • | • | • | • | | • | | | | | | | | | | | |
| 20 | b | | | | | | | | | w | | | | | | | | | | |
| (51) | nb | | R | • | • | • | • | | • | | | | | | | | | | | |
| 14 | b | | | | | | | | | e+ | | | | | | | | | | |
| (31) | b | | R | • | • | • | • | | | | | | | | | | | | | |
| 10 | b | | | | | | | | | | | | | e | | | | | | |
| 5 | b | | | | | | | | | e+ | | | | | | | | | | |
| 4 | b | | | | | | | | | | | w | | e | | | | | | |
| 1 | b | | | | | | | | | | | e | | e | | | | | | |
| (1) | nb | | W | • | • | • | • | | • | | | | | | | | | | | |

*1) Scenic Vista*

**95**

Interstate 95 in New Hampshire runs north to south for 16 miles from the Maine state line to the Massachusetts state line. Exit numbers are based on the consecutive numbering system. Northbound travelers should read up the chart. Southbound travelers read down the chart.

N ↕ S

| Exit(mm) | ↗ | ★ | ▪ | 🚻 | ☎ | ⛱ | ▤ | 🥤 | 🐾 | W | S | K | T | C | Am | FJ | Lo | Pe | Pi | TA |
|---|---|---|---|---|---|---|---|---|---|---|---|---|---|---|---|---|---|---|---|---|
| 7 | b | | | | | | | | | | | | w | | | | | | | |
| 3b | sb | | | | | | | | | | | | | | | | | | | • |
| 3 | nb | | | | | | | | | | | | | | | | | | | • |
| 1 | b | | | | | | | | | | e | w | | | | | | | | |
| (0.5) | nb | | W | • | • | • | • | | • | | | | | | | | | | | |

**293**

Interstate 293 is 11 miles long. It forms an open loop around Manchester. Exit numbers are based on the consecutive numbering system. Northbound travelers should read up the chart. Southbound travelers read down the chart.

| Exit(mm) | ↗ | ★ | ▪ | 🚻 | ☎ | ⛱ | ▤ | 🥤 | 🐾 | W | S | K | T | C | Am | FJ | Lo | Pe | Pi | TA |
|---|---|---|---|---|---|---|---|---|---|---|---|---|---|---|---|---|---|---|---|---|
| 1 | b | | | | | | | | | | s | n | s | | | | | | | |

# New Jersey



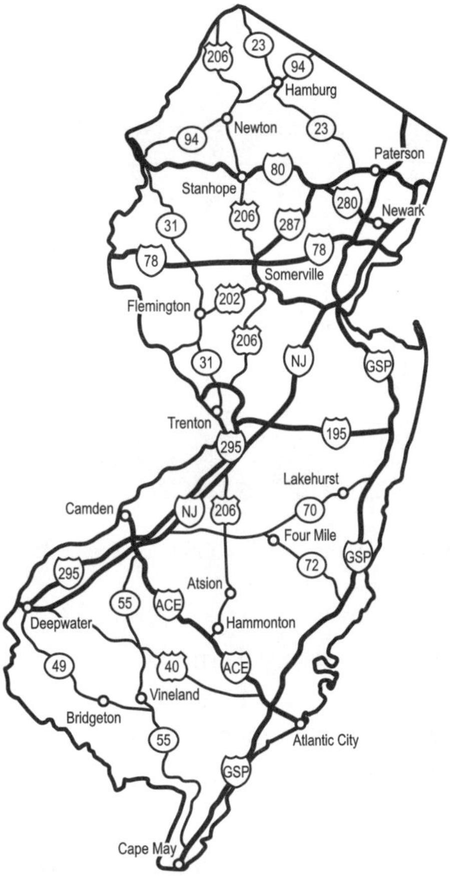


**78** Interstate 78 in New Jersey runs east to west for approximately 68 miles from the Holland Tunnel to the Pennsylvania state line. Eastbound travelers should read up the chart. Westbound travelers read down the chart.

E ↕ W

| Exit(mm) | | * | | | | | | | | W | S | K | T | C | Am | FJ | Lo | Pe | Pi | TA |
|---|---|---|---|---|---|---|---|---|---|---|---|---|---|---|---|---|---|---|---|---|
| (32) | wb | 1 | T | | | | | | | | | | | | | | | | | |
| 15 | b | | | | | | | | | s | | | | s | | | | | | |
| (8) | b | | T | | | • | | | | | | | | | | | | | | |
| 7 | b | | | | | | | | | | | | | | | | | | • | • |
| 3 | b | | | | | | | | | n+ | | | n+ | | | | | | | |

*1) Scenic Vista*

Interstate 80 in New Jersey runs east to west for 68 miles from the George Washington Bridge in Fort Lee to the Pennsylvania state line. Eastbound travelers should read up the chart. Westbound travelers read down the chart.

| Exit(mm) | ⤢ | ★ | 🚗 | 🚻 | 📞 | 🍽 | 🛏 | 🏪 | 🐾 | W | S | K | T | C | Am | FJ | Lo | Pe | Pi | TA |
|---|---|---|---|---|---|---|---|---|---|---|---|---|---|---|---|---|---|---|---|---|
| 53 | b | | | | | | | | | | | | s | | | | | | | |
| 45 | eb | | | | | | | | | | | n | | | | | | | | |
| (32) | b | 1 | R | | | | | | | | | | | | | | | | | |
| 30 | b | | | | | | | | | | | | | n | | | | | | |
| 27a | wb | | | | | | | | | | s | s | | | | | | | | |
| 27 | eb | | | | | | | | | | s | s | | | | | | | | |
| (21) | b | 2 | R | • | • | | | | • | | | | | | | | | | | |
| (7) | eb | | W | • | • | • | • | | • | | | | | | | | | | | |
| (6) | wb | 3 | T | | | | | | | | | | | | | | | | | |
| 4 | eb | | | | | | | | | | | | | | | | | | | • |
| 4c | wb | | | | | | | | | | | | | | | | | | | • |
| (1) | b | | R | • | • | • | | | • | | | | | | | | | | | |

*1) Truck Parking, No Facilities. 2) Scenic Vista (eastbound), No Trucks. 3) Scenic Vista*

 The New Jersey Turnpike is 118 miles long. It runs north to south from US 46 in Ridgefield Park to I-295 in Deepwater. Exit numbers are based on the consecutive numbering system. Northbound travelers should read up the chart. Southbound travelers read down the chart.

| Exit(mm) | ⤢ | ★ | 🚗 | 🚻 | 📞 | 🍽 | 🛏 | 🏪 | 🐾 | W | S | K | T | C | Am | FJ | Lo | Pe | Pi | TA |
|---|---|---|---|---|---|---|---|---|---|---|---|---|---|---|---|---|---|---|---|---|
| (115) | nb | 1 | S | • | • | • | • | | | | | | | | | | | | | |
| (112) | sb | 1 | S | • | • | • | • | | | | | | | | | | | | | |
| (102) | nb | 1 | S | • | • | • | • | | | | | | | | | | | | | |
| (94) | b | 1 | S | • | • | • | • | | | | | | | | | | | | | |
| (79) | nb | 1 | S | • | • | • | • | | | | | | | | | | | | | |
| (72) | sb | 1 | S | • | • | • | • | | | | | | | | | | | | | |
| (59) | b | 1 | S | • | • | • | • | | | | | | | | | | | | | |
| 7 | b | | | | | | | | | | | | | | | | | | • | • |
| 5 | b | | | | | | | | | | | | w | e | | | | | | |
| (39) | nb | 1 | S | • | • | • | • | | | | | | | | | | | | | |
| (30) | sb | 1 | S | • | • | • | • | | | | | | | | | | | | | |
| (5) | b | 1 | S | • | • | • | • | | | | | | | | | | | | | |
| 1 | b | | | | | | | | | | | | | | | | | | | • |

*1) Gas, Food*

Interstate 10 in Alabama runs east to west for 67 miles from the Florida state line to the Mississippi state line. Eastbound travelers should read up the chart. Westbound travelers read down the chart.

| Exit(mm) | ↗ | ★ | 🡽 | 👫 | 📞 | 🍴 | 🛏 | 🏪 | 🐾 | W | S | K | T | C | Am | FJ | Lo | Pe | Pi | TA |
|---|---|---|---|---|---|---|---|---|---|---|---|---|---|---|---|---|---|---|---|---|
| 28a | b |  |  |  |  |  |  |  |  |  |  | s | s |  |  |  |  |  |  |  |
| 5a | b |  |  |  |  |  |  |  |  | s |  |  | s |  |  |  |  |  |  |  |

Interstate 10 in Alabama runs east to west for 67 miles from the Florida state line to the Mississippi state line. Eastbound travelers should read up the chart. Westbound travelers read down the chart.

| Exit(mm) | ↗ | ★ | 🡽 | 👫 | 📞 | 🍴 | 🛏 | 🏪 | 🐾 | W | S | K | T | C | Am | FJ | Lo | Pe | Pi | TA |
|---|---|---|---|---|---|---|---|---|---|---|---|---|---|---|---|---|---|---|---|---|
| (32) | nb |  | R | • | • | • | • |  | • |  |  |  |  |  |  |  |  |  |  |  |
| 13 | sb |  |  |  |  |  |  |  |  |  |  | w |  |  |  |  |  |  |  |  |
| 13b | nb |  |  |  |  |  |  |  |  |  |  | w |  |  |  |  |  |  |  |  |
| 5 | b |  |  |  |  |  |  |  |  | w | w |  |  |  |  |  |  |  |  |  |

E ↕ W

Interstate 10 in Alabama runs east to west for 67 miles from the Florida state line to the Mississippi state line. Eastbound travelers should read up the chart. Westbound travelers read down the chart.

| Exit(mm) | ↗ | ★ | 🡽 | 👫 | 📞 | 🍴 | 🛏 | 🏪 | 🐾 | W | S | K | T | C | Am | FJ | Lo | Pe | Pi | TA |
|---|---|---|---|---|---|---|---|---|---|---|---|---|---|---|---|---|---|---|---|---|
| 67 | b |  |  |  |  |  |  |  |  | e+ |  | e+ |  |  |  |  |  |  |  |  |
| (58) | b | 1 | T |  |  |  |  |  |  |  |  |  |  |  |  |  |  |  |  |  |
| 57 | b |  |  |  |  |  |  |  |  |  |  |  |  |  |  |  |  | • | • |  |
| (50) | b |  | R | • | • | • | • |  | • |  |  |  |  |  |  |  |  |  |  |  |
| 47b | sb |  |  |  |  |  |  |  |  | w | w |  |  |  |  |  |  |  |  |  |
| 47a | nb |  |  |  |  |  |  |  |  |  |  | e |  |  |  |  |  |  |  |  |
| 40 | sb |  |  |  |  |  |  |  |  |  |  | w |  |  |  |  |  |  |  |  |
| 40b | nb |  |  |  |  |  |  |  |  |  |  | w |  |  |  |  |  |  |  |  |
| 36b | b |  |  |  |  |  |  |  |  |  | w |  |  |  |  |  |  |  |  |  |
| 29 | sb |  |  |  |  |  |  |  |  |  | e |  |  |  |  |  |  |  |  |  |
| 29a | nb |  |  |  |  |  |  |  |  |  | e |  |  |  |  |  |  |  |  |  |
| 18a | b |  |  |  |  |  |  |  |  |  |  |  |  |  |  |  |  |  |  | • |
| (2) | nb |  | W | • | • | • | • |  | • |  |  |  |  |  |  |  |  |  |  |  |
| 2c | b |  |  |  |  |  |  |  |  |  |  |  |  |  |  |  | • |  |  |  |
| 2b | b |  |  |  |  |  |  |  |  |  |  |  |  |  |  |  |  |  | • |  |
| 1a | b |  |  |  |  |  |  |  |  |  |  |  | e |  |  |  |  |  |  |  |

E ↕ W

1) Scenic Vista

# New Mexico

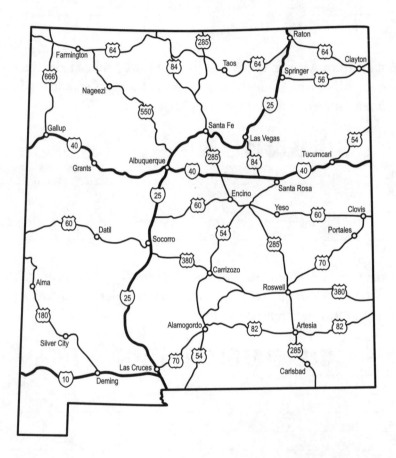

| Interstate | Page |
| --- | --- |
| 10 | 131 |
| 25 | 131 |
| 40 | 132 |

Interstate 10 in New Mexico runs east to west for 164 miles from the Texas state line to the Arizona state line. Eastbound travelers should read up the chart. Westbound travelers read down the chart.

| Exit(mm) | ↗ | ★ | | | | | | | | W | S | K | T | C | Am | FJ | Lo | Pe | Pi | TA |
|---|---|---|---|---|---|---|---|---|---|---|---|---|---|---|---|---|---|---|---|---|
| (164) | wb | | W | • | • | • | • | | • | | | | | | | | | | | |
| 140 | b | | | | | | | | | | | n | | n | | | | | | |
| 139 | b | | | | | | | | | | | | | | | | | | • | • |
| (135) | eb | 1 | R | • | | • | • | | • | | | | | | | | | | | |
| 132 | b | | | | | | | | | | | | | | | | • | | | |
| (120) | eb | 2 | T | | | | | | | | | | | | | | | | | |
| 82b | b | | | | | | | | | | s | | | | | | | | | |
| (61) | wb | | R | • | | • | • | | • | | | | | | | | | | | |
| (53) | eb | | R | • | | • | • | | • | | | | | | | | | | | |
| 24 | b | | | | | | | | | | | | | | | | | | • | |
| 20 | b | | W | • | • | | | | | | | | | | | | • | | | |

*1) Scenic Vista*
*2) No Facilities*

Interstate 25 in New Mexico runs north to south for 462 miles from the Colorado state line to I-10 in Las Cruces. Northbound travelers should read up the chart. Southbound travelers read down the chart.

| Exit(mm) | ↗ | ★ | | | | | | | | W | S | K | T | C | Am | FJ | Lo | Pe | Pi | TA |
|---|---|---|---|---|---|---|---|---|---|---|---|---|---|---|---|---|---|---|---|---|
| 451 | b | | W | • | • | • | | | | | | w | | | | | | | | |
| (434) | b | | R | • | | • | | | • | | | | | | | | | | | |
| (376) | sb | | R | • | • | • | | | • | | | | | | | | | | | |
| (374) | nb | | R | • | • | • | | • | • | | | | | | | | | | | |
| (360) | b | | T | | | • | | | | | | | | | | | | | | |
| (325) | b | | T | | | • | | | | | | | | | | | | | | |
| 278a | b | | | | | | | | | w+ | w+ | | w+ | | | | | | | |
| (269) | nb | | R | • | • | • | | | • | | | | | | | | | | | |
| 231 | b | | | | | | | | | | | | e | | | | | | | |
| 203 | b | | | | | | | | | w | | | | | | | | | | |
| 195 | b | | | | | | | | | w+ | | | | | | | | | | |
| (167) | b | | R | • | | • | • | | • | | | | | | | | | | | |
| (165) | b | 1 | T | | | | | | | | | | | | | | | | | |
| (114) | b | | R | • | | • | • | | • | | | | | | | | | | | |
| (27) | nb | 2 | T | | | • | | | | | | | | | | | | | | |

| Dir | Exit(mm) | ↗ | ★ | | | | | | | | W | S | K | T | C | Am | FJ | Lo | Pe | Pi | TA |
|---|---|---|---|---|---|---|---|---|---|---|---|---|---|---|---|---|---|---|---|---|---|
| N | (23) | b | | R | • | | • | • | | • | | | | | | | | | | | |
| ↕ | 6a | b | | | | | | | | | | e | e | | | | | | | | |
| S | 3 | b | | | | | | | | | w | | | e | | | | | | | |

*1) No Facilities*
*2) Scenic Vista*

Interstate 40 in New Mexico is about 374 miles long. It runs east to west from the Texas state line to the California state line. Eastbound travelers should read up the chart. Westbound travelers read down the chart.

| Dir | Exit(mm) | ↗ | ★ | | | | | | | | W | S | K | T | C | Am | FJ | Lo | Pe | Pi | TA |
|---|---|---|---|---|---|---|---|---|---|---|---|---|---|---|---|---|---|---|---|---|---|
| | (373) | wb | | W | • | • | • | | | • | | | | | | | | | | | |
| | 333 | b | | | | | | | | | | | n+ | | | | | | • | | |
| | (302) | b | | R | • | • | • | | | • | | | | | | | | | | | |
| | 277 | b | | | | | | | | | | | | | | | | | • | | • |
| E | (252) | b | | R | • | • | • | | | • | | | | | | | | | | | |
| ↕ | (220) | b | 1 | T | | | | | | | | | | | | | | | | | |
| W | (207) | b | | R | • | | • | | | • | | | | | | | | | | | |
| | 194 | b | | | | | | | | | | | | | | | | | | | • |
| | 165 | b | | | | | | | | | s | s | | n | | | | | | | |
| | 160 | b | | | | | | | | | | | s | | | | | | | | |
| | 158 | b | | | | | | | | | | | | | | | | • | | | |
| | 155 | b | | | | | | | | | n | | | | | | | | | | |
| | 153 | b | | | | | | | | | | | | | | | | • | | | |
| E | (113) | b | 2 | T | | | | | | | | | | | | | | | | | |
| ↕ | 102 | b | | R | • | • | • | | | • | | | | | | | | • | | | |
| W | 85 | b | | | | | | | | | n | | | | | | | | | | |
| | 79 | b | | | | | | | | | | | | | | | | | • | • | |
| | 39 | b | | | | | | | | | | | | | | | | | | • | |
| | 22 | b | | W | • | • | • | • | • | • | | | | | | | | | | | |
| | 20 | b | | | | | | | | | n | | n | | n | | | | | | |
| | 16 | b | | | | | | | | | | | | | | | | • | | | • |
| | (3) | eb | | R | • | • | • | | | • | | | | | | | | | | | |

*1) No Facilities*
*2) Scenic Vista*

# New York

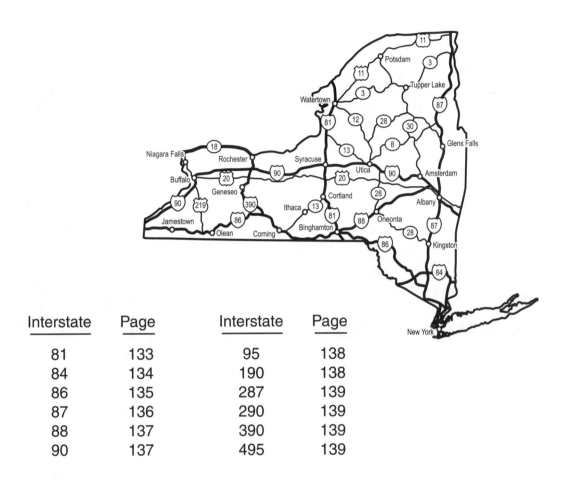

| Interstate | Page | Interstate | Page |
|---|---|---|---|
| 81 | 133 | 95 | 138 |
| 84 | 134 | 190 | 138 |
| 86 | 135 | 287 | 139 |
| 87 | 136 | 290 | 139 |
| 88 | 137 | 390 | 139 |
| 90 | 137 | 495 | 139 |

Interstate 81 in New York runs north to south for 184 miles from the United States/Canada border to the Pennsylvania state line. Exit numbers are based on the consecutive numbering system. Northbound travelers should read up the chart. Southbound travelers read down the chart.

| | Exit(mm) | | ★ | 🚻 | 📞 | ⛽ | 🛏 | 🐕 | W | S | K | T | C | Am | FJ | Lo | Pe | Pi | TA |
|---|---|---|---|---|---|---|---|---|---|---|---|---|---|---|---|---|---|---|---|
| N | (178) sb | | R | • | • | • | | • | | | | | | | | | | | |
| | (174) nb | | R | • | • | • | • | | • | | | | | | | | | | | |
| | (168) sb | | T | | • | | | | | | | | | | | | | | | |
| S | (161) nb 1 | | T | | | | | | | | | | | | | | | | | |

| Exit(mm) | ⇱ | ★ | ↗ | 🚻 | ☎ | ⛱ | 🛢 | 🚮 | 🐾 | W | S | K | T | C | Am | FJ | Lo | Pe | Pi | TA |
|---|---|---|---|---|---|---|---|---|---|---|---|---|---|---|---|---|---|---|---|---|
| 48 | b | | | | | | | | | | | | | | • | | | | | |
| (156) | b | 1 | T | | | | | | | | | | | | | | | | | |
| 46 | b | | | | | | | | | | | | | e | | | | | | |
| 45 | b | | | | | | | | | w | w | w | | | | | | | | |
| (149) | nb | | T | | | • | | | | | | | | | | | | | | |
| (147) | sb | | R | • | • | • | • | | • | | | | | | | | | | | |
| (134) | b | 1 | T | | | | | | | | | | | | | | | | | |
| (101) | sb | | R | • | • | • | • | | • | | | | | | | | | | | |
| 32 | b | | | | | | | | | w | | | | | | | | | | |
| 30 | b | | | | | | | | | | | | | e | | | | | | |
| 26 | b | | | | | | | | | | | e | | | | | | | | |
| 25 | b | | | | | | | | | | | | | | | | | | • | |
| (60) | nb | | R | • | • | • | • | | • | | | | | | | | | | | |
| (45) | nb | | T | | | • | | | | | | | | | | | | | | |
| (33) | sb | | R | • | • | • | • | | • | | | | | | | | | | | |
| (14) | nb | | R | • | • | • | | | | | | | | | | | | | | |
| 5 | b | | | | | | | | | | | | | w | | | | | | |
| 3 | sb | | | | | | | | | | | | | | | | | | • | • |
| 2w | nb | | | | | | | | | | | | | | | | | | | • |
| (2) | nb | | W | • | • | • | • | | • | | | | | | | | | | | |

*Reading direction markers in the left margin: N↕S at exits (149)–(101); N↕S at exits (60)–(14).*

*1) No Facilities*

Interstate 84 in New York runs east to west for 72 miles from the Connecticut state line to the Pennsylvania state line. Exit numbers are based on the consecutive numbering system. Eastbound travelers should read up the chart. Westbound travelers read down the chart.

| Exit(mm) | ⇱ | ★ | ↗ | 🚻 | ☎ | ⛱ | 🛢 | 🚮 | 🐾 | W | S | K | T | C | Am | FJ | Lo | Pe | Pi | TA |
|---|---|---|---|---|---|---|---|---|---|---|---|---|---|---|---|---|---|---|---|---|
| (55) | b | | R | • | • | • | • | | • | | | | | | | | | | | |
| 13 | b | | | | | | | | | n | n | | n | | | | | | | |
| 7 | b | | | | | | | | | s | | | | | | | | | | |
| 6 | b | | | | | | | | | | | | | | | | | | • | |
| 5 | b | | | | | | | | | | | | | | | | | | | • |
| (24) | wb | | R | • | • | • | • | | • | | | | | | | | | | | |
| 4 | b | | | | | | | | | n | n | | | | | | | | | |
| (17) | eb | | R | • | • | • | • | | • | | | | | | | | | | | |
| (3) | b | 1 | T | | | | | | | | | | | | | | | | | |

*Reading direction markers in the left margin: E↕W.*

*1) No Facilities*

Interstate 86 in New York is 386 miles long. It runs east to west between I-87 and the Pennsylvania state line. The Interstate is not entirely completed. Parts are identified as NY Hwy 17. Exit numbers are based on the consecutive numbering system. Eastbound travelers should read up the chart. Westbound travelers read down the chart.

| Exit(mm) | ↗ | * | | | | | | | | W | S | K | T | C | Am | FJ | Lo | Pe | Pi | TA |
|---|---|---|---|---|---|---|---|---|---|---|---|---|---|---|---|---|---|---|---|---|
| 130a | eb | | | | | | | | | s | | | | | | | | | | |
| 120 | b | | | | | | | | | n | n | s | | | | | | | | |
| 105 | b | | | | | | | | | n | | | | | | | | | | |
| (313) | eb | | R | • | • | • | • | | • | | | | | | | | | | | |
| (295) | wb | | R | • | • | • | • | | • | | | | | | | | | | | |
| (276) | wb | 1 | T | | | | | | | | | | | | | | | | | |
| (265) | eb | | T | | | • | | | | | | | | | | | | | | |
| 72 | b | | | | | | | | | | | s | | | | | | | | |
| 67 | b | | | | | | | | | s+ | s+ | | s+ | | | | | | | |
| (222) | wb | | R | • | • | • | • | | • | | | | | | | | | | | |
| (212) | eb | | R | • | • | • | • | | • | | | | | | | | | | | |
| (199) | wb | | R | • | • | • | • | | • | | | | | | | | | | | |
| 51 | b | | | | | | | | | s | s | | | | | | | | | |
| (167) | wb | 1 | T | | | | | | | | | | | | | | | | | |
| (160) | eb | | R | • | • | • | • | | • | | | | | | | | | | | |
| 38 | b | | | | | | | | | | | n | | | | | | | | |
| (147) | wb | | R | • | • | • | • | | • | | | | | | | | | | | |
| 37 | b | | | | | | | | | | | | | | | | | | • | | |
| 34 | b | | | | | | | | | s | | | | | | | | | | |
| (125) | eb | 2 | T | | | | | | | | | | | | | | | | | |
| (101) | eb | | R | • | • | • | • | | • | | | | | | | | | | | |
| (72) | wb | | R | • | • | • | • | | • | | | | | | | | | | | |
| 25 | b | | | | | | | | | s+ | | s+ | | | | | | | | |
| (41) | eb | | T | | • | • | | | | | | | | | | | | | | |
| (39) | wb | | T | | • | • | | | | | | | | | | | | | | |
| (22) | eb | | W | • | • | • | • | | • | | | | | | | | | | | |

*1) No Facilities*
*2) Scenic Vista*

Interstate 87 in New York runs north to south for about 334 miles from the United States/Canada border to I-278 in New York City. Portions are also I-287 and the New York Thruway. Exit numbers are based on the consecutive numbering system. Northbound travelers should read up the chart. Southbound travelers read down the chart.

| Exit(mm) | dir | * | type | ↗ | 🚻 | 📞 | 🏕 | ▢ | ▣ | 🐾 | W | S | K | T | C | Am | FJ | Lo | Pe | Pi | TA |
|---|---|---|---|---|---|---|---|---|---|---|---|---|---|---|---|---|---|---|---|---|---|
| (162) | b | | W | | • | • | • | | | • | | | | | | | | | | | |
| 37 | b | | | | | | | | | | e | e | w | | | | | | | | |
| (123) | b | | R | | • | • | • | | | • | | | | | | | | | | | |
| (111) | nb | | R | | • | • | • | • | | • | | | | | | | | | | | |
| (99) | b | | R | | • | • | • | | | • | | | | | | | | | | | |
| (83) | b | 1 | R | | • | • | • | • | | • | | | | | | | | | | | |
| (65) | sb | | T | | | | • | | | | | | | | | | | | | | |
| (63) | nb | | T | | | | • | | | | | | | | | | | | | | |
| 19 | b | | | | | | | | | | e | | | | | | | | | | |
| (43) | b | | R | | • | • | • | • | | • | | | | | | | | | | | |
| 15 | b | | | | | | | | | | e | | e | | | | | | | | |
| (14) | nb | | R | | • | • | • | • | | • | | | | | | | | | | | |
| 9w | sb | | | | | | | | | | | | w | | | | | | | | |
| 9e | sb | | | | | | | | | | | | | e | | | | | | | |
| 9 | nb | | | | | | | | | | | | w | e | | | | | | | |
| 8a | b | | | | | | | | | | e+ | | | | | | | | | | |
| 6 | b | | | | | | | | | | e | e | w | | | | | | | | |
| 2 | b | | | | | | | | | | | | e | | | | | | | | |
| (139) | sb | | T | | | | • | • | | | | | | | | | | | | | |
| (127) | b | 2 | S | | • | • | • | • | | | | | | | | | | | | | |
| (103) | nb | 2 | S | | • | • | • | • | | | | | | | | | | | | | |
| (99) | nb | | T | | | | • | • | | | | | | | | | | | | | |
| (96) | sb | 2 | S | | • | • | • | • | | | | | | | | | | | | | |
| (66) | sb | 2 | S | | • | • | • | • | | | | | | | | | | | | | |
| (65) | nb | 2 | S | | • | • | • | • | | | | | | | | | | | | | |
| 17 | b | | | | | | | | | | e | | | | | | | | | | |
| 16 | b | | | | | | | | | | w+ | | | | | | | | | | |
| (34) | sb | 2 | S | | • | • | • | • | | | | | | | | | | | | | |
| (33) | nb | 2 | S | | • | • | • | • | | | | | | | | | | | | | |
| 14b | b | | | | | | | | | | w | | | | | | | | | | |
| 14 | b | | | | | | | | | | | | e | | | | | | | | |
| 12 | b | | | | | | | | | | | | w | | | | | | | | |
| (6) | nb | 2 | S | | • | • | • | • | | | | | | | | | | | | | |
| 10 | b | | | | | | | | | | | | w | | | | | | | | |

*1) Scenic Vista (northbound)*
*2) Gas, Food*

Interstate 88 in New York runs east to west for 118 miles from I-90 near Schenectady to I-81 in Binghamton. Exit numbers are based on the consecutive numbering system. Eastbound travelers should read up the chart. Westbound travelers read down the chart.

| Exit(mm) | ↗ | * | type | rr | ph | pic | fl | vn | pt | W | S | K | T | C | Am | FJ | Lo | Pe | Pi | TA |
|---|---|---|---|---|---|---|---|---|---|---|---|---|---|---|---|---|---|---|---|---|
| 21 | b | | | | | | | | | n+ | | | | | | | | | | |
| (79) | wb | | R | • | • | • | • | | • | | | | | | | | | | | |
| (73) | eb | | R | • | • | • | • | | • | | | | | | | | | | | |
| 15 | b | | | | | | | | | | s | | | | | | | | | |
| (43) | wb | | R | • | • | • | • | | • | | | | | | | | | | | |
| (39) | eb | | R | • | • | • | • | | • | | | | | | | | | | | |
| 9 | b | | | | | | | | | | | n | | | | | | | | |

(Left margin: E ↕ W direction indicator)

Interstate 90 in New York runs east to west for 385 miles from the Massachusetts state line to the Pennsylvania state line. Most of it is also the New York Thruway. Exit numbers are based on the consecutive numbering system. Exit numbers and mile markers decrease from west to east, the opposite of the normal numbering system. Eastbound travelers should read up the chart. Westbound travelers read down the chart.

| Exit(mm) | ↗ | * | type | rr | ph | pic | fl | vn | pt | W | S | K | T | C | Am | FJ | Lo | Pe | Pi | TA |
|---|---|---|---|---|---|---|---|---|---|---|---|---|---|---|---|---|---|---|---|---|
| B3 | b | | | | | | | | | | | | | | | | • | | | |
| (18) | wb | | R | • | • | • | • | | • | | | | | | | | | | | |
| 9 | b | | | | | | | | | n | | s | | | | | | | | |
| 1s | b | | | | | | | | | s | s | | | | | | | | | |
| (153) | eb | 1 | S | • | • | • | • | | | | | | | | | | | | | |
| (168) | wb | 1 | S | • | • | • | • | | | | | | | | | | | | | |
| (172) | eb | 1 | S | • | • | • | • | | | | | | | | | | | | | |
| 28 | b | | | | | | | | | | | | | | | | • | | | • |
| (184) | b | | T | | | • | | | | | | | | | | | | | | |
| (210) | b | 1 | S | • | • | • | • | | | | | | | | | | | | | |
| 30 | b | | | | | | | | | n | | n | | | | | | | | |
| (227) | wb | 1 | S | • | • | • | • | | | | | | | | | | | | | |
| 31 | b | | | | | | | | | n+ | | | | | | | | | | |
| (244) | eb | 1 | S | • | • | • | • | | | | | | | | | | | | | |
| (250) | eb | | T | | • | • | | | | | | | | | | | | | | |
| (256) | wb | | T | | • | • | | | | | | | | | | | | | | |
| (266) | wb | 1 | S | • | • | • | • | | | | | | | | | | | | | |
| (280) | eb | 1 | S | • | • | • | • | | | | | | | | | | | | | |
| 36 | b | | | | | | | | | | | | | | | | | | | • |

(Left margin: E ↕ W direction indicators)

| | Exit(mm) | | ★ | 🚐 | 🚻 | ☎ | 🍽 | ♿ | 🥤 | 🐾 | W | S | K | T | C | Am | FJ | Lo | Pe | Pi | TA |
|---|---|---|---|---|---|---|---|---|---|---|---|---|---|---|---|---|---|---|---|---|---|
| | (292) | wb | 1 | S | • | • | • | • | | | | | | | | | | | | | |
| | (310) | eb | 1 | S | • | • | • | • | | | | | | | | | | | | | |
| | (318) | wb | | T | | | • | • | | | | | | | | | | | | | |
| | 41 | b | | | | | | | | | | | | | | | | | • | | | |
| E ↕ W | (324) | wb | 1 | S | • | • | • | • | • | | | | | | | | | | | | |
| | 42 | b | | | | | | | | | | | | | | | • | | | | | |
| | (337) | eb | 1 | S | • | • | • | • | | | | | | | | | | | | | |
| | (350) | wb | 1 | S | • | • | • | • | • | | | | | | | | | | | | |
| | (353) | eb | | T | | | • | • | | | | | | | | | | | | | |
| | (366) | eb | 1 | S | • | • | • | • | • | | | | | | | | | | | | |
| | (376) | wb | 1 | S | • | • | • | • | • | | | | | | | | | | | | |
| | 48 | b | | | | | | | | | | s+ | | | | | | | | | | |
| | (397) | eb | 1 | S | • | • | • | • | | | | | | | | | | | | | |
| E ↕ W | 48a | b | | | | | | | | | | | | | | | | | • | | | • |
| | (412) | wb | 1 | S | • | • | • | • | | | | | | | | | | | | | |
| | 49 | b | | | | | | | | | | n+ | | n+ | n+ | n+ | | | | | | |
| | 52 | b | | | | | | | | | | | | s | n | | • | | | | | |
| | 55 | b | | | | | | | | | | | | | s | | | | | | | |
| | (442) | b | | T | | | • | • | | | | | | | | | | | | | | |
| | (447) | b | 1 | S | • | • | • | • | | | | | | | | | | | | | |
| | 59 | b | | | | | | | | | | | | s | s | | | | | | | |

*1) Gas, Food*

Interstate 95 in New York runs north to south for 24 miles from the Connecticut state line to the New Jersey state line. Exit numbers are based on the consecutive numbering system. Northbound travelers should read up the chart. Southbound travelers read down the chart.

| Exit(mm) | | ★ | 🚐 | 🚻 | ☎ | 🍽 | ♿ | 🥤 | 🐾 | W | S | K | T | C | Am | FJ | Lo | Pe | Pi | TA |
|---|---|---|---|---|---|---|---|---|---|---|---|---|---|---|---|---|---|---|---|---|
| 11 | b | | | | | | | | | | | | e | | | | | | | |

Interstate 190 in New York is 28 miles long. It generally runs north to south from the United States/Canada border in Lewiston to I-90 in Buffalo. Exit numbers are based on the consecutive numbering system. Northbound travelers should read up the chart. Southbound travelers read down the chart.

| Exit(mm) | | ★ | 🚐 | 🚻 | ☎ | 🍽 | ♿ | 🥤 | 🐾 | W | S | K | T | C | Am | FJ | Lo | Pe | Pi | TA |
|---|---|---|---|---|---|---|---|---|---|---|---|---|---|---|---|---|---|---|---|---|
| 23 | b | | | | | | | | | w | w | e | | | | | | | | |
| 22 | b | | | | | | | | | | | | e | | | | | | | |

Interstate 287 in New York is 31 miles long. It runs from I-95 to the New Jersey state line. Portions are shared with I-87 and the New York Thruway. Exit numbers are based on the consecutive numbering system.

| Exit(mm) | ↗ | ★ | 🡒 | 👥 | 📞 | 🍽 | ⛽ | 🏧 | 🐾 | W | S | K | T | C | Am | FJ | Lo | Pe | Pi | TA |
|---|---|---|---|---|---|---|---|---|---|---|---|---|---|---|---|---|---|---|---|---|
| 14b | b | | | | | | | | | s | | | | | | | | | | |
| 14 | b | | | | | | | | | | | | n | | | | | | | |
| 12 | b | | | | | | | | | | | | s | | | | | | | |

Interstate 290 in Buffalo is about 10 miles long. It connects I-90 with I-190. Exit numbers are based on the consecutive numbering system.

| Exit(mm) | ↗ | ★ | 🡒 | 👥 | 📞 | 🍽 | ⛽ | 🏧 | 🐾 | W | S | K | T | C | Am | FJ | Lo | Pe | Pi | TA |
|---|---|---|---|---|---|---|---|---|---|---|---|---|---|---|---|---|---|---|---|---|
| 3 | wb | | | | | | | | | n | | s | s | | | | | | | |
| 3b | eb | | | | | | | | | n | | | | | | | | | | |
| 3a | eb | | | | | | | | | | | s | s | | | | | | | |

Interstate 390 is about 80 miles long. It generally runs north to south from Rochester to I-86 near Bath. Exit numbers are based on the consecutive numbering system. Northbound travelers should read up the chart. Southbound travelers read down the chart.

N ↕ S

| Exit(mm) | ↗ | ★ | 🡒 | 👥 | 📞 | 🍽 | ⛽ | 🏧 | 🐾 | W | S | K | T | C | Am | FJ | Lo | Pe | Pi | TA |
|---|---|---|---|---|---|---|---|---|---|---|---|---|---|---|---|---|---|---|---|---|
| 13 | b | | | | | | | | | | w | w | | w | e | | | | | | |
| (38) | b | R | • | • | • | | | | • | | | | | | | | | | | | |
| 5 | b | | | | | | | | | | | | | | | | | | • | | |

Interstate 495 on Long Island is 66 miles long. It begins in New York City and runs east to Calverton. Exit numbers are based on the consecutive numbering system. Eastbound travelers should read up the chart. Westbound travelers read down the chart.

| Exit(mm) | ↗ | ★ | 🡒 | 👥 | 📞 | 🍽 | ⛽ | 🏧 | 🐾 | W | S | K | T | C | Am | FJ | Lo | Pe | Pi | TA |
|---|---|---|---|---|---|---|---|---|---|---|---|---|---|---|---|---|---|---|---|---|
| 64 | b | | | | | | | | | | | | n | | | | | | | |
| (51) | b | T | | | • | | | | | | | | | | | | | | | |

# North Carolina

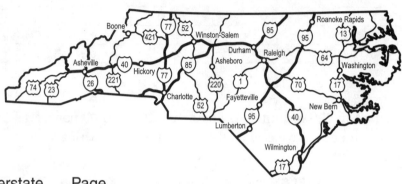

| Interstate | Page |
|---|---|
| 26 | 140 |
| 40 | 141 |
| 77 | 142 |
| 85 | 142 |
| 95 | 143 |
| 240 | 144 |
| 440 | 144 |

**26** Interstate 26 in North Carolina runs east to west for 71 miles from the South Carolina state line to the Tennessee state line. Eastbound travelers should read up the chart. Westbound travelers read down the chart.

| Exit(mm) | ↗ | * | | | | | | | | W | S | K | T | C | Am | FJ | Lo | Pe | Pi | TA |
|---|---|---|---|---|---|---|---|---|---|---|---|---|---|---|---|---|---|---|---|---|
| (67) | wb | | W | • | • | • | | • | | | | | | | | | | | | |
| 53 | b | | | | | | | | | | | | | | s | | | | | |
| 49a | b | | | | | | | | | | | n | | | | | | | | |
| 49b | b | | | | | | | | | | | | s | | | | | | | |
| (41) | b | | R | • | • | • | | • | | | | | | | | | | | | |
| 33 | b | | | | | | | | | | | | s | | | | | | | |
| (8) | wb | 1 | T | | | | | | | | | | | | | | | | | |
| (6) | eb | | W | • | • | • | | • | | | | | | | | | | | | |

*1) Scenic Vista*

Interstate 40 in North Carolina runs east to west for 420 miles from Wilmington to the Tennessee state line. Part of it is also I-85. Eastbound travelers should read up the chart. Westbound travelers read down the chart.

| Exit(mm) | ↗ | ★ | ↗ | 👥 | ☎ | ⛱ | 🛒 | 🏨 | 🐾 | W | S | K | T | C | Am | FJ | Lo | Pe | Pi | TA |
|---|---|---|---|---|---|---|---|---|---|---|---|---|---|---|---|---|---|---|---|---|
| 364 | b | | R | • | • | • | • | | • | | | | | | | | | | | |
| (324) | b | | R | • | • | • | • | | • | | | | | | | | | | | |
| 312 | b | | | | | | | | | | | | | n | | | | | | |
| 298a | b | | | | | | | | | | s | | | | | | | | | |
| 284 | b | | | | | | | | | | | | | s | | | | | | |
| 270 | b | | | | | | | | | n | | | | | | | | | | |
| 157 | b | | | | | | | | | | | | | | | | • | | | |
| 153 | b | | | | | | | | | | | | | s | | | | | | |
| 152 | b | | | | | | | | | | | | | | | | | | • | |
| 150 | b | | | | | | | | | | | | | | • | | | | | |
| 141 | b | | | | | | | | | n | | n | | n | | | | | | |
| (139) | b | | R | • | • | • | • | | | | | | | | | | | | | |
| 138 | b | | | | | | | | | | | | | | | | | | | • |
| 220 | b | | | | | | | | | | | e | | | | | | | | |
| 214 | wb | | | | | | | | | s | s | s | s | | | | | | | |
| 214a | eb | | | | | | | | | s | s | s | s | | | | | | | |
| 213 | b | | | | | | | | | | | | s | | | | | | | |
| 192 | b | | | | | | | | | | | s | | | | | | | | |
| 189 | b | | | | | | | | | | | s | s | | | | | | | |
| 188 | wb | 1 | | | | | | | | n | | | | | | | | | | |
| 184 | b | | | | | | | | | | | s | | s | | | | | | |
| (177) | b | | R | • | • | • | • | | • | | | | | | | | | | | |
| 170 | b | | | | | | | | | s | | | | | • | | | | | |
| 151 | b | | | | | | | | | n | | | n | | | | | | | |
| (136) | b | | R | • | • | • | • | | • | | | | | | | | | | | |
| 130 | b | | | | | | | | | | | | n | | | | | | | |
| 126 | b | | | | | | | | | s | s | s | | | | | | | | |
| 125 | b | | | | | | | | | | | | | s | | | | | | |
| 103 | b | | | | | | | | | s | | | | | | | | | | |
| 86 | b | | | | | | | | | | | | | | | | | • | | |
| (82) | b | | R | • | • | • | • | • | • | | | | | | | | | | | |
| 44 | b | | | | | | | | | | | | n | | | | | | | |
| 37 | b | | | | | | | | | | | | | | | | | | | • |
| 27 | b | | | | | | | | | s+ | | | | | | | | | | |
| 24 | b | | | | | | | | | | | | | | | | • | | | |
| (10) | b | 2 | W | • | • | • | • | | • | | | | | | | | | | | |

*1) Wal-Mart is off US 421. 2) Welcome Center (eastbound), Rest Area (westbound)*

Interstate 77 in North Carolina runs north to south for 105 miles from the Virginia state line to the South Carolina state line. Northbound travelers should read up the chart. Southbound travelers read down the chart.

| Exit(mm) | | ★ | Facilities | W | S | K | T | C | Am | FJ | Lo | Pe | Pi | TA |
|---|---|---|---|---|---|---|---|---|---|---|---|---|---|---|
| (105) | sb | | W • • • • • • | | | | | | | | | | | |
| 82 | b | | | | | | | e | | | | | | |
| (72) | nb | | R • • • • • • | | | | | | | | | | | |
| (63) | sb | | R • • • • • • | | | | | | | | | | | |
| 50 | b | | | | | e | | | | | | | | |
| (39) | b | | R • • • • • • | | | | | | | | | | | |
| 36 | b | | | | e | | e | w | | | | | | |
| 25 | b | | | | | | e | | | | | | | |
| 16b | b | | | | | | | | | | | • | | |
| 13a | b | 1 | | | | | | | | | | | • | |
| 5 | b | | | | | | | e | | | | | | |
| (1) | nb | | W • • • • • • | | | | | | | | | | | |

*N ↕ S*

*1) Pilot Travel Center is on Statesville Ave*

Interstate 85 in North Carolina runs north to south for 234 miles from the Virginia state line to the South Carolina state line. Part of it is shared with I-40. Northbound travelers should read up the chart. Southbound travelers read down the chart.

| Exit(mm) | | ★ | Facilities | W | S | K | T | C | Am | FJ | Lo | Pe | Pi | TA |
|---|---|---|---|---|---|---|---|---|---|---|---|---|---|---|
| (231) | sb | | W • • • • • | | | | | | | | | | | |
| 213 | b | | | | | w | | | | | | | | |
| 212 | b | | | | w | | e | | | | | | | |
| 204 | b | | | | w | | | | | | | | | |
| (199) | b | | R • • • • • • | | | | | | | | | | | |
| 177a | b | | | | | w | | | | | | | | |
| 173 | b | | | | | | e | | | | | | | |
| 165 | b | | | | e | | | | | | | | | |
| 157 | b | | | | | | | | | | | • | | |
| 153 | b | | | | | | e | | | | | | | |
| 152 | b | | | | | | | | | | | | • | |
| 150 | b | | | | | | | | | | • | | | |
| 141 | b | | | | w | w | w | | | | | | | |
| (139) | b | | R • • • • | | | | | | | | | | | |

*N ↕ S*

| Exit(mm) | | ★ | | | | | | | | W | S | K | T | C | Am | FJ | Lo | Pe | Pi | TA |
|---|---|---|---|---|---|---|---|---|---|---|---|---|---|---|---|---|---|---|---|---|
| 138 | b | | | | | | | | | | | | | | | | | | | • |
| 103 | b | | | | | | | | | e | | e | | | | | | | | |
| (100) | b | | R | • | • | • | • | • | • | | | | | | | | | | | |
| 91 | b | | | | | | | | | w | | | w | | | | | | | |
| 76b | b | | | | | | | | | | | w | | | | | | | | |
| 75 | b | | | | | | | | | w | | | | | | | | | | |
| 63 | b | | | | | | | | | | | | | | | | | | • | |
| 60 | b | | | | | | | | | w | w | | e | | | | | | | |
| (59) | b | | R | • | • | • | • | • | • | | | | | | | | | | | |
| 58 | b | | | | | | | | | | | | w | | | | | | | |
| 45 | b | | | | | | | | | e | e | | | | | | | | | |
| 39 | b | | | | | | | | | | | | | | | | | | • | |
| 33 | b | | | | | | | | | | | | w | | | | | | | |
| 22 | b | | | | | | | | | | e | | | | | | | | | |
| 21 | b | | | | | | | | | e | | e | | | | | | | | |
| 20 | b | | | | | | | | | | | e | e | w | | | | | | |
| 5 | b | | | | | | | | | | | | | | • | | | | | |
| (2) | nb | | W | • | • | • | • | • | • | | | | | | | | | | | |

*(left margin: N ↕ S)*

Interstate 95 in North Carolina is 182 miles long. It runs north to south from the Virginia state line to the South Carolina state line. Northbound travelers should read up the chart. Southbound travelers read down the chart.

| Exit(mm) | | ★ | | | | | | | | W | S | K | T | C | Am | FJ | Lo | Pe | Pi | TA |
|---|---|---|---|---|---|---|---|---|---|---|---|---|---|---|---|---|---|---|---|---|
| (181) | sb | | W | • | • | • | • | • | • | | | | | | | | | | | |
| 180 | b | | | | | | | | | | | | | | | | | | • | |
| 173 | b | | | | | | | | | w | | | w | | | | | | | |
| (142) | b | | R | • | • | • | • | • | • | | | | | | | | | | | |
| 121 | b | | | | | | | | | e+ | | e+ | w | | | | | | | |
| 106 | b | | | | | | | | | | | | | | | | | | | • |
| (99) | b | | R | • | • | • | • | • | • | | | | | | | | | | | |
| 95 | b | | | | | | | | | | | | w | | | | | | | |
| 77 | b | | | | | | | | | | | | | | | | | | • | |
| 73 | b | | | | | | | | | | | | | e | | | | | | |
| 49 | b | | | | | | | | | | | | w | | | | | | | |
| (48) | b | | R | • | • | • | • | • | • | | | | | | | | | | | |
| 22 | b | | | | | | | | | e | | | | | | | | | | |
| 20 | b | | | | | | | | | | | e | w | | | | | | | |
| (5) | nb | | W | • | • | • | • | • | • | | | | | | | | | | | |

*(left margin: N ↕ S)*

Interstate 240 in Asheville is 9 miles long. It departs I-40 at exit 46 and rejoins it at exit 53. Eastbound travelers should read up the chart. Westbound travelers read down the chart.

| Exit(mm) | ↗ | * | 🛈 | 🚻 | 🛗 | 🍴 | ⛽ | 🏨 | ✈ | W | S | K | T | C | Am | FJ | Lo | Pe | Pi | TA |
|---|---|---|---|---|---|---|---|---|---|---|---|---|---|---|---|---|---|---|---|---|
| 7 | b | | | | | | | | | | | s | | | | | | | | |
| 3a | b | | | | | | | | | | n | n | | | | | | | | |

Interstate 440 forms a 16-mile partial loop around Raleigh. Exit numbering begins at I-40 exit 293 and increases in a clockwise direction.

| Exit(mm) | ↗ | * | 🛈 | 🚻 | 🛗 | 🍴 | ⛽ | 🏨 | ✈ | W | S | K | T | C | Am | FJ | Lo | Pe | Pi | TA |
|---|---|---|---|---|---|---|---|---|---|---|---|---|---|---|---|---|---|---|---|---|
| 13b | b | | | | | | | | | | | e+ | | | | | | | | |
| 2b | b | | | | | | | | | | | w | | | | | | | | |

# North Dakota

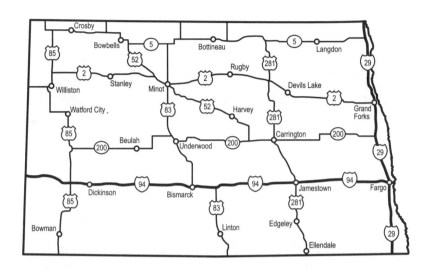

| Interstate | Page |
| --- | --- |
| 29 | 145 |
| 94 | 146 |

**29**    Interstate 29 in North Dakota runs north to south for 218 miles from the United States/Canada border to the South Dakota state line. Northbound travelers should read up the chart. Southbound travelers read down the chart.

| Exit(mm) | ↗ | ★ | | | | | | | | W | S | K | T | C | Am | FJ | Lo | Pe | Pi | TA |
| --- | --- | --- | --- | --- | --- | --- | --- | --- | --- | --- | --- | --- | --- | --- | --- | --- | --- | --- | --- | --- |
| (216) | b | 1 | W | • | • | • | • | | • | | | | | | | | | | | |
| (179) | b | | R | • | • | • | • | | • | | | | | | | | | | | |
| 138 | b | | | | | | | | | e | e | e | e | | • | | | | | |
| (99) | b | | R | • | • | • | • | | • | | | | | | | | | | | |
| (74) | b | | R | • | • | • | • | | • | | | | | | | | | | | |
| 64 | b | | | | | | | | | w | w | w | w | | | | | | | |
| 62 | b | | | | | | | | | | | | | | | | • | | | |
| (40) | b | | R | • | • | • | • | | • | | | | | | | | | | | |
| (3) | nb | | W | • | • | • | | | • | | | | | | | | | | | |

N ↕ S

*1) Welcome Center (southbound), Turnout (northbound)*

Interstate 94 in North Dakota runs east to west for 352 miles from the Minnesota state line to the Montana state line. Eastbound travelers should read up the chart. Westbound travelers read down the chart.

| Exit(mm) | ↗ | * | | | | | | | | W | S | K | T | C | Am | FJ | Lo | Pe | Pi | TA |
|---|---|---|---|---|---|---|---|---|---|---|---|---|---|---|---|---|---|---|---|---|
| 351 | b | | | | | | | | | | s | | | | | | | | | |
| 348 | b | | W | • | • | • | • | | • | n+ | n+ | | n+ | | | | | | • | |
| (304) | b | | R | • | • | • | • | | • | | | | | | | | | | | |
| 258 | b | | | | | | | | | s | | s | | | | | | | | |
| (254) | b | | R | • | • | • | • | | • | | | | | | | | | | | |
| (224) | wb | | R | • | • | • | • | | • | | | | | | | | | | | |
| (221) | eb | | R | • | • | • | • | | • | | | | | | | | | | | |
| (168) | b | | R | • | • | • | • | | • | | | | | | | | | | | |
| 159 | b | | | | | | | | | | | n | | | | | | | | |
| 157 | b | | | | | | | | | | | | | n | | | | | | |
| (152) | eb | 1 | T | | | | | | | | | | | | | | | | | |
| (135) | wb | 1 | T | | | | | | | | | | | | | | | | | |
| (119) | b | | R | • | • | • | | | • | | | | | | | | | | | |
| 61 | b | | | | | | | | | n | | n | | | | | | | | |
| (32) | b | 2 | R | • | • | • | • | | • | | | | | | | | | | | |
| (21) | eb | 1 | T | | | | | | | | | | | | | | | | | |
| (12) | eb | | W | • | • | • | | | • | | | | | | | | | | | |
| 1 | b | | | | | | | | | | | | | | | | • | | | |

E ↕ W (directional indicator at left, between exits 168 and 159)

1) Scenic Vista
2) Theodore Roosevelt National Park Visitor Center

# Ohio

| Interstate | Page | | Interstate | Page |
|---|---|---|---|---|
| 70 | 148 | | 270 | 153 |
| 71 | 148 | | 271 | 153 |
| 74 | 149 | | 275 | 153 |
| 75 | 149 | | 280 | 154 |
| 76 | 150 | | 475 | 154 |
| 77 | 151 | | 480 | 154 |
| 80 | 151 | | 675 | 154 |
| 90 | 152 | | | |

Interstate 70 in Ohio runs east to west for 226 miles from the West Virginia state line to the Indiana state line. Eastbound travelers should read up the chart. Westbound travelers read down the chart.

| Exit(mm) | ↗ | ★ | 🛈 | 👫 | ♿ | 🍴 | ⛽ | 🏧 | 🐾 | W | S | K | T | C | Am | FJ | Lo | Pe | Pi | TA |
|---|---|---|---|---|---|---|---|---|---|---|---|---|---|---|---|---|---|---|---|---|
| 218 | b | | | | | | | | | n | n | | s | | | | | | | |
| (211) | b | 1 | W | • | • | • | • | | • | | | | | | | | | | | |
| (189) | eb | | R | • | • | • | • | | • | | | | | | | | | | | |
| 178 | b | | | | | | | | | s | | s | n | | | | | | • | |
| (163) | wb | | R | • | • | • | • | | • | | | | | | | | | | | |
| 160 | b | | | | | | | | | | | | | | | | • | | | |
| 155 | b | | | | | | | | | | | | s | | | | | | | |
| (131) | b | | R | • | • | • | • | | • | | | | | | | | | | | |
| 126 | b | | | | | | | | | | | | | | | | | | • | • |
| 122 | b | | | | | | | | | | | | | | | | • | | | |
| 112 | wb | | | | | | | | | n | n | | s | | | | | | | |
| 112a | eb | | | | | | | | | n | n | | s | | | | | | | |
| 110 | wb | | | | | | | | | | s | s | | | | | | | | |
| 110a | eb | | | | | | | | | | s | s | | | | | | | | |
| 94 | b | | | | | | | | | | s | | | | | | | | • | |
| 91b | wb | | | | | | | | | n | n | | n | | | | | | | |
| 91 | eb | | | | | | | | | n | n | | n | | | | | | | |
| 79 | b | | | | | | | | | | | | | | | | | | • | • |
| (71) | b | | R | • | • | • | • | | • | | | | | | | | | | | |
| 54 | b | | | | | | | | | | | | n | | | | | | | |
| 36 | b | | | | | | | | | n | | s | n | | | | | | | |
| 10 | b | | | | | | | | | | | | | | | | | | • | • |
| (3) | b | 2 | W | • | • | • | • | | • | | | | | | | | | | | |

1) Welcome Center (westbound), Rest Area (eastbound)
2) Welcome Center (eastbound), Rest Area (westbound)

Interstate 71 in Ohio runs north to south for 248 miles from I-90 in Cleveland to the Kentucky state line. Northbound travelers should read up the chart. Southbound travelers read down the chart.

| Exit(mm) | ↗ | ★ | 🛈 | 👫 | ♿ | 🍴 | ⛽ | 🏧 | 🐾 | W | S | K | T | C | Am | FJ | Lo | Pe | Pi | TA |
|---|---|---|---|---|---|---|---|---|---|---|---|---|---|---|---|---|---|---|---|---|
| 235 | b | | | | | | | | | | | | w | | | | | | | |
| 234 | b | | | | | | | | | | w | | | | | | | | | |
| 231a | sb | | | | | | | | | | | | | w | | | | | | |
| 231 | nb | | | | | | | | | | | | | w | | | | | | |

Legend columns (left to right): Exit(mm), exit-direction arrow, ★, then amenity icons (type [R/W], restroom, phone, picnic, icon5, icon6, pet), then the service columns **W · S · K · T · C · Am · FJ · Lo · Pe · Pi · TA**.

| Exit(mm) | Dir | ★ | Type | (icon2) | (icon3) | (icon4) | (icon5) | (icon6) | (pet) | W | S | K | T | C | Am | FJ | Lo | Pe | Pi | TA |
|---|---|---|---|---|---|---|---|---|---|---|---|---|---|---|---|---|---|---|---|---|
| 226 | b | | | | | | | | | | | w | | | | | | | | |
| (225) | nb | | R | • | • | • | | | • | | | | | | | | | | | |
| (224) | sb | | R | • | • | • | | | • | | | | | | | | | | | |
| 218 | b | | | | | | | | | | | | | e | | | | | | |
| 209 | b | | | | | | | | | | | | | | | | | • | | • |
| 204 | b | | | | | | | | | | | | | | | | | • | | |
| (196) | b | | R | • | • | • | • | | • | | | | | | | | | | | |
| 186 | b | | | | | | | | | | | | | | | | | | | • |
| 169 | b | | | | | | | | | | | | | e | | | | | | |
| 140 | b | | | | | | | | | | | | | | | | | • | | |
| 131 | b | | | | | | | | | | | | | w | | • | | • | | |
| (128) | b | | R | • | • | • | • | | • | | | | | | | | | | | |
| 121 | b | | | | | | | | | w | | | w | | | | | | | |
| 100 | b | | | | | | | | | | | w | w | | | | | | | |
| 69 | b | | | | | | | | | | | | | | | | • | | | |
| (68) | b | | R | • | • | • | • | | • | | | | | | | | | | | |
| 65 | b | | | | | | | | | | | | | | • | | | | | • |
| 50 | b | | | | | | | | | | | | | | | | | • | | |
| (34) | b | 1 | W | • | • | • | • | | • | | | | | | | | | | | |
| 19 | b | | | | | | | | | e | | | e | e | | | | | | |
| 8 | b | | | | | | | | | | e | | e | | | | | | | |

(Left-margin reading-direction indicators: N ↕ S shown beside rows 218–196 and rows 100–68.)

*1) Scenic Vista*

Interstate 74 in Ohio is 19 miles long. It runs east to west from I-75 in Cincinnati to the Indiana state line. Eastbound travelers should read up the chart. Westbound travelers read down the chart.

| Exit(mm) | Dir | ★ | Type | (icon2) | (icon3) | (icon4) | (icon5) | (icon6) | (pet) | W | S | K | T | C | Am | FJ | Lo | Pe | Pi | TA |
|---|---|---|---|---|---|---|---|---|---|---|---|---|---|---|---|---|---|---|---|---|---|
| 14 | b | | | | | | | | | | | | n | | | | | | | | |
| 1 | b | | | | | | | | | | | | s | | n | | | | | | |

Interstate 75 in Ohio runs north to south for 211 miles from the Michigan state line to the Kentucky state line. Northbound travelers should read up the chart. Southbound travelers read down the chart.

| Exit(mm) | Dir | ★ | Type | (icon2) | (icon3) | (icon4) | (icon5) | (icon6) | (pet) | W | S | K | T | C | Am | FJ | Lo | Pe | Pi | TA |
|---|---|---|---|---|---|---|---|---|---|---|---|---|---|---|---|---|---|---|---|---|---|
| 210 | b | | | | | | | | | | | | | | | | | | | | • |

| Exit(mm) | ⤴ | * | 🔷 | 🚻 | 🛉 | ⛱ | ⛽ | 🏪 | 🐾 | W | S | K | T | C | Am | FJ | Lo | Pe | Pi | TA |
|---|---|---|---|---|---|---|---|---|---|---|---|---|---|---|---|---|---|---|---|---|
| 207 | b | | | | | | | | | | | | e | | | | | | | |
| 193 | b | | | | | | | | | | | | e | e | | | | | | |
| (179) | b | | W | • | • | • | • | | • | | | | | | | | | | | |
| 167 | b | | | | | | | | | | | | | | | | | | • | |
| 164 | b | | | | | | | | | | | | | | | | | | | • |
| 159 | b | | | | | | | | | | | | | w | | | | | | |
| (153) | b | | R | • | • | • | • | | • | | | | | | | | | | | |
| 135 | b | | | | | | | | | | | | | | | | | • | | • |
| 125a | sb | | | | | | | | | e | e | e | | e | | | | | | |
| 125 | nb | | | | | | | | | e | e | e | | e | | | | | | |
| (114) | b | | R | • | • | • | • | | • | | | | | | | | | | | |
| 92 | b | | | | | | | | | w | | | | | | | | | | |
| 82 | b | | | | | | | | | | | | | w | | | | | | |
| (81) | b | | R | • | • | • | • | | • | | | | | | | | | | | |
| 74b | sb | | | | | | | | | w | | | | | | | | | | |
| 74 | nb | | | | | | | | | w | | | | | | | | | | |
| 60 | b | | | | | | | | | | w | | | w | | | | | | |
| 44 | b | | | | | | | | | e | | | | | | | | | | |
| 38 | b | | | | | | | | | | | | e | | | | | | | |
| 36 | b | | | | | | | | | | | | | | | | | | • | |
| 32 | b | | | | | | | | | | | w | w | | | | | | | |
| (27) | b | | W | • | • | • | • | | • | | | | | | | | | | | |
| 22 | b | | | | | | | | | w | | | | | | | | | | |

N ↕ S

**76** Interstate 76 in Ohio runs east to west for 82 miles from the Pennsylvania state line to I-71 south of Medina. Part of it is also the Ohio Turnpike. Eastbound travelers should read up the chart. Westbound travelers read down the chart.

| Exit(mm) | ⤴ | * | 🔷 | 🚻 | 🛉 | ⛱ | ⛽ | 🏪 | 🐾 | W | S | K | T | C | Am | FJ | Lo | Pe | Pi | TA |
|---|---|---|---|---|---|---|---|---|---|---|---|---|---|---|---|---|---|---|---|---|
| (237) | b | 1 | S | • | • | • | • | | | | | | | | | | | | | |
| 232 | b | | | | | | | | | | | | | | | | | | • | |
| (45) | b | | R | • | • | • | | | • | | | | | | | | | | | |
| 38 | wb | | | | | | | | | | | | | s | | | | | | |
| 38a | eb | | | | | | | | | | | | | s | | | | | | |
| 9 | b | | | | | | | | | | | | n | | n | | | | | | |

E ↕ W

1) Gas, Food

Interstate 77 in Ohio is 160 miles long. It runs north to south from I-90 in Cleveland to the West Virginia state line. Northbound travelers should read up the chart. Southbound travelers read down the chart.

N ↕ S

| Exit(mm) | ↗ | ★ | ↗ | 👥 | ♿ | ⛱ | ⛽ | 🚐 | 🐾 | W | S | K | T | C | Am | FJ | Lo | Pe | Pi | TA |
|---|---|---|---|---|---|---|---|---|---|---|---|---|---|---|---|---|---|---|---|---|
| 145 | nb | | | | | | | | | | | | | | | | | | • | |
| (141) | b | | R | • | • | • | • | | • | | | | | | | | | | | |
| 137a | b | | | | | | | | | e | e | | | e | | | | | | |
| 120 | b | | | | | | | | | e | | | | | | | | | | |
| 111 | b | | | | | | | | | | | | | w | | | | | | • |
| 109 | sb | | | | | | | | | | | | w | | | | | | | |
| 109a | nb | | | | | | | | | | | | w | | | | | | | |
| (85) | b | | R | • | • | • | | | • | | | | | | | | | | | |
| 81 | b | | | | | | | | | e | | | | | | | | | | |
| (39) | nb | | R | • | • | • | • | • | • | | | | | | | | | | | |
| (36) | sb | | R | • | • | • | • | | • | | | | | | | | | | | |
| 25 | b | | | | | | | | | | | | | | | | | | • | |
| (3) | nb | | W | • | • | • | • | | • | | | | | | | | | | | |
| 1 | b | | | | | | | | | e | | w | | | | | | | | |

Interstate 80 in Ohio runs east to west for 237 miles from the Pennsylvania state line to the Indiana state line. Portions are also I-90 and the Ohio Turnpike. Eastbound travelers should read up the chart. Westbound travelers read down the chart.

E ↕ W

| Exit(mm) | ↗ | ★ | ↗ | 👥 | ♿ | ⛱ | ⛽ | 🚐 | 🐾 | W | S | K | T | C | Am | FJ | Lo | Pe | Pi | TA |
|---|---|---|---|---|---|---|---|---|---|---|---|---|---|---|---|---|---|---|---|---|
| (237) | wb | | W | • | • | • | • | | • | | | | | | | | | | | |
| 234 | wb | | | | | | | | | | | | | | | | • | | | |
| 234b | eb | | | | | | | | | | | | | | | | • | | | |
| 226 | b | | | | | | | | | | | | | | | | | | • | • |
| 223b | wb | | | | | | | | | | | | | | | | | | | • |
| 223a | wb | | | | | | | | | | | | | s | • | | | | | • |
| 223 | eb | | | | | | | | | | | | | s | • | | | | | • |
| (197) | b | 1 | S | • | • | • | • | • | • | • | | | | | | | | | | |
| 187 | b | | | | | | | | | | S+ | | S+ | | | | | | | | |
| 173 | b | | | | | | | | | | | | | | | | | | | • |
| (170) | b | 2 | S | • | • | • | • | | • | | | | | | | | | | | |
| 161 | b | 3 | | | | | | | | | n | | | | | | | | | |
| (139) | b | 1 | S | • | • | • | • | • | • | | | | | | | | | | | |
| (100) | b | 2 | S | • | • | • | | | • | | | | | | | | | | | |

| Exit(mm) | ↗ | ★ | 🡥 | 👫 | ) | ⛱ | 📷 | 💾 | 🐾 | W | S | K | T | C | Am | FJ | Lo | Pe | Pi | TA |
|---|---|---|---|---|---|---|---|---|---|---|---|---|---|---|---|---|---|---|---|---|
| (77) | b | 1 | S | • | • | • | • | • | • | | | | | | | | | | | |
| 71 | b | 4 | | | | | | | | | | | | | | | | • | • | • |
| 59 | b | | | | | | | | | | n | | | | | | | | | |
| (49) | b | 2 | S | • | • | • | • | | • | | | | | | | | | | | |
| 34 | b | | | | | | | | | s+ | | | | | | | | | | |
| (21) | eb | 2 | S | • | • | • | • | | • | | | | | | | | | | | |
| (21) | wb | 5 | S | • | • | • | • | • | • | | | | | | | | | | | |

1) Gas, Food, Overnight RV parking with hookups
2) Gas, Food
3) Wal-Mart is on US 42
4) Petro Stopping Center is off I-280 Exit 1b; TA Travel Center is on Libbey Rd
5) Gas, Food, Overnight RV parking

Interstate 90 in Ohio runs east to west for 245 miles from the Pennsylvania state line to the Indiana state line. Part of it is also I-80 and the Ohio Turnpike. Eastbound travelers should read up the chart. Westbound travelers read down the chart.

| Exit(mm) | ↗ | ★ | 🡥 | 👫 | ) | ⛱ | 📷 | 💾 | 🐾 | W | S | K | T | C | Am | FJ | Lo | Pe | Pi | TA |
|---|---|---|---|---|---|---|---|---|---|---|---|---|---|---|---|---|---|---|---|---|
| (242) | wb | | W | • | • | • | • | | • | | | | | | | | | | | |
| 241 | b | | | | | | | | | | n | | | | | | | | | |
| 235 | b | | | | | | | | | | | | | | | | | | | • |
| 223 | b | | | | | | | | | | | | | | | | • | | • | |
| 200 | b | | | | | | | | | | | | s | | | | | | | |
| (198) | b | | R | • | • | • | • | | • | | | | | | | | | | | |
| 189 | b | | | | | | | | | | | | | | n | | | | | |
| 187 | b | | | | | | | | | | | s | | | | | | | | |
| 186 | b | | | | | | | | | | | | s | | | | | | | |
| 156 | b | | | | | | | | | | | | s | | | | | | | |
| 153 | b | | | | | | | | | | n | | | s | | | | | | |
| 151 | b | | | | | | | | | | | | | | | | | | • | |
| 148 | b | | | | | | | | | | | | s | | s | | | | | |
| 145 | b | | | | | | | | | | s | | | | | | | | | |
| (139) | b | 1 | S | • | • | • | • | • | • | | | | | | | | | | | |
| (100) | b | 2 | S | • | • | • | • | | • | | | | | | | | | | | |
| (77) | b | 1 | S | • | • | • | • | • | • | | | | | | | | | | | |
| 71 | b | 3 | | | | | | | | | | | | | | | | • | • | • |
| 59 | b | | | | | | | | | | | n | | | | | | | | | |
| (49) | b | 2 | S | • | • | • | • | | • | | | | | | | | | | | |

| Exit(mm) | ↗ | ★ | 🚹 | 🚻 | 📞 | 🍴 | ⛽ | 🏪 | 🐾 | W | S | K | T | C | Am | FJ | Lo | Pe | Pi | TA |
|---|---|---|---|---|---|---|---|---|---|---|---|---|---|---|---|---|---|---|---|---|
| 34 | b | | | | | | | | | s+ | | | | | | | | | | |
| (21) | eb | 2 | S | • | • | • | • | | • | | | | | | | | | | | |
| (21) | wb | 4 | S | • | • | • | • | • | • | | | | | | | | | | | |

*1) Gas, Food, Overnight RV parking with hookups*
*2) Gas, Food*
*3) Petro Stopping Center is off I-280 Exit 1b; TA Travel Center is on Libbey Rd*
*4) Gas, Food, Overnight RV parking*

Interstate 270 is a 55-mile loop around Columbus. Exit numbering begins at US 62 and increases in a clockwise direction.

| Exit(mm) | ↗ | ★ | 🚹 | 🚻 | 📞 | 🍴 | ⛽ | 🏪 | 🐾 | W | S | K | T | C | Am | FJ | Lo | Pe | Pi | TA |
|---|---|---|---|---|---|---|---|---|---|---|---|---|---|---|---|---|---|---|---|---|
| 52a | b | | | | | | | | | n | | | | | | | | | | |
| 32 | b | | | | | | | | | w | w | | w | | | | | | | |
| 15 | b | | | | | | | | | w | | | | | | | | | | |

Interstate 271 in Ohio is about 40 miles long. It runs north to south from I-90 near Willoughby Hills to I-71 near Medina. Part of it is also I-480. Northbound travelers should read up the chart. Southbound travelers read down the chart.

| Exit(mm) | ↗ | ★ | 🚹 | 🚻 | 📞 | 🍴 | ⛽ | 🏪 | 🐾 | W | S | K | T | C | Am | FJ | Lo | Pe | Pi | TA |
|---|---|---|---|---|---|---|---|---|---|---|---|---|---|---|---|---|---|---|---|---|
| 23 | b | | | | | | | | | | | e | | | | | | | | | |
| 19 | sb | | | | | | | | | | | | w | | | | | | | | |
| 18 | b | | | | | | | | | w | | | | | | | | | | | |
| (8) | b | | R | • | • | • | | | • | | | | | | | | | | | |

Interstate 275 around Cincinnati is 56 miles long. It is part of an 84-mile loop that also runs through Kentucky and Indiana. Exit numbers increase in a clockwise direction.

| Exit(mm) | ↗ | ★ | 🚹 | 🚻 | 📞 | 🍴 | ⛽ | 🏪 | 🐾 | W | S | K | T | C | Am | FJ | Lo | Pe | Pi | TA |
|---|---|---|---|---|---|---|---|---|---|---|---|---|---|---|---|---|---|---|---|---|
| 39 | b | | | | | | | | | | | | | s | | | | | | | |
| 59 | b | | | | | | | | | | | | | e | | | | | | | |

Interstate 280 is 12 miles long and runs north to south. It connects I-80/90 with I-75 in Toledo. Northbound travelers should read up the chart. Southbound travelers read down the chart.

| Exit(mm) | ↗ | ★ | ⤢ | 🚻 | 🚰 | ⛽ | 🏪 | 📷 | 🐾 | W | S | K | T | C | Am | FJ | Lo | Pe | Pi | TA |
|---|---|---|---|---|---|---|---|---|---|---|---|---|---|---|---|---|---|---|---|---|
| 1b | b | | | | | | | | | | | | | | | | • | | • | |

Interstate 475 in Ohio is 20 miles long. It forms a partial loop around Toledo. Exit numbers increase in a clockwise direction.

| Exit(mm) | ↗ | ★ | ⤢ | 🚻 | 🚰 | ⛽ | 🏪 | 📷 | 🐾 | W | S | K | T | C | Am | FJ | Lo | Pe | Pi | TA |
|---|---|---|---|---|---|---|---|---|---|---|---|---|---|---|---|---|---|---|---|---|
| 13 | b | | | | | | | | | | | | e | | | | | | | |
| 8b | sb | | | | | | | | | | | w | w | | | | | | | |
| 8 | nb | | | | | | | | | | | w | w | | | | | | | |
| 6 | b | | | | | | | | | | | | | w | | | | | | |

Interstate 480 in Ohio is 42 miles long. It runs east to west from I-80 near Streetsboro to I-80 near North Ridgeville. Eastbound travelers should read up the chart. Westbound travelers read down the chart.

| Exit(mm) | ↗ | ★ | ⤢ | 🚻 | 🚰 | ⛽ | 🏪 | 📷 | 🐾 | W | S | K | T | C | Am | FJ | Lo | Pe | Pi | TA |
|---|---|---|---|---|---|---|---|---|---|---|---|---|---|---|---|---|---|---|---|---|
| 36 | b | | | | | | | | | | | | | | n | | | | | |
| 23 | b | | | | | | | | | | | n | | | | | | | | |
| 21 | b | | | | | | | | | | s | | | | | | | | | |
| 15 | b | | | | | | | | | | | s | | | | | | | | |
| 13 | b | | | | | | | | | | | | | | s | | | | | |
| 6 | b | | | | | | | | | | | n | | | | | | | | |

E ↕ W

Interstate 675 in Dayton is about 27 miles long. It runs north to south from I-75 near Miamisburg to I-70 near Fairborn. Northbound travelers should read up the chart. Southbound travelers read down the chart.

| Exit(mm) | ↗ | ★ | ⤢ | 🚻 | 🚰 | ⛽ | 🏪 | 📷 | 🐾 | W | S | K | T | C | Am | FJ | Lo | Pe | Pi | TA |
|---|---|---|---|---|---|---|---|---|---|---|---|---|---|---|---|---|---|---|---|---|
| 7 | b | | | | | | | | | | | | | s | | | | | | |

# Oklahoma

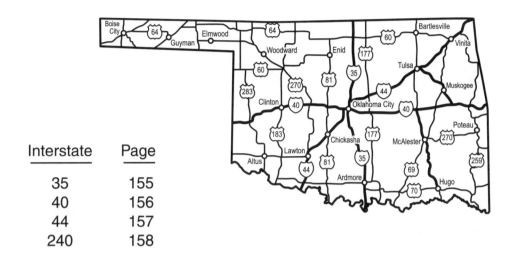

| Interstate | Page |
|:----------:|:----:|
| 35 | 155 |
| 40 | 156 |
| 44 | 157 |
| 240 | 158 |

**(35)** Interstate 35 in Oklahoma runs north to south for 236 miles from the Kansas state line to the Texas state line. Portions are also shared with I-40 and I-44. Northbound travelers should read up the chart. Southbound travelers read down the chart.

| Exit(mm) | ↰ | ★ | ⛶ | 🚻 | 🚹 | ⛽ | 🛏 | 🏪 | 🦟 | W | S | K | T | C | Am | FJ | Lo | Pe | Pi | TA |
|:--------:|:-:|:-:|:-:|:-:|:-:|:-:|:-:|:-:|:-:|:-:|:-:|:-:|:-:|:-:|:--:|:--:|:--:|:--:|:--:|:--:|
| (225) | b | 1 | W | • | • | • | • | • | • | | | | | | | | | | | |
| 211 | b | | | | | | | | | | | | | | | | | • | | |
| (209) | b | 2 | T | | | | | | | | | | | | | | | | | |
| (195) | b | 2 | T | | | | | | | | | | | | | | | | | |
| (173) | sb | 2 | T | | | | | | | | | | | | | | | | | |
| (171) | nb | 2 | T | | | | | | | | | | | | | | | | | |
| 157 | b | | | | | | | | | | | | | | | | | • | | |
| 137 | b | | | | | | | | | | | | | w | | | • | | • | |
| 127 | b | | | | | | | | | | | | | | | | | | • | |
| 120 | b | | | | | | | | | | | | | | | | | | • | |
| 116 | b | | | | | | | | | w | | | | | | | | | | |
| 110b | sb | | | | | | | | | | | | w | | | | | | | |
| 110 | nb | | | | | | | | | | | | w | | | | | | | |
| 109 | b | | | | | | | | | | e | | e | | | | | | | |

| Exit(mm) | ⤢ | ★ | ↗ | 🚻 | ☎ | 🍽 | ⛽ | 🛒 | 🐾 | ✈ | W | S | K | T | C | Am | FJ | Lo | Pe | Pi | TA |
|---|---|---|---|---|---|---|---|---|---|---|---|---|---|---|---|---|---|---|---|---|---|
| 106 | b | | | | | | | | | | | | | | | | | | • | | |
| 72 | b | | | | | | | | | | e+ | | | | | | | | • | | |
| (59) | b | | R | • | • | • | • | | • | • | | | | | | | | | | | |
| (49) | b | 3 | T | | | | | | | | | | | | | | | | | | |
| (46) | b | 3 | T | | | | | | | | | | | | | | | | | | |
| 32 | b | | | | | | | | | | e+ | | | | | | | | • | | |
| (3) | b | 4 | W | • | • | • | • | | | • | | | | | | | | | | | |

(N ↕ S indicator at left)

1) Welcome Center (southbound), Rest Area (northbound)
2) No Facilities
3) Scenic Vista
4) Welcome Center (northbound), Rest Area (southbound)

Interstate 40 in Oklahoma runs east to west for 331 miles from the Arkansas state line to the Texas state line. Part of it is shared with I-35. Eastbound travelers should read up the chart. Westbound travelers read down the chart.

| Exit(mm) | ⤢ | ★ | ↗ | 🚻 | ☎ | 🍽 | ⛽ | 🛒 | 🐾 | ✈ | W | S | K | T | C | Am | FJ | Lo | Pe | Pi | TA |
|---|---|---|---|---|---|---|---|---|---|---|---|---|---|---|---|---|---|---|---|---|---|
| 325 | b | | | | | | | | | | | | | | | | | | | • | |
| (316) | eb | | R | • | • | • | • | • | • | • | | | | | | | | | | | |
| (314) | wb | | W | • | • | • | • | • | • | • | | | | | | | | | | | |
| 308 | b | | | | | | | | | | n | | | | | | | | | | |
| 287 | b | | | | | | | | | | | | | | | | | | • | | |
| (283) | b | 1 | T | | | | | | | | | | | | | | | | | | |
| 264b | b | 2 | | | | | | | | | n+ | | | | | | | • | | | |
| (251) | b | 3 | T | | | | | | | | | | | | | | | | | | |
| 240b | b | | | | | | | | | | n | | | | | | | | | | |
| 221 | b | | | | | | | | | | | | | | | | | | • | | |
| 200 | b | | | | | | | | | | | | | | | | | | • | | |
| (197) | b | | R | • | • | • | | | • | • | | | | | | | | | | | |
| 185 | b | | | | | | | | | | n | | | | s | | | | | | |
| 176 | b | | | | | | | | | | | | | | | | | | • | | |
| 166 | b | | | | | | | | | | | | | | | | | | • | | |
| 157a | b | | | | | | | | | | | s | | | | | | | | | |
| 127 | b | | | | | | | | | | | | | | | | | | • | | |
| 145 | b | | | | | | | | | | | | | | s | | | | | | |
| 144 | b | | | | | | | | | | n | s | | | | | | | | | |
| 142 | b | | | | | | | | | | | | | | | | | | | | • |
| 140 | b | | | | | | | | | | | | | | | | • | • | | • | • |
| 136 | b | | | | | | | | | | n | | | | | | | | | | |

(E ↕ W indicators at left)

| Exit(mm) | ↗ | ★ | ➡ | 🚻 | ☎ | 🍴 | ⛽ | 🏪 | 🐾 | W | S | K | T | C | Am | FJ | Lo | Pe | Pi | TA |
|---|---|---|---|---|---|---|---|---|---|---|---|---|---|---|---|---|---|---|---|---|
| 123 | b | | | | | | | | | n | | | | | | | | | | |
| (111) | eb | | T | | | • | | | | | | | | | | | | | | |
| 108 | b | | | | | | | | | | | | | | | | | • | | |
| 101 | b | | | | | | | | | | | | | | • | | | | | |
| (94) | wb | | T | | | • | | | | | | | | | | | | | | |
| 82 | b | | | | | | | | | n | | | | | | | | | | |
| 71 | b | | | | | | | | | | | | | | | | • | | | |
| 65 | b | | | | | | | | | | | n | | | | | | | | |
| 41 | b | | | | | | | | | | | | | | | | • | | | |
| 26 | b | | | | | | | | | | | | | | | | | | | • |
| 20 | b | | | | | | | | | | | | | | | • | | | | |
| (10) | b | 4 | W | • | • | • | | • | • | | | | | | | | | | | |
| 7 | b | | | | | | | | | | | | | | | | • | | | |

*(Read direction: E ↕ W)*

1) Scenic Vista
2) Services are north of exit off US 69 at US 266
3) No Facilities
4) Welcome Center (eastbound), Rest Area (westbound)

Interstate 44 runs east to west for about 329 miles from the Missouri state line to the Texas state line. Part of it is shared with I-35. Much of I-44 is part of Oklahoma's toll-highway system. Eastbound travelers should read up the chart. Westbound travelers read down the chart.

| Exit(mm) | ↗ | ★ | ➡ | 🚻 | ☎ | 🍴 | ⛽ | 🏪 | 🐾 | W | S | K | T | C | Am | FJ | Lo | Pe | Pi | TA |
|---|---|---|---|---|---|---|---|---|---|---|---|---|---|---|---|---|---|---|---|---|
| (314) | wb | 1 | S | • | • | • | | | | | | | | | | | | | | |
| (312) | eb | | T | | • | • | | | | | | | | | | | | | | |
| (310) | wb | | T | | • | • | | | | | | | | | | | | | | |
| (299) | eb | | T | | | • | | | | | | | | | | | | | | |
| 289 | b | | | | | | | | | n | | | | | | | | | | |
| (288) | b | 2 | S | • | • | • | | | | | | | | | | | | | | |
| 283 | b | | | | | | | | | | | | | | • | | | | | |
| (271) | wb | | T | | | • | | | | | | | | | | | | | | |
| (269) | eb | | T | | | • | | | | | | | | | | | | | | |
| (256) | wb | | T | | • | • | | | | | | | | | | | | | | |
| 236 | b | | | | | | | | | | | | | | • | | | | | |
| 233 | wb | | | | | | | | | | | | s | | | | | | | |
| 231 | b | | | | | | | | | | | | | s | | | | | | |
| 228 | b | | | | | | | | | | | | s | | | | | | | |

*(Read direction: E ↕ W)*

| Exit(mm) | ↗ | ★ | 🡭 | 🚻 | ☎ | ⛱ | 🏪 | 💾 | 🐾 | W | S | K | T | C | Am | FJ | Lo | Pe | Pi | TA |
|---|---|---|---|---|---|---|---|---|---|---|---|---|---|---|---|---|---|---|---|---|
| (207) | wb | 1 | S | • | • | • | | | | | | | | | | | | | | |
| (205) | wb | | T | | | • | | | | | | | | | | | | | | |
| (204) | eb | | T | | | • | | | | | | | | | | | | | | |
| (197) | eb | 2 | S | • | • | • | | | | | | | | | | | | | | |
| (191) | wb | | T | | | • | | | | | | | | | | | | | | |
| (189) | eb | | T | | | • | | | | | | | | | | | | | | |
| (178) | b | 2 | S | • | • | • | | | | | | | | | | | | | | |
| (171) | eb | | T | | • | • | | | | | | | | | | | | | | |
| (166) | wb | | T | | • | • | | | | | | | | | | | | | | |
| (153) | b | | T | | • | • | | | | | | | | | | | | | | |
| 137 | b | | | | | | | | | | | | | | n | | | • | • | | |
| 125b | b | | | | | | | | | | n | | | | | | | | | | |
| 112 | b | | | | | | | | | | | | | | | | | | | • | |
| 108 | b | | | | | | | | | | n | | | | | | | | | | |
| (100) | eb | | T | | | • | | | | | | | | | | | | | | |
| (96) | wb | | T | | | • | | | | | | | | | | | | | | |
| (85) | b | 2 | S | • | • | • | | | | | | | | | | | | | | |
| 80 | b | | | | | | | | | | s | | | | | | | | | | |
| (63) | wb | | T | | | • | | | | | | | | | | | | | | |
| (60) | eb | | T | | | • | | | | | | | | | | | | | | |
| 45 | b | | | | | | | | | | | | | | | | | | • | | |
| 37 | b | | | | | | | | | | | | | n | | | | | | | |
| (20) | b | 2 | S | • | • | • | • | | | | | | | | | | | | | |

(Left margin directional indicators: E ↕ W at the upper group and again at the lower group.)

1) Gas
2) Gas, Food

Interstate 240 in Oklahoma City is 16 miles long. It runs east to west between I-40 and I-44. Eastbound travelers should read up the chart. Westbound travelers read down the chart.

| Exit(mm) | ↗ | ★ | 🡭 | 🚻 | ☎ | ⛱ | 🏪 | 💾 | 🐾 | W | S | K | T | C | Am | FJ | Lo | Pe | Pi | TA |
|---|---|---|---|---|---|---|---|---|---|---|---|---|---|---|---|---|---|---|---|---|
| 3b | b | | | | | | | | | | s | | | | | | | | | | |

# Oregon

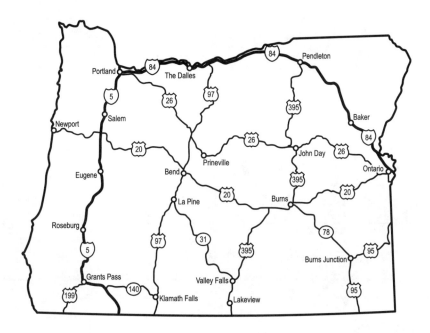

| Interstate | Page |
|:---:|:---:|
| 5 | 160 |
| 82 | 161 |
| 84 | 161 |
| 205 | 162 |

Interstate 5 in Oregon runs north to south for 308 miles from the Washington state line to the California state line. Northbound travelers should read up the chart. Southbound travelers read down the chart.

| Exit(mm) | ↗ | * | ↗ | 🚻 | ☎ | ⛱ | ⛽ | 🚰 | 🐾 | W | S | K | T | C | Am | FJ | Lo | Pe | Pi | TA |
|---|---|---|---|---|---|---|---|---|---|---|---|---|---|---|---|---|---|---|---|---|
| 308 | b | | | | | | | | | | w | w | | | | | | | | |
| 307 | b | 1 | W | • | • | | | | | | | | | | • (Am) | | | | | |
| 289 | b | | | | | | | | | | w | | | | | | | | | |
| 286 | b | | | | | | | | | | | e | | | | | | | | |
| (281) | b | | R | • | • | • | • | | • | | | | | | | | | | | |
| 278 | b | | | | | | | | | | | | | | | | | | | • |
| 271 | b | | | | | | | | | e | | | | | | | | | | |
| 263 | b | | | | | | | | | | | | | | | | | • | | |
| 256 | b | | | | | | | | | | | e | | | | | | | | |
| 253 | b | | | | | | | | | | w | | | | | | | | | |
| (240) | b | | R | • | • | • | • | • | • | | | | | | | | | | | |
| 234 | b | | | | | | | | | | w | | | | | | | | | |
| (206) | b | | R | • | • | • | • | | • | | | | | | | | | | | |
| 199 | b | | | | | | | | | | | | | | | | | | | • |
| 195a | b | | | | | | | | | | | e | | | | | | | | |
| (178) | b | | R | • | • | • | • | | • | | | | | | | | | | | |
| 174 | b | | | | | | | | | e | | | | | | | | | | |
| 148 | b | | | | | | | | | | | | | | | | | | | • |
| (144) | sb | | R | • | • | • | • | | • | | | | | | | | | | | |
| (143) | nb | | R | • | • | • | • | | • | | | | | | | | | | | |
| 127 | b | | | | | | | | | | w | w | | | | | | | | |
| 119 | b | | | | | | | | | | | | | | | | | • | | |
| 112 | b | | R | • | • | • | • | | • | | | | | | | | | | | |
| (82) | b | | R | • | • | • | • | | • | | | | | | | | | | | |
| (63) | b | | R | • | • | • | • | | • | | | | | | | | | | | |
| 55 | b | | | | | | | | | | w | | | | | | | | | |
| 45b | b | 2 | R | • | • | • | | • | • | | | | | | | | | | | |
| 33 | b | | | | | | | | | | | | | | | | | | | • |
| 30 | b | | | | | | | | | | | w | | | | | | | | |
| 27 | b | | | | | | | | | | | w | | | | | | | | |
| 24 | b | | | | | | | | | | | | | | | | | • | | |
| (22) | sb | | R | • | • | • | • | | • | | | | | | | | | | | |
| 21 | b | | | | | | | | | w | | | | | | | | | | |
| 19 | b | | W | • | • | • | • | | | | | | | | | | | | | |

N ↕ S

1) Welcome Center located at AmBest truck stop
2) Camping in Valley of the Rogue State Park

Interstate 82 in Oregon is a short 11-mile route running from the Washington state line to I-84 exit 179. Eastbound travelers should read up the chart. Westbound travelers read down the chart.

| Exit(mm) | 🡕 | * | 🡖 | 🚻 | 📞 | ⛱ | ⛽ | 🏪 | 🐾 | W | S | K | T | C | Am | FJ | Lo | Pe | Pi | TA |
|---|---|---|---|---|---|---|---|---|---|---|---|---|---|---|---|---|---|---|---|---|
| 1 | b | | W | • | • | | | | | | | | | | | | | | | |

Interstate 84 in Oregon runs east to west for approximately 378 miles from the Idaho state line to I-5 in Portland. Eastbound travelers should read up the chart. Westbound travelers read down the chart.

| Exit(mm) | 🡕 | * | 🡖 | 🚻 | 📞 | ⛱ | ⛽ | 🏪 | 🐾 | W | S | K | T | C | Am | FJ | Lo | Pe | Pi | TA |
|---|---|---|---|---|---|---|---|---|---|---|---|---|---|---|---|---|---|---|---|---|
| (377) | wb | | W | • | • | • | • | | • | | | | | | | | | | | |
| 376b | b | | | | | | | | | n | | n | | | | | | | | |
| 376a | b | | | | | | | | | | | | | | | | | | • | |
| 374 | b | 1 | R | • | | • | • | | | | | | | | | | | | | |
| 335 | b | | R | • | • | • | • | | • | | | | | | | | | | | |
| 304 | b | | | | | | | | | | | | | | • | | | | | |
| (295) | b | | R | • | • | • | • | | • | | | | | | | | | | | |
| (269) | b | | R | • | • | • | • | • | • | | | | | | | | | | | |
| 265 | b | | | | | | | | | | | | | | | • | | | | |
| 261 | b | | | | | | | | | n | | | | | | | | | | |
| (254) | b | 2 | T | | | | | | | | | | | | | | | | | |
| 252 | b | 3 | R | • | | • | | | | | | | | | | | | | | |
| 228 | b | | R | • | • | • | • | • | • | | | | | | | | | | | |
| (223) | wb | 2 | T | | | | | | | | | | | | | | | | | |
| (221) | eb | 2 | T | | | | | | | | | | | | | | | | | |
| 209 | b | | | | | | | | | n | | s | | | | | | | | |
| 188 | b | | | | | | | | | | | | | | | | | | • | |
| (187) | b | | R | • | • | • | • | | • | | | | | | | | | | | |
| (160) | b | | R | • | • | • | • | | • | | | | | | | | | | | |
| (136) | wb | 2 | T | | | • | | | | | | | | | | | | | | |
| (112) | b | 4 | T | | | | | | | | | | | | | | | | | |
| 104 | b | | | | | | | | | | | | | | | | | | • | |
| (73) | b | 5 | R | • | • | • | | • | • | | | | | | | | | | | |
| (66) | wb | 6 | R | • | | • | | | | | | | | | | | | | | |
| 62 | b | | | | | | | | | s | | | | | | | | | | |
| (61) | wb | 4 | T | | | | | | | | | | | | | | | | | |

(Left margin direction markers: "E ↕ W" beside exit 304 and beside exit 188.)

| Exit(mm) | | * | ⤴ | 🚻 | ☎ | ⛺ | 🅿 | 🛢 | 🐾 | W | S | K | T | C | Am | FJ | Lo | Pe | Pi | TA |
|---|---|---|---|---|---|---|---|---|---|---|---|---|---|---|---|---|---|---|---|---|
| (58) eb | 2 | T | | | | | | | | | | | | | | | | | | |
| (55) eb | 7 | T | • | | | | | | | | | | | | | | | | | |
| (49) eb | 4 | T | | | | | | | | | | | | | | | | | | |
| (23) wb | 2 | T | | | | | | | | | | | | | | | | | | |
| 17 b | | | | | | | | | | | | | | | | | | • | | • |
| 16 b | | | | | | | | | | n | | | | | | | | | | |

(E ↕ W directional indicator at left)

1) Camping in Ontario State Park
2) Scenic Vista
3) Camping in Hilgard Junction State Park
4) No Facilities
5) Camping in Memaloose State Park (eastbound), RV Dump Station eastbound only
6) Access to Koberg Beach State Park
7) Access to Starvation Creek State Park

Interstate 205 is a 37-mile route running north and south in Oregon and Washington. It forms an open loop around the Portland area. Northbound travelers should read up the chart. Southbound travelers read down the chart.

| Exit(mm) | | * | ⤴ | 🚻 | ☎ | ⛺ | 🅿 | 🛢 | 🐾 | W | S | K | T | C | Am | FJ | Lo | Pe | Pi | TA |
|---|---|---|---|---|---|---|---|---|---|---|---|---|---|---|---|---|---|---|---|---|
| 30 b | 1 | | | | | | | | | | | | w | | | | | | | |
| 28 b | 1 | | | | | | | | | w | | | | | | | | | | |
| 14 b | | | | | | | | | | | | | w | | | | | | | |
| 13 b | | | | | | | | | | | | w | | | | | | | | |
| (7) nb | 2 | T | | | | | | | | | | | | | | | | | | |

(N ↕ S directional indicator at left)

1) This exit is in Washington
2) Scenic Vista

# Pennsylvania

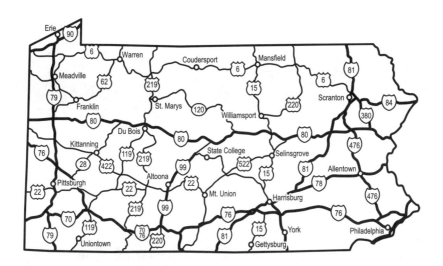

| Interstate | Page | Interstate | Page |
|---|---|---|---|
| 70 | 163 | 84 | 168 |
| 76 | 164 | 90 | 168 |
| 78 | 165 | 95 | 169 |
| 79 | 165 | 99 | 169 |
| 80 | 166 | 276 | 169 |
| 81 | 167 | 476 | 170 |
| 83 | 168 | | |

Interstate 70 in Pennsylvania runs east to west for about 171 miles from the Maryland state line to the West Virginia state line. Portions are also shared with I-76, I-79, and the Pennsylvania Turnpike. Eastbound travelers should read up the chart. Westbound travelers read down the chart.

| Exit(mm) | | ★ | | | | | | | | | W | S | K | T | C | Am | FJ | Lo | Pe | Pi | TA |
|---|---|---|---|---|---|---|---|---|---|---|---|---|---|---|---|---|---|---|---|---|---|
| (171) | wb | W | • | • | | • | | • | | | | | | | | | | | | | |
| (153) | eb | R | • | • | | • | | • | | | | | | | | | | | | | |
| 147 | wb | | | | | | | | | | | | | | | | | | • | | • |
| 161 | eb | | | | | | | | | | | | | | | | | | • | | • |
| (150) | wb | 1 | T | | | | | | | | | | | | | | | | | | |

| Exit(mm) | ↗ | ★ | ➘ | 🚻 | ☎ | ⛱ | 🏪 | 💾 | 🐴 | W | S | K | T | C | Am | FJ | Lo | Pe | Pi | TA |
|---|---|---|---|---|---|---|---|---|---|---|---|---|---|---|---|---|---|---|---|---|
| (148) | b | 2 | S | • | • | • | • |  | • |  |  |  |  |  |  |  |  |  |  |  |
| (142) | wb | 1 | T |  |  |  |  |  |  |  |  |  |  |  |  |  |  |  |  |  |
| (112) | b | 2 | S | • | • | • | • |  | • |  |  |  |  |  |  |  |  |  |  |  |
| (78) | wb | 2 | S | • | • | • | • |  | • |  |  |  |  |  |  |  |  |  |  |  |
| 57 | b |  |  |  |  |  |  |  |  |  |  |  |  | s |  |  |  |  |  |  |
| 43a | wb |  |  |  |  |  |  |  |  | s |  | s |  |  |  |  |  |  |  |  |
| 43 | eb |  |  |  |  |  |  |  |  | s |  | s |  |  |  |  |  |  |  |  |
| 32b | b |  |  |  |  |  |  |  |  |  |  |  |  |  |  |  |  |  | • |  |
| 19b | b |  |  |  |  |  |  |  |  | n | n |  | n |  | n |  |  |  |  |  |
| 19a | b |  |  |  |  |  |  |  |  |  | s |  |  |  |  |  |  |  |  |  |
| 6 | b |  |  |  |  |  |  |  |  |  |  |  |  |  |  |  |  |  | • |  |
| (5) | eb |  | W | • | • | • | • |  | • |  |  |  |  |  |  |  |  |  |  |  |

*(Left side: E ↕ W directional indicators shown between rows 57 and 32b.)*

*1) No Facilities. 2) Gas, Food.*

Interstate 76 in Pennsylvania runs east to west for about 350 miles from the New Jersey state line to the Ohio state line. Nearly all of I-76 is also the Pennsylvania Turnpike. Part of the Interstate is shared with I-70. Eastbound travelers should read up the chart. Westbound travelers read down the chart.

| Exit(mm) | ↗ | ★ | ➘ | 🚻 | ☎ | ⛱ | 🏪 | 💾 | 🐴 | W | S | K | T | C | Am | FJ | Lo | Pe | Pi | TA |
|---|---|---|---|---|---|---|---|---|---|---|---|---|---|---|---|---|---|---|---|---|
| (325) | eb | 1 | S | • | • | • | • | • | • |  |  |  |  |  |  |  |  |  |  |  |
| (305) | wb | 1 | S | • | • | • | • |  | • |  |  |  |  |  |  |  |  |  |  |  |
| (290) | eb | 1 | S | • | • | • | • |  | • |  |  |  |  |  |  |  |  |  |  |  |
| (259) | wb | 1 | S | • | • | • | • | • | • |  |  |  |  |  |  |  |  |  |  |  |
| (250) | eb | 1 | S | • | • | • | • |  | • |  |  |  |  |  |  |  |  |  |  |  |
| 226 | b |  |  |  |  |  |  |  |  |  |  |  |  |  | • |  |  | • |  |  |
| (219) | eb | 1 | S | • | • | • | • |  | • |  |  |  |  |  |  |  |  |  |  |  |
| (203) | wb | 1 | S | • | • | • | • |  | • |  |  |  |  |  |  |  |  |  |  |  |
| (172) | b | 1 | S | • | • | • | • | • | • |  |  |  |  |  |  |  |  |  |  |  |
| 161 | b |  |  |  |  |  |  |  |  |  |  |  |  |  |  |  |  | • |  | • |
| (150) | wb | 2 | T |  |  |  |  |  |  |  |  |  |  |  |  |  |  |  |  |  |
| (148) | b | 1 | S | • | • | • | • |  | • |  |  |  |  |  |  |  |  |  |  |  |
| (142) | wb | 2 | T |  |  |  |  |  |  |  |  |  |  |  |  |  |  |  |  |  |
| (112) | b | 1 | S | • | • | • | • |  | • |  |  |  |  |  |  |  |  |  |  |  |
| (78) | wb | 1 | S | • | • | • | • |  | • |  |  |  |  |  |  |  |  |  |  |  |
| (75) | eb | 1 | S | • | • | • | • |  | • |  |  |  |  |  |  |  |  |  |  |  |
| (61) | eb | 2 | T |  |  |  |  |  |  |  |  |  |  |  |  |  |  |  |  |  |
| (49) | eb | 1 | S | • | • | • | • |  | • |  |  |  |  |  |  |  |  |  |  |  |
| (41) | eb | 2 | T |  |  |  |  |  |  |  |  |  |  |  |  |  |  |  |  |  |
| 39 | b |  |  |  |  |  |  |  |  | n |  |  |  |  |  |  |  |  |  |  |

*(Left side: E ↕ W directional indicators shown at two points in the chart.)*

| Exit(mm) | ↗ | ★ | | | | | | | | W | S | K | T | C | Am | FJ | Lo | Pe | Pi | TA |
|---|---|---|---|---|---|---|---|---|---|---|---|---|---|---|---|---|---|---|---|---|
| (31) | wb | 1 | S | • | • | • | • | | • | | | | | | | | | | | |
| 28 | b | | | | | | | | | n | | n | | | | | | | | |
| (23) | eb | 2 | T | | | | | | | | | | | | | | | | | |
| (22) | eb | 1 | S | • | • | • | • | | • | | | | | | | | | | | |
| (17) | eb | 2 | T | | | | | | | | | | | | | | | | | |
| (13) | eb | 2 | T | | | | | | | | | | | | | | | | | |
| (6) | eb | 2 | T | | | | | | | | | | | | | | | | | |
| (2) | eb | 2 | T | | | | | | | | | | | | | | | | | |

*1) Gas, Food. 2) No Facilities.*

Interstate 78 in Pennsylvania is approximately 77 miles long. It runs east to west from the New Jersey state line to I-81 east of Harrisburg. Eastbound travelers should read up the chart. Westbound travelers read down the chart.

| Exit(mm) | ↗ | ★ | | | | | | | | W | S | K | T | C | Am | FJ | Lo | Pe | Pi | TA |
|---|---|---|---|---|---|---|---|---|---|---|---|---|---|---|---|---|---|---|---|---|
| (76) | wb | | W | • | • | • | • | | • | | | | | | | | | | | |
| 49b | b | | | | | | | | | | | | n | | | | | | | |
| 29b | b | | | | | | | | | | | | n | | | | | | | |

Interstate 79 in Pennsylvania runs north to south for 183 miles from Erie to the West Virginia state line. A small segment is shared with I-70. Northbound travelers should read up the chart. Southbound travelers read down the chart.

| Exit(mm) | ↗ | ★ | | | | | | | | W | S | K | T | C | Am | FJ | Lo | Pe | Pi | TA |
|---|---|---|---|---|---|---|---|---|---|---|---|---|---|---|---|---|---|---|---|---|
| 182 | b | | | | | | | | | | | w | | | | | | | | |
| 166 | b | | | | | | | | | e | | | | | | | | | | |
| (163) | b | 1 | W | • | • | • | • | | • | | | | | | | | | | | |
| 147b | b | | | | | | | | | w | | w | | | | | | | | |
| 147a | b | | | | | | | | | | | | | e | | | | | | |
| (135) | b | | R | • | • | • | • | | • | | | | | | | | | | | |
| (110) | sb | | R | • | • | • | • | | • | | | | | | | | | | | |
| (107) | nb | | R | • | • | • | • | | • | | | | | | | | | | | |
| (81) | b | | T | | • | • | | | | | | | | | | | | | | |
| 78 | b | | | | | | | | | w | | w | e | | | | | | | |
| 55 | b | | | | | | | | | | | e+ | | | | | | | | |
| (50) | b | | R | • | • | • | • | | • | | | | | | | | | | | |
| 19b | b | | | | | | | | | e | e | | e | e | | | | | | |
| 19a | b | | | | | | | | | | | w | | | | | | | | |

| Exit(mm) | ↗ | ★ | 🅿 | 🚻 | ☎ | 🍽 | 🏪 | 🗑 | 🐴 | W | S | K | T | C | Am | FJ | Lo | Pe | Pi | TA |
|---|---|---|---|---|---|---|---|---|---|---|---|---|---|---|---|---|---|---|---|---|
| (31) | sb | 2 | T | | | | | | | | | | | | | | | | | |
| (6) | nb | | W | • | • | • | • | | • | | | | | | | | | | | |

*1) Welcome Center (southbound), Rest Area (northbound). 2) No Facilities.*

Interstate 80 in Pennsylvania runs east to west for 311 miles from the New Jersey state line to the Ohio state line. Eastbound travelers should read up the chart. Westbound travelers read down the chart.

| Exit(mm) | ↗ | ★ | 🅿 | 🚻 | ☎ | 🍽 | 🏪 | 🗑 | 🐴 | W | S | K | T | C | Am | FJ | Lo | Pe | Pi | TA |
|---|---|---|---|---|---|---|---|---|---|---|---|---|---|---|---|---|---|---|---|---|
| 310 | b | | W | • | • | • | • | | • | | | | | | | | | | | |
| 308 | b | | | | | | | | | n+ | | n+ | | | | | | | | |
| 302b | eb | | | | | | | | | | | | | | | | • | | | |
| 302 | wb | | | | | | | | | | | | | | | | • | | | |
| (295) | eb | | R | • | • | • | • | | • | | | | | | | | | | | |
| (270) | eb | | R | • | • | • | • | | • | | | | | | | | | | | |
| 256 | b | | | | | | | | | | | | | | | | | | | • |
| (246) | b | | R | • | • | • | • | | • | | | | | | | | | | | |
| 241a | wb | | | | | | | | | s+ | | | | | | | | | | |
| 241 | eb | | | | | | | | | s+ | | | | | | | | | | |
| 232 | b | | | | | | | | | s | | | n | | | | | | | • |
| (219) | b | | R | • | • | • | • | | • | | | | | | | | | | | |
| 215 | b | | | | | | | | | | | | | | | | | • | | |
| (194) | b | | R | • | • | • | • | | • | | | | | | | | | | | |
| 178 | b | 1 | | | | | | | | n+ | | n+ | | | | | | | | |
| 173 | b | | | | | | | | | | | | | | | | • | | • | • |
| 158 | b | | | | | | | | | | | | | | | | | | | • |
| (146) | b | | R | • | • | • | • | | • | | | | | | | | | | | |
| 120 | b | | | | | | | | | s | | s | | | | | | | | |
| 101 | b | | | | | | | | | s+ | | s+ | | | | | | | | |
| 97 | b | | | | | | | | | | | | | | | | | | • | |
| (87) | b | | R | • | • | • | • | | • | | | | | | | | | | | |
| 78 | b | | | | | | | | | | | | | | | | • | | | • |
| 62 | b | | | | | | | | | n | | n | | | | | | | | |
| (56) | b | 2 | T | | | | | | | | | | | | | | | | | |
| (30) | b | | R | • | • | • | • | | • | | | | | | | | | | | |
| 29 | b | | | | | | | | | | | | | | | | | | | • |
| (1) | eb | | W | • | • | • | • | | • | | | | | | | | | | | |

*1) Services located 5 miles north of exit*
*2) No Facilities*

Interstate 81 in Pennsylvania runs north to south 233 miles from the New York state line to the Maryland state line. Northbound travelers should read up the chart. Southbound travelers read down the chart.

| Exit(mm) | ↗ | * | ⤢ | 🚻 | ☎ | ⛱ | ⛽ | 🍽 | 🐾 | W | S | K | T | C | Am | FJ | Lo | Pe | Pi | TA |
|---|---|---|---|---|---|---|---|---|---|---|---|---|---|---|---|---|---|---|---|---|
| 219 | b | | | | | | | | | | | | | | • | | | | | |
| (209) | sb | | W | • | • | • | • | | • | | | | | | | | | | | |
| (203) | nb | | R | • | • | • | • | | • | | | | | | | | | | | |
| 191a | b | | | | | | | | | e | | e | | | | | | | | |
| 190 | b | | | | | | | | | | e | | | | | | | | | |
| 178b | b | | | | | | | | | | | | | | | | • | | | |
| 175b | sb | | | | | | | | | w | | | | | | | | | • | |
| 175 | nb | | | | | | | | | w | | | | | | | | | • | |
| 168 | b | | | | | | | | | w | w | | w | w | | | | | | |
| 165 | sb | | | | | | | | | | | w | | | | | | | | |
| 165b | nb | | | | | | | | | | | w+ | | | | | | | | |
| (157) | sb | | R | • | • | • | • | | • | | | | | | | | | | | |
| (156) | nb | | R | • | • | • | • | | • | | | | | | | | | | | |
| (135) | nb | 1 | T | | | | | | | | | | | | | | | | | |
| (132) | b | 2 | T | | | | | | | | | | | | | | | | | |
| 124a | b | | | | | | | | | | | e | | e | | | | | | |
| (79) | b | | R | • | • | • | • | | • | | | | | | | | | | | |
| 77 | b | | | | | | | | | | | | | | | | | | • | • |
| 72 | sb | | | | | | | | | | | e | | | | | | | | |
| 72a | nb | | | | | | | | | | | e | | | | | | | | |
| 69 | b | | | | | | | | | | | | | e | | | | | | |
| 65 | b | | | | | | | | | | | e+ | | | | | | | | |
| 52 | sb | | | | | | | | | | | | | | | • | | | • | • |
| 52b | nb | | | | | | | | | | | | | | | | | | • | • |
| 52a | nb | | | | | | | | | | | | | | | • | | | | |
| 48 | nb | | | | | | | | | | | w+ | | | | | | | | |
| 47a | sb | | | | | | | | | | | | | e | | | | | | |
| 47 | nb | | | | | | | | | | | | | e | | | | | | |
| 45 | b | | | | | | | | | | | e | | | | | | | | |
| (38) | b | | R | • | • | • | • | | • | | | | | | | | | | | |
| 14 | b | | | | | | | | | | | w | | e | | | | | | |
| 5 | b | | | | | | | | | | | | | | | | | | | • |
| (2) | nb | | W | • | • | • | • | | • | | | | | | | | | | | |

*1) Scenic Vista*
*2) No Facilities*

Interstate 83 in Pennsylvania is 51 miles long. It runs north to south from I-81 in Harrisburg to the Maryland state line. Northbound travelers should read up the chart. Southbound travelers read down the chart.

N ↕ S

| Exit(mm) | | ★ | ↗ | 🚻 | ☎ | 🌳 | ⛽ | 🏨 | 🐾 | W | S | K | T | C | Am | FJ | Lo | Pe | Pi | TA |
|---|---|---|---|---|---|---|---|---|---|---|---|---|---|---|---|---|---|---|---|---|
| 50a | b | | | | | | | | | | | | | e | | | | | | |
| (35) | sb | 1 | T | | | | | | | | | | | | | | | | | |
| (33) | nb | 1 | T | | | | | | | | | | | | | | | | | |
| 18 | b | | | | | | | | | | | | e | | | | | | | |
| 16a | b | | | | | | | | | | | | | | e | | | | | |
| 4 | b | | | | | | | | | w | | | | | | | | | | |
| (2) | nb | | W | • | • | • | • | | • | | | | | | | | | | | |

*1) No Facilities*

Interstate 84 in Pennsylvania runs east to west for 54 miles from the New York state line to I-81 in Scranton. Eastbound travelers should read up the chart. Westbound travelers read down the chart.

E ↕ W

| Exit(mm) | | ★ | ↗ | 🚻 | ☎ | 🌳 | ⛽ | 🏨 | 🐾 | W | S | K | T | C | Am | FJ | Lo | Pe | Pi | TA |
|---|---|---|---|---|---|---|---|---|---|---|---|---|---|---|---|---|---|---|---|---|
| 53 | b | | W | • | • | • | • | | • | | s | s | | | | | | | | |
| (26) | b | | R | • | • | • | • | | • | | | | | | | | | | | |
| 17 | b | | | | | | | | | | | | | | • | | | | | |

Interstate 90 in Pennsylvania runs east to west for 46 miles from the New York state line to the Ohio state line. Eastbound travelers should read up the chart. Westbound travelers read down the chart.

E ↕ W

| Exit(mm) | | ★ | ↗ | 🚻 | ☎ | 🌳 | ⛽ | 🏨 | 🐾 | W | S | K | T | C | Am | FJ | Lo | Pe | Pi | TA |
|---|---|---|---|---|---|---|---|---|---|---|---|---|---|---|---|---|---|---|---|---|
| (46) | wb | | W | • | • | • | • | | • | | | | | | | | | | | |
| 35 | b | | | | | | | | | | | | | | | | | | | • |
| 27 | b | | | | | | | | | | | | | | | | | | • | |
| 24 | b | | | | | | | | | n | n | n | n | n | | | | | | |
| (2) | eb | | W | • | • | • | • | | • | | | | | | | | | | | |

Interstate 95 in Pennsylvania runs north to south for 51 miles from the New Jersey state line to the Delaware state line. Northbound travelers should read up the chart. Southbound travelers read down the chart.

N ↕ S

| Exit(mm) | ↗ | ★ | ◤ | 🚻 | ☎ | 🍴 | ⛽ | 🏨 | 🐾 | W | S | K | T | C | Am | FJ | Lo | Pe | Pi | TA |
|---|---|---|---|---|---|---|---|---|---|---|---|---|---|---|---|---|---|---|---|---|
| (49) | sb | | W | • | • | • | • | | • | | | | | | | | | | | |
| 44 | b | | | | | | | | | | e | e | | | | | | | | |
| 35 | b | 1 | | | | | | | | w+ | | | | | | | | | | |
| 32 | b | | | | | | | | | | | w | | | | | | | | |
| 20 | b | | | | | | | | | | e | | e | | | | | | | |
| 19 | b | 2 | | | | | | | | | | w | | | | | | | | |
| 8 | b | 3 | | | | | | | | w+ | | | | | | | | | | |
| 6 | b | 3 | | | | | | | | e+ | | | | | | | | | | |
| (0.5) | nb | | W | • | • | • | • | | • | | | | | | | | | | | |

1) Wal-Mart is off PA 63 at Millbrook Rd
2) K-Mart is on Oregon Ave
3) Wal-Mart is on US 13 and is accessed from either Exit 6 or 8

Interstate 99 in Pennsylvania is 53 miles long. It runs north to south between Bald Eagle and I-70/I-76 near Bedford. Northbound travelers should read up the chart. Southbound travelers read down the chart.

| Exit(mm) | ↗ | ★ | ◤ | 🚻 | ☎ | 🍴 | ⛽ | 🏨 | 🐾 | W | S | K | T | C | Am | FJ | Lo | Pe | Pi | TA |
|---|---|---|---|---|---|---|---|---|---|---|---|---|---|---|---|---|---|---|---|---|
| 31 | b | | | | | | | | | | | e | e | | e | w | | | | |

Interstate 276 in Pennsylvania is about 33 miles long. It runs east to west from the New Jersey state line to I-76. It is also part of the Pennsylvania Turnpike. Eastbound travelers should read up the chart. Westbound travelers read down the chart.

E ↕ W

| Exit(mm) | ↗ | ★ | ◤ | 🚻 | ☎ | 🍴 | ⛽ | 🏨 | 🐾 | W | S | K | T | C | Am | FJ | Lo | Pe | Pi | TA |
|---|---|---|---|---|---|---|---|---|---|---|---|---|---|---|---|---|---|---|---|---|
| (352) | b | 1 | S | • | • | • | • | • | • | | | | | | | | | | | |
| 351 | b | 2 | | | | | | | | | | | n | | | | | | | |
| (328) | wb | 1 | S | • | • | • | | | | | | | | | | | | | | |

1) Gas, Food
2) Target is off US 1 at Rock Hill Rd

Interstate 476 in Pennsylvania is a 131-mile route that runs north to south from US 6 in Clarks Summit to I-95 in Crum Lynne. Portions of it are part of Pennsylvania's turnpike system. Northbound travelers should read up the chart. Southbound travelers read down the chart.

| Exit(mm) | ↗ | * | 🚗 | 🚻 | 🅿 | 🏕 | ⛽ | 🔌 | 🖥 | 🐾 | W | S | K | T | C | Am | FJ | Lo | Pe | Pi | TA |
|---|---|---|---|---|---|---|---|---|---|---|---|---|---|---|---|---|---|---|---|---|---|
| 115 | b | | | | | | | | | | w | | | | | | | | | • | |
| (103) | sb | 1 | T | | | | | | | | | | | | | | | | | | |
| (100) | b | 1 | T | | | | | | | | | | | | | | | | | | |
| (97) | b | 1 | T | | | | | | | | | | | | | | | | | | |
| (90) | sb | 1 | T | | | | | | | | | | | | | | | | | | |
| (86) | b | 2 | S | • | • | • | • | | • | | | | | | | | | | | | |
| (56) | b | 2 | S | • | • | • | • | • | • | | | | | | | | | | | | |
| (37) | sb | 1 | T | | | | | | | | | | | | | | | | | | |
| 18 | sb | | | | | | | | | | | | | | e | | | | | | |
| 18b | nb | | | | | | | | | | | | | | e | | | | | | |

N ↕ S

*1) No Facilities*
*2) Gas, Food*

# Rhode Island

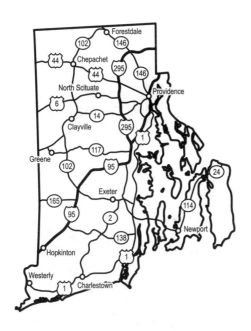

| Interstate | Page |
|---|---|
| 95 | 171 |
| 295 | 171 |

Interstate 95 in Rhode Island runs north to south for 43 miles from the Massachusetts state line to the Connecticut state line. Exit numbers are based on the consecutive numbering system. Northbound travelers should read up the chart. Southbound travelers read down the chart.

| Exit(mm) | ⬀ | ★ | 🚐 | 🚻 | 🚹 | ⛽ | 🅿 | 🏪 | 🐾 | W | S | K | T | C | Am | FJ | Lo | Pe | Pi | TA |
|---|---|---|---|---|---|---|---|---|---|---|---|---|---|---|---|---|---|---|---|---|
| N   7 | b | | | | | | | | | | | | | w | | | | | | |
| (10) | nb | | T | | • | | | | | | | | | | | | | | | |
| S   (6) | nb | | W | • | • | • | • | | • | | | | | | | | | | | |

Interstate 295 is a 27-mile route around Providence. Exit numbers are based on the consecutive numbering system. Northbound travelers should read up the chart. Southbound travelers read down the chart.

| Exit(mm) | ⬀ | ★ | 🚐 | 🚻 | 🚹 | ⛽ | 🅿 | 🏪 | 🐾 | W | S | K | T | C | Am | FJ | Lo | Pe | Pi | TA |
|---|---|---|---|---|---|---|---|---|---|---|---|---|---|---|---|---|---|---|---|---|
| N   1a | b | 1 | | | | | | | | e | | | e | | | | | | | |
| 7b | b | | | | | | | | | | | | w | | | | | | | |
| S   2 | b | | | | | | | | | w | w | | | | | | | | | |

1) This exit is in Massachusetts

# South Carolina

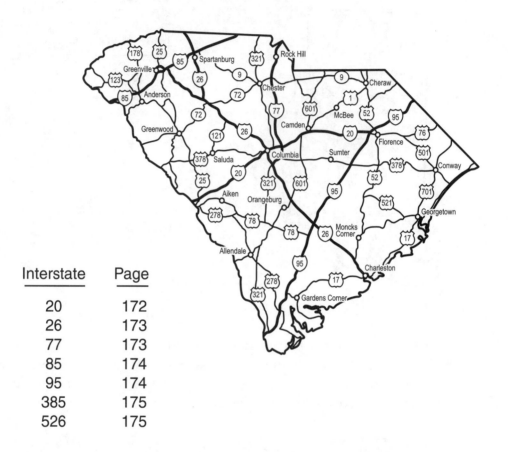

| Interstate | Page |
|:---:|:---:|
| 20 | 172 |
| 26 | 173 |
| 77 | 173 |
| 85 | 174 |
| 95 | 174 |
| 385 | 175 |
| 526 | 175 |

Interstate 20 in South Carolina runs east to west for 142 miles from I-95 near Florence to the Georgia state line. Eastbound travelers should read up the chart. Westbound travelers read down the chart.

| Exit(mm) | ⤴ | ★ | ◪ | 👪 | 🚹 | 🍴 | 🛏 | 🏪 | ✈ | W | S | K | T | C | Am | FJ | Lo | Pe | Pi | TA |
|:---:|:---:|:---:|:---:|:---:|:---:|:---:|:---:|:---:|:---:|:---:|:---:|:---:|:---:|:---:|:---:|:---:|:---:|:---:|:---:|:---:|
| (93) | b | | R | • | • | • | • | | • | | | | | | | | | | | |
| 92 | b | | | | | | | | | | | | | | | | | | | • |
| 70 | b | | | | | | | | | | | | | | | | • | | | |
| 63 | b | | | | | | | | | | | | | n | | | | | | |
| (0.5) | eb | | W | • | • | • | • | | • | | | | | | | | | | | |

E ↕ W

Interstate 26 in South Carolina is an east-west route that is 221 miles long. It runs from US 17 in Charleston to the North Carolina state line. Eastbound travelers should read up the chart. Westbound travelers read down the chart.

| Exit(mm) | ↗ | ★ | ◩ | 🚻 | ☎ | ⛱ | ⛽ | 🏪 | 🐕 | W | S | K | T | C | Am | FJ | Lo | Pe | Pi | TA |
|---|---|---|---|---|---|---|---|---|---|---|---|---|---|---|---|---|---|---|---|---|
| 211b | b | | | | | | | | | | | n | | | | | | | | |
| 209 | b | | | | | | | | | n | | n | s | | | | | | | |
| (204) | eb | | R | ● | ● | ● | ● | | ● | | | | | | | | | | | |
| (202) | wb | | R | ● | ● | ● | ● | | ● | | | | | | | | | | | |
| 199b | b | | | | | | | | | | | | | | | | | | ● | |
| 199a | b | | | | | | | | | s | | s | | | | | | | | |
| 159 | b | | | | | | | | | | | | | | | | | | ● | |
| (152) | wb | | R | ● | ● | ● | ● | | ● | | | | | | | | | | | |
| (150) | eb | | R | ● | ● | ● | ● | | ● | | | | | | | | | | | |
| 145a | b | | | | | | | | | | | | s | | | | | | | |
| (123) | b | | R | ● | ● | ● | ● | | ● | | | | | | | | | | | |
| 115 | b | | | | | | | | | | | | | | | | | | ● | |
| 111b | b | | | | | | | | | n | | | | | | | | | | |
| 108 | b | | | | | | | | | | | n | | | | | | | | |
| 103 | b | | | | | | | | | s | s | s | | | | | | | | |
| 76 | b | | | | | | | | | s+ | | | | | | | | | | |
| (63) | b | | R | ● | ● | ● | ● | | ● | | | | | | | | | | | |
| 52 | b | | | | | | | | | | | | | | | | | | ● | |
| 21b | b | | | | | | | | | n | | | | | | | | | | |
| 21a | b | | | | | | | | | | | s | s | | | | | | | |
| (9) | b | 1 | T | | | | | | | | | | | | | | | | | |
| (3) | eb | | W | ● | ● | ● | ● | | ● | | | | | | | | | | | |

*1) No Facilities*

Interstate 77 in South Carolina runs north to south for 91 miles from the North Carolina state line to I-26 in Columbia. Northbound travelers should read up the chart. Southbound travelers read down the chart.

| Exit(mm) | ↗ | ★ | ◩ | 🚻 | ☎ | ⛱ | ⛽ | 🏪 | 🐕 | W | S | K | T | C | Am | FJ | Lo | Pe | Pi | TA |
|---|---|---|---|---|---|---|---|---|---|---|---|---|---|---|---|---|---|---|---|---|
| (89) | sb | | W | ● | ● | ● | ● | | ● | | | | | | | | | | | |
| 82b | b | | | | | | | | | | | w | | | | | | | | |
| 79 | b | | | | | | | | | e | | w | e | | | | | | | |
| (66) | b | | R | ● | ● | ● | ● | | ● | | | | | | | | | | | |
| 19 | b | | | | | | | | | | | | e | | | | | | | |
| 12 | b | | | | | | | | | w | w | | | | | | | | | |
| 9a | b | | | | | | | | | e | | w | | | | | | | | |

Interstate 85 in South Carolina runs north to south for 106 miles from the North Carolina state line to the Georgia state line. Northbound travelers should read up the chart. Southbound travelers read down the chart.

**N ↕ S**

| Exit(mm) | ↗ | ★ | type | | | | | | 🐾 | W | S | K | T | C | Am | FJ | Lo | Pe | Pi | TA |
|---|---|---|---|---|---|---|---|---|---|---|---|---|---|---|---|---|---|---|---|---|
| (103) | sb | | W | • | • | • | • | | • | | | | | | | | | | | |
| 102 | b | | | | | | | | | | | | | | | | | | • | |
| 92 | b | | | | | | | | | e | | | | | | | | | | |
| 90 | b | | | | | | | | | | | | w | | | | | | • | |
| (89) | b | | R | • | • | • | • | | • | | | | | | | | | | | |
| 63 | b | | | | | | | | | | | | | | | | | | • | • |
| 51 | b | | | | | | | | | e+ | e | | w | | | | | | | |
| 50 | b | | | | | | | | | | | | w | | | | | | | |
| 35 | b | | | | | | | | | | | | | | | | | | • | |
| (23) | sb | | R | • | • | • | • | | • | | | | | | | | | | | |
| 19b | b | | | | | | | | | | | | w | | | | | | | |
| (18) | nb | | R | • | • | • | • | | • | | | | | | | | | | | |
| (0.5) | nb | | W | • | • | • | • | | • | | | | | | | | | | | |

Interstate 95 in South Carolina runs north to south for 198 miles from the North Carolina state line to the Georgia state line. Northbound travelers should read up the chart. Southbound travelers read down the chart.

**N ↕ S**

| Exit(mm) | ↗ | ★ | type | | | | | | 🐾 | W | S | K | T | C | Am | FJ | Lo | Pe | Pi | TA |
|---|---|---|---|---|---|---|---|---|---|---|---|---|---|---|---|---|---|---|---|---|
| (196) | sb | | W | • | • | • | • | | • | | | | | | | | | | | |
| 181 | b | | | | | | | | | | | | | | | | | | • | |
| (172) | b | | R | • | • | • | • | | • | | | | | | | | | | | |
| 170 | b | | | | | | | | | | | | | | | | | | | • |
| 169 | b | | | | | | | | | | | | | | | | | • | | |
| 164 | b | | | | | | | | | | | | | e | | | | | • | • |
| 160a | b | | | | | | | | | e | e+ | e+ | | | | | | | | |
| (139) | b | | R | • | • | • | • | | • | | | | | | | | | | | |
| 119 | b | | | | | | | | | e+ | | | | | | | | | | • |
| (99) | b | 1 | W | • | • | • | • | | • | | | | | | | | | | | |
| 98 | b | | | | | | | | | | | | w | | | | | | | |
| 57 | b | | | | | | | | | e | | e | | | | | | | | |
| 53 | b | | | | | | | | | | | | w | | | | | | | |
| (47) | b | | R | • | • | • | • | | • | | | | | | | | | | | |
| (17) | b | 2 | T | | | | | | | | | | | | | | | | | |

| Exit(mm) | ⤴ | ★ | ◣ | ♿ | 🚶 | ☎ | ⛱ | 🛏 | 🏪 | 🐾 | W | S | K | T | C | Am | FJ | Lo | Pe | Pi | TA |
|---|---|---|---|---|---|---|---|---|---|---|---|---|---|---|---|---|---|---|---|---|---|
| (4) | nb | | W | • | • | | • | | • | | | | | | | | | | | | |

1) Welcome Center (southbound), Rest Area (northbound)
2) No Facilities

Interstate 385 in South Carolina is 42 miles long. It runs north to south, connecting US 276 in Greenville to I-26 near Clinton. Northbound travelers should read up the chart. Southbound travelers read down the chart.

| Exit(mm) | ⤴ | ★ | ◣ | ♿ | 🚶 | ☎ | ⛱ | 🛏 | 🏪 | 🐾 | W | S | K | T | C | Am | FJ | Lo | Pe | Pi | TA |
|---|---|---|---|---|---|---|---|---|---|---|---|---|---|---|---|---|---|---|---|---|---|
| 37 | b | | | | | | | | | | | | | | w | | | | | | |
| 35 | b | | | | | | | | | | e | w | | w+ | | | | | | | |
| 27 | b | | | | | | | | | | w | | | | w | | | | | | |
| (6) | b | | R | • | • | | • | • | | • | | | | | | | | | | | |

N ↑↓ S

Interstate 526 in South Carolina is 19 miles long. It forms an open loop around Charleston. Exit numbers increase in a clockwise direction.

| Exit(mm) | ⤴ | ★ | ◣ | ♿ | 🚶 | ☎ | ⛱ | 🛏 | 🏪 | 🐾 | W | S | K | T | C | Am | FJ | Lo | Pe | Pi | TA |
|---|---|---|---|---|---|---|---|---|---|---|---|---|---|---|---|---|---|---|---|---|---|
| 32 | b | | | | | | | | | | | s | | | | | | | | | |

# South Dakota

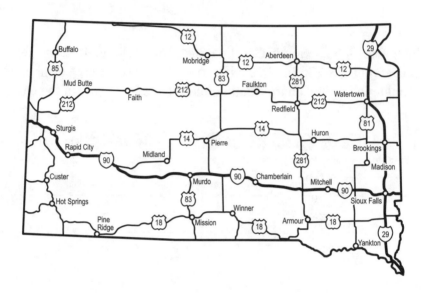

| Interstate | Page |
|---|---|
| 29 | 176 |
| 90 | 177 |
| 229 | 178 |

Interstate 29 in South Dakota runs north to south for 253 miles from the North Dakota state line to the Iowa state line. Northbound travelers should read up the chart. Southbound travelers read down the chart.

| Exit(mm) | ⤴ | ★ | 🚗 | 🚻 | 🔌 | ⛽ | 📞 | 🏧 | ✈ | W | S | K | T | C | Am | FJ | Lo | Pe | Pi | TA |
|---|---|---|---|---|---|---|---|---|---|---|---|---|---|---|---|---|---|---|---|---|
| (251) sb | W | | • | • | • | | | • | | | | | | | | | | | | |
| 213 b | R | | • | • | • | | | • | • | | | | | | | | | | | |
| 177 b | | | | | | | | | | | W+ | | W+ | W+ | | | | | | |
| (161) b | R | | • | • | • | • | • | • | • | | | | | | | | | | | |
| 132 b | | | | | | | | | | | w | | w | | | | | | | |

N ↑ ↓ S

| Exit(mm) | ↗ | * | | 🚻 | ☎ | ⛽ | 🍴 | 🏪 | 🐕 | W | S | K | T | C | Am | FJ | Lo | Pe | Pi | TA |
|---|---|---|---|---|---|---|---|---|---|---|---|---|---|---|---|---|---|---|---|---|
| 121 | b | | R | • | • | • | • | • | • | | | | | | | | | | | |
| (103) | b | 1 | T | | | | | | | | | | | | | | | | | |
| 83 | b | | | | | | | | | | | | | | | • | | | | |
| 79 | b | | | | | | | | | | | e | | | | | | | | |
| 78 | b | | | | | | | | | | e | | | e | | | | | | |
| 77 | b | | | | | | | | | e | | | e | | | | | | | |
| (40) | sb | 1 | T | | | | | | | | | | | | | | | | | |
| 26 | b | | W | • | • | • | | • | • | | | | | | | | | | | |

*(N ↕ S)*

1) No Facilities

Interstate 90 in South Dakota runs east to west for 413 miles from the Minnesota state line to the Wyoming state line. Eastbound travelers should read up the chart. Westbound travelers read down the chart.

| Exit(mm) | ↗ | * | | 🚻 | ☎ | ⛽ | 🍴 | 🏪 | 🐕 | W | S | K | T | C | Am | FJ | Lo | Pe | Pi | TA |
|---|---|---|---|---|---|---|---|---|---|---|---|---|---|---|---|---|---|---|---|---|
| (412) | b | 1 | W | • | • | • | | • | • | | | | | | | | | | | |
| 399 | b | | | | | | | | | | | | | | | | | | • | |
| (363) | b | | R | • | • | • | • | • | • | | | | | | | | | | | |
| 353 | b | | | | | | | | | | | | | | | | | | | • |
| (337) | b | 2 | T | | | | | | | | | | | | | | | | | |
| 332 | b | | | | | | | | | | s | | n | | | • | | | | | |
| (302) | wb | | R | • | • | • | | • | | | | | | | | | | | | |
| (301) | eb | | R | • | • | • | | • | | | | | | | | | | | | |
| (293) | b | 2 | T | | | | | | | | | | | | | | | | | |
| (264) | b | 3 | R | • | • | • | | • | | | | | | | | | | | | |
| (221) | wb | | R | • | • | • | | • | • | | | | | | | | | | | |
| (218) | eb | | R | • | • | • | | • | • | | | | | | | | | | | |
| (194) | b | 2 | T | | | | | | | | | | | | | | | | | |
| (188) | b | 2 | T | | | | | | | | | | | | | | | | | |
| (167) | wb | | R | • | • | • | | • | • | | | | | | | | | | | |
| (165) | eb | | R | • | • | • | | • | • | | | | | | | | | | | |
| (138) | wb | 3 | T | • | | | | | | | | | | | | | | | | |
| (129) | eb | 3 | T | | | | | | | | | | | | | | | | | |
| (100) | b | | R | • | • | • | • | • | • | | | | | | | | | | | |
| (69) | b | 2 | T | | | | | | | | | | | | | | | | | |
| 61 | b | | | | | | | | | | | | | | | | | | • | | |
| 59 | b | | | | | | | | | | | s | s | | | | | | | | |
| 58 | b | | | | | | | | | | | | | n | | | | | | | |

*(E ↕ W)*

| Exit(mm) | 🡕 | ★ | 🢅 | 🚻 | ☎ | ⛱ | ⛽ | 🚮 | 🐾 | W | S | K | T | C | Am | FJ | Lo | Pe | Pi | TA |
|---|---|---|---|---|---|---|---|---|---|---|---|---|---|---|---|---|---|---|---|---|
| 55 | b | | | | | | | | | | | | | | • | | | | | |
| (42) | b | R | • | • | • | • | • | • | • | | | | | | | | | | | |
| 14 | b | | | | | | | | | | | s | | | | | | | | |
| 10 | b | | | | | | | | | s | | | | | | | | | | |
| (1) | eb | W | • | • | • | | • | • | | | | | | | | | | | | |

*1) Welcome Center (westbound), Rest Area (eastbound), RV Dump Station westbound only*
*2) No Facilities*
*3) Scenic Vista*

Interstate 229 in Sioux Falls is 11 miles long. It connects I-29 with I-90. Northbound travelers should read up the chart. Southbound travelers read down the chart.

| Exit(mm) | 🡕 | ★ | 🢅 | 🚻 | ☎ | ⛱ | ⛽ | 🚮 | 🐾 | W | S | K | T | C | Am | FJ | Lo | Pe | Pi | TA |
|---|---|---|---|---|---|---|---|---|---|---|---|---|---|---|---|---|---|---|---|---|
| 6 | b | | | | | | | | | | | e | | | | | | | | |
| 3 | b | | | | | | | | | | | w+ | | | | | | | | |

# Tennessee

| Interstate | Page | | Interstate | Page |
|---|---|---|---|---|
| 24 | 179 | | 75 | 183 |
| 26 | 180 | | 81 | 184 |
| 40 | 180 | | 155 | 184 |
| 55 | 182 | | 640 | 184 |
| 65 | 182 | | | |

Interstate 10 in Alabama runs east to west for 67 miles from the Florida state line to the Mississippi state line. Eastbound travelers should read up the chart. Westbound travelers read down the chart.

| Exit(mm) | ↗ | * | ◤ | 🚻 | ⛽ | 🍴 | 🛏 | 🏕 | 🐾 | W | S | K | T | C | Am | FJ | Lo | Pe | Pi | TA |
|---|---|---|---|---|---|---|---|---|---|---|---|---|---|---|---|---|---|---|---|---|
| 184 | b | | | | | | | | | | | | s | | | | | | | |
| 174 | b | | | | | | | | | | | | | s | | | | | | |
| (172) | eb | | W | • | • | • | • | | • | | | | | | | | | | | |
| 169 | b | | | | | | | | | | | | | | | | | | • | |
| (160) | b | 1 | W | • | • | • | • | | • | | | | | | | | | | | |
| 152 | b | | | | | | | | | n | | | | | | | | | | |
| (133) | b | | R | • | • | • | • | | • | | | | | | | | | | | |
| (119) | b | 2 | T | | | | | | | | | | | | | | | | | |
| 114 | b | | | | | | | | | n | | | | | | | | | | |
| 110 | b | | | | | | | | | | | | n | | | | | | | |
| 89 | b | | | | | | | | | | | | | | | | | • | | |
| 81 | wb | | | | | | | | | | | | n | | | | | | | |
| 81b | eb | | | | | | | | | | | | n | | | | | | | |
| 78 | wb | | | | | | | | | n | s | | n | n | | | | | | |

E ↕ W

| Exit(mm) | | ★ | ⬈ | 🚻 | ☎ | 🍴 | ⛽ | 🏪 | 🛒 | 🔭 | W | S | K | T | C | Am | FJ | Lo | Pe | Pi | TA |
|---|---|---|---|---|---|---|---|---|---|---|---|---|---|---|---|---|---|---|---|---|---|
| 78b | eb | | | | | | | | | | n | | | n | n | | | | | | |
| 78a | eb | | | | | | | | | | | s | | | | | | | | | |
| 66 | wb | | | | | | | | | | | | | | | s | | | | | | |
| 66a | eb | | | | | | | | | | | | | | | s | | | | | | |
| 64 | b | | | | | | | | | | | | | | | | | | | • | | |
| 62 | b | | | | | | | | | | | | | | | | | | | | | • |
| 60 | b | | | | | | | | | | | | | | s | | | | | | | |
| 59 | b | | | | | | | | | | | | | | | n | | | | | | |
| 56 | b | | | | | | | | | | | | n | | | | | | | | | |
| 85 | b | | | | | | | | | | | | | | | | | | | | | • |
| 87 | b | | | | | | | | | | | | | | | | | | | | • | |
| 4 | b | | | | | | | | | | | s | n | s | s | n | | | | | | |
| (0.5) | eb | | W | • | • | • | • | • | | • | | | | | | | | | | | | |

1) Welcome Center (westbound), Rest Area (eastbound)
2) Trucks Only, No Facilities

Interstate 26 in Tennessee is a 46-mile route between the North Carolina state line and Interstate 81. Eastbound travelers should read up the chart. Westbound travelers read down the chart.

| Exit(mm) | | ★ | ⬈ | 🚻 | ☎ | 🍴 | ⛽ | 🏪 | 🛒 | 🔭 | W | S | K | T | C | Am | FJ | Lo | Pe | Pi | TA |
|---|---|---|---|---|---|---|---|---|---|---|---|---|---|---|---|---|---|---|---|---|---|---|
| 38 | b | | | | | | | | | | | | | | | s | | | | | | |
| 36 | b | | | | | | | | | | | n | | s | | | | | | | | |
| (7) | wb | 1 | T | | | | | | | | | | | | | | | | | | | |
| (1) | eb | 1 | T | | | | | | | | | | | | | | | | | | | |

1) Scenic Vista

Interstate 40 in Tennessee runs east to west for about 455 miles from the North Carolina state line to the Arkansas state line. Portions are also shared with I-24 and I-75. Eastbound travelers should read up the chart. Westbound travelers read down the chart.

| Exit(mm) | | ★ | ⬈ | 🚻 | ☎ | 🍴 | ⛽ | 🏪 | 🛒 | 🔭 | W | S | K | T | C | Am | FJ | Lo | Pe | Pi | TA |
|---|---|---|---|---|---|---|---|---|---|---|---|---|---|---|---|---|---|---|---|---|---|---|
| (446) | wb | 1 | W | • | • | • | • | • | | • | | | | | | | | | | | | |
| 435 | b | | | | | | | | | | | | | s | | s | | | | | | |
| (425) | wb | | R | • | • | • | • | • | | • | | | | | | | | | | | | |

| Exit(mm) | dir | * | ↗ | 🚻 | ☎ | 🍽 | 🔥 | 🚮 | 🐾 | W | S | K | T | C | Am | FJ | Lo | Pe | Pi | TA |
|---|---|---|---|---|---|---|---|---|---|---|---|---|---|---|---|---|---|---|---|---|
| (420) | eb | | R | • | • | • | • | | • | | | | | | | | | | | |
| 417 | b | | | | | | | | | | | | | | | | | | • | |
| 412 | b | | | | | | | | | | | | | | | | • | | | |
| 398 | b | | | | | | | | | | | | | s | | | | | • | |
| 380 | b | | | | | | | | | | | | s | | | | | | | |
| 379 | b | | | | | | | | | n | n | | | | | | | | | |
| 378 | b | | | | | | | | | | | | | n | | | | | | |
| 374 | b | | | | | | | | | s | | | s | | | | | • | • | |
| 373 | b | | | | | | | | | | | | | s | | | | | | |
| 369 | b | | | | | | | | | | | | | | | • | | • | | • |
| (363) | wb | | T | | • | | | | | | | | | | | | | | | |
| (362) | eb | | T | | • | | | | | | | | | | | | | | | |
| 347 | b | | | | | | | | | s+ | ' | | | s | | | | | | |
| (336) | eb | 2 | T | | | | | | | | | | | | | | | | | |
| (327) | wb | | R | • | • | • | • | | • | | | | | | | | | | | |
| (324) | eb | | R | • | • | • | • | | • | | | | | | | | | | | |
| 317 | b | | | | | | | | | s+ | | | | s | | | | | | |
| (306) | wb | 2 | T | | | | | | | | | | | | | | | | | |
| 287 | b | | | | | | | | | n | | n | | n | | | | | • | |
| (267) | b | | W | • | • | • | • | | • | | | | | | | | | | | |
| (252) | b | | T | | | • | | | | | | | | | | | | | | |
| 238 | b | | | | | | | | | n | | | | n | | | | | • | |
| 226 | wb | | | | | | | | | | | | | s | | | | | | |
| 226a | eb | | | | | | | | | | | | | s | | | | | | |
| 219 | b | | | | | | | | | | | | | s | | | | | | |
| 216 | wb | | | | | | | | | | | n | | | | | | | | |
| 216c | eb | | | | | | | | | | | n | | | | | | | | |
| 201 | wb | | | | | | | | | n | | | | n | | | | | | |
| 201b | eb | | | | | | | | | n | | | | n | | | | | | |
| 199 | b | | | | | | | | | | s | | | | | | | | | |
| 188 | b | | | | | | | | | | | | | | | | • | | | |
| 182 | b | | | | | | | | | | | | | | | • | | | | |
| 172 | b | | | | | | | | | | | | | n | | | | | • | |
| (170) | b | | R | • | • | • | • | | • | | | | | | | | | | | |
| 143 | b | | | | | | | | | | | | | | | | | | • | |
| (130) | b | | R | • | • | • | • | | • | | | | | | | | | | | |
| (103) | eb | | T | | • | | | | | | | | | | | | | | | |
| (102) | wb | 2 | T | | | | | | | | | | | | | | | | | |
| 87 | b | | | | | | | | | | | | | | | | • | | | |
| 82b | b | | | | | | | | | | | | | n | | | | | | |
| 80b | b | | | | | | | | | n | n | | | | | | | | | |
| 80a | b | | | | | | | | | | | s | | | | | | | | |

Direction: E ▲▼ W

| Exit(mm) | ↗ | ⋆ | 🛈 | 🚻 | ☎ | ⛱ | 🛢 | 🏪 | 📬 | 🐾 | W | S | K | T | C | Am | FJ | Lo | Pe | Pi | TA |
|---|---|---|---|---|---|---|---|---|---|---|---|---|---|---|---|---|---|---|---|---|---|
| (73) | b | | R | • | • | • | • | | • | | | | | | | | | | | | |
| 68 | b | | | | | | | | | | | | | | | | | | | | • |
| 66 | b | | | | | | | | | | | | | | • | | | | | | |
| 42 | b | | | | | | | | | | | | | | | | | | • | | |
| 20 | b | | | | | | | | | | | | | | n | | | | | | |
| 18 | b | | | | | | | | | | | n | n | | | | | | | | |
| 16b | wb | | | | | | | | | | | | | n | | | | | | | |
| 16 | eb | | | | | | | | | | | | | n | | | | | | | |
| 12 | b | | | | | | | | | | | | | | n | | | | | | |
| 12a | b | | | | | | | | | | | | s | | | | | | | | |
| 10 | b | | | | | | | | | | | n | | | | | | | | | |

1) No Trucks
2) No Facilities

**55** Interstate 55 in Tennessee is 12 miles long. It runs north to south from the Arkansas state line to the Mississippi state line. Northbound travelers should read up the chart. Southbound travelers read down the chart.

| Exit(mm) | ↗ | ⋆ | 🛈 | 🚻 | ☎ | ⛱ | 🛢 | 🏪 | 📬 | 🐾 | W | S | K | T | C | Am | FJ | Lo | Pe | Pi | TA |
|---|---|---|---|---|---|---|---|---|---|---|---|---|---|---|---|---|---|---|---|---|---|
| (3) | nb | | W | • | • | • | • | | • | | | | | | | | | | | | |

**65** Interstate 65 in Tennessee runs north to south for 122 miles from the Kentucky state line to the Alabama state line. Part of it is shared with I-24 and I-40. Northbound travelers should read up the chart. Southbound travelers read down the chart.

Direction: N ▲▼ S

| Exit(mm) | ↗ | ⋆ | 🛈 | 🚻 | ☎ | ⛱ | 🛢 | 🏪 | 📬 | 🐾 | W | S | K | T | C | Am | FJ | Lo | Pe | Pi | TA |
|---|---|---|---|---|---|---|---|---|---|---|---|---|---|---|---|---|---|---|---|---|---|
| (121) | sb | | W | • | • | • | • | | • | | | | | | | | | | | | |
| 108 | b | | | | | | | | | | | | | | | e | | | | | |
| 97 | b | | | | | | | | | | | | | | e | e | | | | | |
| 96 | b | 1 | | | | | | | | | | e+ | e+ | | e+ | | | | | | |
| 90b | sb | | | | | | | | | | | | e | | | | | | | | |
| 90 | nb | | | | | | | | | | | | e | | | | | | | | |
| 87 | b | | | | | | | | | | | | | | | | | | | • | |
| 85 | b | | | | | | | | | | | | | | | | | | | | • |
| 78 | b | | | | | | | | | | | | | | | e | | | | | |

| Exit(mm) | ↗ | ★ | 🔲 | 🚻 | ☎ | 🍴 | 🛢 | 🍽 | ✈ | W | S | K | T | C | Am | FJ | Lo | Pe | Pi | TA |
|---|---|---|---|---|---|---|---|---|---|---|---|---|---|---|---|---|---|---|---|---|
| 69 | b | | | | | | | | | | | | w | | | | | | | |
| 68b | b | | | | | | | | | w | w | | | | | | | | | |
| 65 | b | | | | | | | | | | | | | e | | | | | | |
| 61 | b | | | | | | | | | | | | | | | | | | • | |
| (48) | nb | 2 | T | | | | | | | | | | | | | | | | | |
| 46 | b | | | | | | | | | | | | | w | | | | | | |
| (25) | sb | 2 | T | | | | | | | | | | | | | | | | | |
| (24) | nb | 2 | T | | | | | | | | | | | | | | | | | |
| 22 | b | | | | | | | | | | | | | | | | | | • | |
| (3) | nb | | W | • | • | • | • | • | | • | | | | | | | | | | | |

1) Discount stores are on Gallatin Pike (US 31E)
2) No Facilities

Interstate 75 in Tennessee runs north to south for 162 miles from the Kentucky state line to the Georgia state line. Portions are shared with I-640 and I-40. Northbound travelers should read up the chart. Southbound travelers read down the chart.

| Exit(mm) | ↗ | ★ | 🔲 | 🚻 | ☎ | 🍴 | 🛢 | 🍽 | ✈ | W | S | K | T | C | Am | FJ | Lo | Pe | Pi | TA |
|---|---|---|---|---|---|---|---|---|---|---|---|---|---|---|---|---|---|---|---|---|
| (161) | sb | | W | • | • | • | • | • | | • | | | | | | | | | | | |
| 141 | b | | | | | | | | | | | | | | | | | | | • | |
| 129 | b | | | | | | | | | | | | | | w | | | | | | |
| 117 | b | | | | | | | | | | | | | | | | | | | • | |
| 108 | b | | | | | | | | | | | | w+ | | e | | | | | | |
| 380 | b | | | | | | | | | | | | e | | | | | | | | |
| 379 | b | | | | | | | | | | w | w | | | | | | | | | |
| 378 | b | | | | | | | | | | | | | | w | | | | | | |
| 374 | b | | | | | | | | | | e | | | e | | | | | | • | • |
| 373 | b | | | | | | | | | | | | | | e | | | | | | |
| 369 | b | | | | | | | | | | | | | | | | • | | • | | • |
| 60 | b | | | | | | | | | | | | | | w | | | | | | |
| (45) | b | | R | • | • | • | • | • | | • | | | | | | | | | | | |
| 27 | b | | | | | | | | | | e+ | | e+ | | | | | | | | |
| 25 | b | | | | | | | | | | | | | | e | | | | | | |
| (23) | nb | 1 | T | | | | | | | | | | | | | | | | | |
| (16) | sb | 2 | T | | | | | | | | | | | | | | | | | |
| (13) | sb | | T | | | | • | | | | | | | | | | | | | | |
| 5 | b | | | | | | | | | | e | | | | w | | | | | | |
| (1.5) | nb | | W | • | • | • | • | • | | • | | | | | | | | | | | |

| Exit(mm) | | ⤢ | ★ | 🚻 | ☎ | 🍴 | 🏧 | 🏪 | 🐾 | W | S | K | T | C | Am | FJ | Lo | Pe | Pi | TA |
|---|---|---|---|---|---|---|---|---|---|---|---|---|---|---|---|---|---|---|---|---|
| 1 | sb | | | | | | | | | | | | w | | | | | | | |
| 1b | nb | | | | | | | | | | | | w | | | | | | | |

1) No Facilities
2) Scenic Vista

---

**81** Interstate 81 in Tennessee runs north to south for 76 miles from the Virginia state line to I-40 near Dandridge. Northbound travelers should read up the chart. Southbound travelers read down the chart.

N ↕ S

| Exit(mm) | | ⤢ | ★ | 🚻 | ☎ | 🍴 | 🏧 | 🏪 | 🐾 | W | S | K | T | C | Am | FJ | Lo | Pe | Pi | TA |
|---|---|---|---|---|---|---|---|---|---|---|---|---|---|---|---|---|---|---|---|---|
| (75) | sb | W | • | • | • | • | | | • | | | | | | | | | | | |
| 63 | b | | | | | | | | | | w | | | e | | | | | | |
| (41) | sb | R | • | • | • | • | | | • | | | | | | | | | | | |
| (38) | nb | R | • | • | • | • | | | • | | | | | | | | | | | |
| 36 | b | | | | | | | | | | | | | | | | | • | | • | |
| 8 | b | | | | | | | | | | | | | | w | | | | | | |
| 4 | b | | | | | | | | | | | | | | | | | | | • | |
| (2) | sb | R | • | • | • | | | | • | | | | | | | | | | | |

---

**155** Interstate 155 in Tennessee is 16 miles long. It runs east to west between Dyersburg and the Arkansas state line. Eastbound travelers should read up the chart. Westbound travelers read down the chart.

| Exit(mm) | | ⤢ | ★ | 🚻 | ☎ | 🍴 | 🏧 | 🏪 | 🐾 | W | S | K | T | C | Am | FJ | Lo | Pe | Pi | TA |
|---|---|---|---|---|---|---|---|---|---|---|---|---|---|---|---|---|---|---|---|---|
| (9) | nb | W | • | • | • | • | | | • | | | | | | | | | | | |

---

**640** Interstate 640 is 7 miles long. It forms a partial loop around Knoxville. Part of it is shared with I-75. Exit numbering begins at TN 62 and increases in a clockwise direction.

| Exit(mm) | | ⤢ | ★ | 🚻 | ☎ | 🍴 | 🏧 | 🏪 | 🐾 | W | S | K | T | C | Am | FJ | Lo | Pe | Pi | TA |
|---|---|---|---|---|---|---|---|---|---|---|---|---|---|---|---|---|---|---|---|---|
| 8 | b | | | | | | | | | | | n | n | | n | | | | | |
| 6 | b | | | | | | | | | | | | s | n | | | | | | |

# Texas

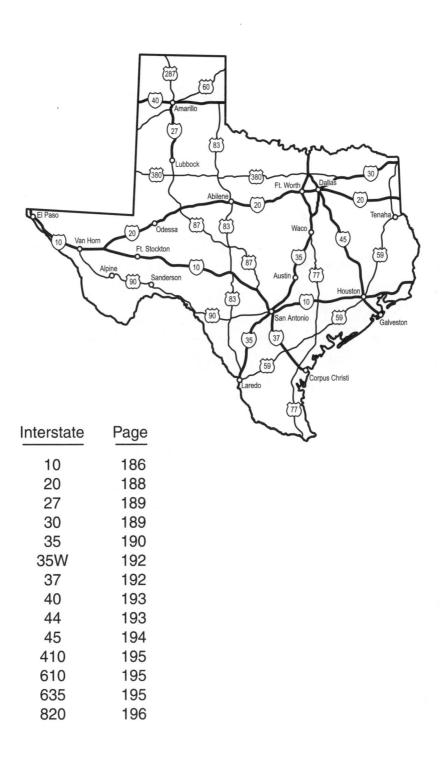

**10** Interstate 10 in Texas runs east to west for 881 miles from the Louisiana state line to the New Mexico state line. Part of it is shared with I-35. Eastbound travelers should read up the chart. Westbound travelers read down the chart.

| Exit(mm) | | * | ↗ | 🚻 | 🧍 | ⛱ | ⛽ | 🥤 | 🐦 | W | S | K | T | C | Am | FJ | Lo | Pe | Pi | TA |
|---|---|---|---|---|---|---|---|---|---|---|---|---|---|---|---|---|---|---|---|---|
| (879) | wb | W | • | • | • | • |  |  | • |  |  |  |  |  |  |  |  |  |  |  |
| 873 | b |  |  |  |  |  |  |  |  |  |  |  |  |  |  | • |  |  | • |  |
| (868) | b | R | • |  | • | • |  |  |  |  |  |  |  |  |  |  |  |  |  |  |
| 851 | b |  |  |  |  |  |  |  |  |  | s |  |  |  |  |  |  |  |  |  |
| 848 | b |  |  |  |  |  |  |  |  |  |  |  |  | s |  |  |  |  | • |  |
| (837) | b | T |  |  | • |  |  |  |  |  |  |  |  |  |  |  |  |  |  |  |
| 792 | b |  |  |  |  |  |  |  |  |  |  |  |  | n |  |  |  |  |  |  |
| 789 | b |  |  |  |  |  |  |  |  |  |  |  |  |  |  |  |  |  | • | • |
| (789) | b | R | • | • | • |  |  |  | • |  |  |  |  |  |  |  |  |  |  |
| 779b | wb |  |  |  |  |  |  |  | s | s |  |  |  |  |  |  |  |  |  |  |
| 780 | eb |  |  |  |  |  |  |  | s | s |  |  |  |  |  |  |  |  |  |  |
| 758a | b |  |  |  |  |  |  |  |  |  |  | s |  |  |  |  |  |  |  |  |
| 757 | b |  |  |  |  |  |  |  | n | n |  |  |  |  |  |  |  |  |  |  |
| 751 | b |  |  |  |  |  |  |  |  | n |  |  |  |  |  |  |  |  |  |  |
| 748 | b |  |  |  |  |  |  |  |  |  |  |  | s |  |  |  |  |  |  |  |
| 747 | b |  |  |  |  |  |  |  | n | n |  | s |  |  |  |  |  |  |  |  |
| 745 | b |  |  |  |  |  |  |  |  |  | s |  |  |  |  |  |  |  |  |  |
| 741 | b |  |  |  |  |  |  |  | s |  |  |  |  |  |  |  |  |  |  |  |
| 737 | b |  |  |  |  |  |  |  |  |  |  |  |  |  |  | • |  |  |  |  |
| 732 | b |  |  |  |  |  |  |  |  |  |  |  |  |  | • |  |  |  |  |  |
| (730) | b | T |  |  | • |  |  |  |  |  |  |  |  |  |  |  |  |  |  |  |
| 720 | b |  |  |  |  |  |  |  | s |  |  |  |  |  |  |  |  |  |  |  |
| (701) | wb | T |  |  | • |  |  |  |  |  |  |  |  |  |  |  |  |  |  |  |
| 696 | b |  |  |  |  |  |  |  | n |  |  |  |  |  |  |  |  |  |  |  |
| (692) | b | R | • | • | • | • |  |  | • |  |  |  |  |  |  |  |  |  |  |
| (657) | b | T |  |  | • |  |  |  |  |  |  |  |  |  |  |  |  |  |  |  |
| 632 | b |  |  |  |  |  |  |  |  |  |  |  |  |  |  |  |  |  | • |  |
| (621) | b | R | • | • | • | • |  |  | • |  |  |  |  |  |  |  |  |  |  |
| (590) | b | R | • | • | • |  |  | • | • |  |  |  |  |  |  |  |  |  |  |
| 583 | b |  |  |  |  |  |  |  |  |  |  |  |  |  | • |  |  |  |  | • |
| 582 | b |  |  |  |  |  |  |  |  |  |  |  |  |  |  |  |  |  | • | • |
| 565a | b |  |  |  |  |  |  |  |  |  |  |  | s |  |  |  |  |  |  |  |
| 560 | b |  |  |  |  |  |  |  |  |  |  |  |  | s |  |  |  |  |  |  |
| 558 | b |  |  |  |  |  |  |  | s |  |  | n |  |  |  |  |  |  |  |  |
| 543 | b |  |  |  |  |  |  |  | n |  |  |  |  |  |  |  |  |  |  |  |
| (531) | wb | T |  |  | • |  |  |  |  |  |  |  |  |  |  |  |  |  |  |  |
| (529) | eb | T |  |  | • |  |  |  |  |  |  |  |  |  |  |  |  |  |  |  |

Direction markers along left edge: E ↑ / ↕ / W (repeated at several points down the chart)

| Exit(mm) | 🡵 | * | 🡵 | 🚻 | ☎ | 🏕 | 🛢 | 🏠 | 🐾 | W | S | K | T | C | Am | FJ | Lo | Pe | Pi | TA |
|---|---|---|---|---|---|---|---|---|---|---|---|---|---|---|---|---|---|---|---|---|
| (514) | b | | R | • | • | • | • | • | • | | | | | | | | | | | |
| 508 | b | | | | | | | | | | | | | s | | | | | | |
| 505 | b | | | | | | | | | s+ | | | | | | | | | | |
| (503) | b | 1 | T | | | | | | | | | | | | | | | | | |
| (497) | b | | T | | | • | | | | | | | | | | | | | | |
| (461) | eb | | T | | | • | | | | | | | | | | | | | | |
| (459) | wb | | T | | | • | | | | | | | | | | | | | | |
| (423) | b | 2 | T | | | | | | | | | | | | | | | | | |
| (394) | b | | R | • | • | • | | • | • | | | | | | | | | | | |
| 372 | b | | | | | | | | | | | | | | | | | • | | |
| (349) | wb | 2 | T | | | | | | | | | | | | | | | | | |
| (346) | eb | 2 | T | | | | | | | | | | | | | | | | | |
| (308) | b | | R | • | • | • | | | • | | | | | | | | | | | |
| (279) | eb | | T | | | • | | | | | | | | | | | | | | |
| 257 | b | | | | | | | | | s | | | | | | | | | | |
| (233) | b | | R | • | • | • | | | • | | | | | | | | | | | |
| (185) | b | | T | | | • | | | | | | | | | | | | | | |
| (144) | b | | R | • | | • | | | • | | | | | | | | | | | |
| 140b | b | | | | | | | | | | | | | | | | | | • | |
| 140a | b | | | | | | | | | | | | | | | | | | | • |
| (136) | wb | 1 | T | | | • | | | | | | | | | | | | | | |
| (98) | eb | | T | | | • | | | | | | | | | | | | | | |
| (77) | wb | 3 | T | | | | | | | | | | | | | | | | | |
| (51) | b | | R | • | | • | | | • | | | | | | | | | | | |
| 37 | b | | | | | | | | | | | | | | • | | | • | • | |
| 28b | b | | | | | | | | | n | | | | | | | | | | |
| 28a | b | | | | | | | | | | n | | | | | | | | | |
| 26 | b | | | | | | | | | n | n | | | | | | | | | |
| 24 | wb | | | | | | | | | | | | n | | | | | | | |
| 24b | eb | | | | | | | | | | | | n | | | | | | | |
| 13 | b | | | | | | | | | | | | n | | | | | | | |
| 11 | b | | | | | | | | | n | s | | n | | | | | | | |
| 2 | b | | | | | | | | | | | | | | | | | | • | |
| (1) | eb | | W | • | • | • | | | • | | | | | | | | | | | |
| 0 | b | | | | | | | | | | | | | | • | | | | | • |

1) Scenic Vista
2) No Facilities
3) Truck Parking, No Facilities

Interstate 20 in Texas runs east to west for 636 miles from the Louisiana state line to I-10 near Kent. Eastbound travelers should read up the chart. Westbound travelers read down the chart.

| Exit(mm) | ↗ | * | 🔲 | 👥 | 📞 | 🍴 | ⛽ | 🏪 | 🐾 | W | S | K | T | C | Am | FJ | Lo | Pe | Pi | TA |
|---|---|---|---|---|---|---|---|---|---|---|---|---|---|---|---|---|---|---|---|---|
| (635) | b | 1 | W | • | • | • | | | • | | | | | | | | | | | |
| (608) | b | | R | • | • | • | • | | | | | | | | | | | | | |
| (574) | b | | T | | | • | | | | | | | | | | | | | | |
| 556 | b | | | | | | | | | | | | | s | | | | | | |
| 540 | b | | | | | | | | | | | | | | | | • | | | |
| (538) | b | | R | • | • | • | • | | • | | | | | | | | | | | |
| 503 | b | | | | | | | | | | | | | | | | | | | • |
| 472 | b | | | | | | | | | | | | | | | • | | | | • |
| 470 | b | | | | | | | | | | | | | | | | | | • | |
| 466 | b | | | | | | | | | | | | | | | • | | | | |
| 465 | b | | | | | | | | | | s | | | | | | | | | |
| 463 | b | | | | | | | | | | | s | s | | | | | | | |
| 456 | b | | | | | | | | | | | | | n | | | | | | |
| 454 | b | | | | | | | | | s | s | | | | | | | | | |
| 449 | b | | | | | | | | | s | | s | n | | | | | | | |
| 448 | b | | | | | | | | | | | | | n | | | | | | |
| 439 | b | | | | | | | | | | s | | | | | | | | | |
| 431 | b | | | | | | | | | | n | | s | | | | | | | |
| 429b | b | | | | | | | | | | | | | n | | | | | | |
| 410 | b | | | | | | | | | | | | | | | | • | | | |
| 409 | b | | | | | | | | | | | | | | | | | • | | |
| 408 | b | | | | | | | | | n | | | | | | | | | | |
| 406 | b | | | | | | | | | | | | | | | | | | | • |
| (390) | b | | R | • | • | • | • | | • | | | | | | | | | | | |
| (362) | b | | T | | | • | | | | | | | | | | | | | | |
| 349 | b | | | | | | | | | | | | | | | | • | | | |
| 343 | b | | | | | | | | | n | | | | | | | | | | |
| (329) | wb | | T | | | • | | | | | | | | | | | | | | |
| (327) | eb | | T | | | • | | | | | | | | | | | | | | |
| (296) | b | | R | • | • | • | | | • | | | | | | | | | | | |
| 277 | b | | | | | | | | | | | | | | | • | | | | |
| (257) | b | | R | • | • | • | • | | • | | | | | | | | | | | |
| 244 | b | | | | | | | | | | | s | | | | | | | | |
| 242 | b | | | | | | | | | | | | | | | | | | | • |
| (229) | wb | | T | | | • | | | | | | | | | | | | | | |
| (228) | eb | | T | | | • | | | | | | | | | | | | | | |
| (204) | wb | | R | • | • | • | | | • | | | | | | | | | | | |
| (191) | eb | | R | • | • | • | | | • | | | | | | | | | | | |

| Exit(mm) | ↗ | * | 🅿 | 🚻 | ☎ | ⛱ | ℹ | 🚽 | 🐾 | W | S | K | T | C | Am | FJ | Lo | Pe | Pi | TA |
|---|---|---|---|---|---|---|---|---|---|---|---|---|---|---|---|---|---|---|---|---|
| 177 | b | | | | | | | | | | | | | | | | | | | • |
| (168) | b | | T | | | • | | | | | | | | | | | | | | |
| (142) | b | | T | | | • | | | | | | | | | | | | | | |
| 121 | b | 1 | | | | | | | | | n+ | n+ | | | | | | | | |
| (103) | eb | 2 | T | | | | | | | | | | | | | | | | | |
| (69) | b | | R | • | • | • | | | • | | | | | | | | | | | |
| 42 | b | | | | | | | | | | n | | | | | | • | | | |
| (25) | b | | T | | | • | | | | | | | | | | | | | | |

(direction indicator on chart: E ↕ W)

1) Welcome Center (westbound), Turnout (eastbound - no facilities)
2) Wal-Mart and Sam's Club are 3 miles north on TX 191
3) No Facilities

Interstate 27 in Texas runs north to south for 124 miles from Amarillo to Lubbock. Northbound travelers should read up the chart. Southbound travelers read down the chart.

| Exit(mm) | ↗ | * | 🅿 | 🚻 | ☎ | ⛱ | ℹ | 🚽 | 🐾 | W | S | K | T | C | Am | FJ | Lo | Pe | Pi | TA |
|---|---|---|---|---|---|---|---|---|---|---|---|---|---|---|---|---|---|---|---|---|
| 116 | b | | | | | | | | | | | | | | | | | | • | |
| (97) | b | 1 | T | | | | | | | | | | | | | | | • | | |
| 74 | b | | | | | | | | | | | | | | | | | • | | |
| (70) | b | 1 | T | | | | | | | | | | | | | | | • | | |
| 49 | b | | | | | | | | | | | w | | | | | | | | |
| (29) | b | | R | • | • | • | | | • | | | | | | | | | | | |
| 1c | sb | | | | | | | | | | | | | | | | | • | | |
| 1a | nb | | | | | | | | | | | | | | | | | • | | |

(direction indicator on chart: N ↕ S)

1) No Facilities

Interstate 30 in Texas runs east to west for 224 miles from the Arkansas state line to I-20, west of Fort Worth. Eastbound travelers should read up the chart. Westbound travelers read down the chart.

| Exit(mm) | ↗ | * | 🅿 | 🚻 | ☎ | ⛱ | ℹ | 🚽 | 🐾 | W | S | K | T | C | Am | FJ | Lo | Pe | Pi | TA |
|---|---|---|---|---|---|---|---|---|---|---|---|---|---|---|---|---|---|---|---|---|
| 223a | b | | | | | | | | | | | s | | | | | | | | |
| (223) | wb | | W | • | • | • | • | | • | | | | | | | | | | | |
| 220b | b | | | | | | | | | | | | | n | s | n | | | | |
| 220a | b | | | | | | | | | | | s | | | | | | | | |
| 201 | b | | | | | | | | | | | s | | | | | | | | |
| (191) | b | | R | • | • | • | • | | • | | | | | | | | | | | |
| 147 | b | | | | | | | | | | | | | | | | | | • | |

(direction indicator on chart: E ↕ W)

| Exit(mm) | ⤢ | ★ | ⬈ | 🚻 | ☎ | 🍽 | 🛒 | 🏨 | 🐾 | W | S | K | T | C | Am | FJ | Lo | Pe | Pi | TA |
|---|---|---|---|---|---|---|---|---|---|---|---|---|---|---|---|---|---|---|---|---|
| (143) | b | | R | • | • | • | • | | • | | | | | | | | | | | |
| 124 | b | | | | | | | | | s+ | | | | | | | | | | |
| 122 | b | | | | | | | | | | | | | | | | | | • | |
| 93a | b | | | | | | | | | s | | | | s | | | | | | |
| 87 | b | | | | | | | | | | | | | | • | | | | | |
| 70 | b | | | | | | | | | | | | | | | | • | | | |
| 68 | b | | | | | | | | | | | | | | | | | | | • |
| 67b | b | | | | | | | | | n | | s | | | | | | | | |
| 59 | b | | | | | | | | | n | | | | | | | | | | |
| 53a | b | | | | | | | | | s | s | s | | | | | | | | |
| 30 | b | | | | | | | | | | | s | | | | | | | | |
| 24 | b | | | | | | | | | n | n | | s | | | | | | | |
| 7a | b | | | | | | | | | n | n | | s | | | | | | | |

Interstate 35 in Texas runs north to south for 504 miles from the Oklahoma state line to Laredo. I-35 splits into I-35E and I-35W near Hillsboro and comes together again in Denton. Northbound travelers should read up the chart. Southbound travelers read down the chart.

| Exit(mm) | ⤢ | ★ | ⬈ | 🚻 | ☎ | 🍽 | 🛒 | 🏨 | 🐾 | W | S | K | T | C | Am | FJ | Lo | Pe | Pi | TA |
|---|---|---|---|---|---|---|---|---|---|---|---|---|---|---|---|---|---|---|---|---|
| (503) | b | 1 | T | | | | | | | | | | | | | | | | | |
| (502) | sb | | W | • | • | • | | | | | | | | | | | | | | |
| 500 | b | | | | | | | | | | | | | | • | | | | | |
| (492) | sb | | T | | | • | | | | | | | | | | | | | | |
| (490) | nb | | T | | | • | | | | | | | | | | | | | | |
| 473 | b | | | | | | | | | | | | | | | | | • | | |
| 471 | b | | | | | | | | | | | | | | | | | | | • |
| 469 | b | | | | | | | | | | | e | | e | | | | | | |
| 464 | b | | | | | | | | | e | | | | | | | | | | |
| 458 | b | | | | | | | | | w | | | | | | | | | | |
| 451 | b | | | | | | | | | | | | | w | | | | | | |
| 448a | b | | | | | | | | | | | | e | | | | | | | |
| 421b | b | | | | | | | | | | w | | | | | | | | | |
| 421a | b | | | | | | | | | | | | e | | | | | | | |
| 416 | b | | | | | | | | | | | | | w | | | | | | |
| 415 | b | | | | | | | | | | w | | | | | | | | | |
| 414 | b | | | | | | | | | e | | | | | | | | | | |
| (392) | b | | R | • | • | • | • | | • | | | | | | | | | | | |
| 368a | b | | | | | | | | | w | | | | | | | | • | | |
| (345) | b | | T | | | • | | | | | | | | | | | | | | |
| 339 | b | | | | | | | | | e | | | | w | | | | | | |

| Exit(mm) | ↗ | * | ➤ | 👫 | ☎ | ⛱ | 🛒 | 🚐 | 🐾 | W | S | K | T | C | Am | FJ | Lo | Pe | Pi | TA |
|---|---|---|---|---|---|---|---|---|---|---|---|---|---|---|---|---|---|---|---|---|
| 337 | b | | | | | | | | | | e | | | | | | | | | |
| 331 | b | | | | | | | | | | | | | | | | | • | | |
| 330 | b | | | | | | | | | | w+ | | | | | | | | | |
| 328 | b | | | | | | | | | | | | | | | | | | | • |
| (318) | b | | T | | | • | | | | | | | | | | | | | | |
| 306 | b | | | | | | | | | | | | | | | | | • | | |
| 299 | b | | | | | | | | | | | | e | | | | | | | |
| (281) | b | | R | • | • | • | • | | • | | | | | | | | | | | |
| 261 | b | | | | | | | | | | w | | | | | | | | | |
| (256) | sb | | R | • | • | • | • | | • | | | | | | | | | | | |
| (255) | nb | | R | • | • | • | • | | • | | | | | | | | | | | |
| 254 | b | | | | | | | | | | | | | | w | | | | | |
| 250 | b | | | | | | | | | | e | w | | e | | | | | | |
| 239 | b | | | | | | | | | | e | | | | | | | | | |
| 229 | b | | | | | | | | | | e | e | | | | | | | | |
| 228 | b | | | | | | | | | | | | e | e | | | | | | |
| (211) | b | | R | • | • | • | • | | • | | | | | | | | | | | |
| 205 | b | | | | | | | | | | e | | | e | | | | | | |
| 200 | b | | | | | | | | | | | | | | e | | | | | |
| 193 | b | | | | | | | | | | | | | | | | | | | • |
| 189 | b | | | | | | | | | | | | e | | | | | | | |
| 186 | b | | | | | | | | | | e | | | w | | | | | | |
| (180) | b | | R | • | • | • | • | • | • | | | | | | | | | | | |
| 173 | b | | | | | | | | | | | | | e | | | | | | |
| 170 | b | | | | | | | | | | | w | | | | | | | | | |
| 169 | b | | | | | | | | | | | | w | | | | | | | | |
| 165 | b | | | | | | | | | | e | | | e | | | | | | |
| 164a | b | | | | | | | | | | | | | e | | | | | | |
| 150b | b | | | | | | | | | | | | w | | | | | | | |
| 144 | b | | | | | | | | | | | | | | | | | • | | |
| (129) | b | | R | • | • | • | • | | • | | | | | | | | | | | |
| (93) | b | | T | | | • | | | | | | | | | | | | | | |
| (59) | b | | T | | | • | | | | | | | | | | | | | | |
| 39 | b | | | | | | | | | | | | | | | | | • | | |
| 18 | b | | W | • | • | • | • | | • | | | | | | | | | | | |
| (15) | sb | | T | | | • | | | | | | | | | | | | | | |
| 13 | b | | | | | | | | | | | | | | | | | | | • |
| 4 | b | | | | | | | | | | | | | e | | | | | | |
| 3b | b | | | | | | | | | | w | | | | | | | | | |
| 3a | b | | | | | | | | | | | w | e | | | | | | | |

Direction segments (left margin): N ↕ S markers appear between rows 306/299, 205/200, 189/144, and (129)/39.

1) No Facilities

Interstate 35W in Texas runs north to south for 85 miles. It splits from I-35 near Hillsboro and rejoins I-35 in Denton. Northbound travelers should read up the chart. Southbound travelers read down the chart.

| Exit(mm) | ↗ | ★ | ◻ | 👫 | ☎ | ⛱ | ⛽ | 🏬 | 🐾 | ✈ | W | S | K | T | C | Am | FJ | Lo | Pe | Pi | TA |
|---|---|---|---|---|---|---|---|---|---|---|---|---|---|---|---|---|---|---|---|---|---|
| (76) | b | T | | | | • | | | | | | | | | | | | | | | |
| 65 | b | | | | | | | | | | | | | | | | | | | • | |
| 56a | b | | | | | | | | | | | | | | w | | | | | | |
| 40 | b | | | | | | | | | | | | | | | | | | • | | |
| 38 | b | | | | | | | | | | | w | | e | | | | | | | |
| (33) | sb | R | • | • | • | | | | | | | | | | | | | | | | |
| (31) | nb | R | • | • | • | | | | | | | | | | | | | | | | |
| 8 | sb | T | | | • | | | | | | | | | | | | | | | | |
| 7 | nb | T | | | • | | | | | | | | | | | | | | | | |

N ↕ S

Interstate 37 in Texas runs north to south for 143 miles from I-35 in San Antonio to Corpus Christi. Northbound travelers should read up the chart. Southbound travelers read down the chart.

| Exit(mm) | ↗ | ★ | ◻ | 👫 | ☎ | ⛱ | ⛽ | 🏬 | 🐾 | ✈ | W | S | K | T | C | Am | FJ | Lo | Pe | Pi | TA |
|---|---|---|---|---|---|---|---|---|---|---|---|---|---|---|---|---|---|---|---|---|---|
| 135 | b | | | | | | | | | | | | w | | | | | | | | |
| (112) | b | T | | | • | | | | | | | | | | | | | | | | |
| (82) | sb | R | • | • | • | | | | | | | | | | | | | | | | |
| (78) | nb | R | • | • | • | | | | | | | | | | | | | | | | |
| (56) | sb 1 | T | | | | | | | | | | | | | | | | | | | |
| (44) | sb 1 | T | | | | | | | | | | | | | | | | | | | |
| (42) | nb 1 | T | | | | | | | | | | | | | | | | | | | |
| (19) | b | R | • | • | • | • | | • | | | | | | | | | | | | | |
| 16 | b | T | | | • | | | | | | | | | | | | | | | | |
| 14 | b | | | | | | | | | | w+ | | | | | | | | | | |
| 4a | b 2 | | | | | | | | | | w+ | | | | | | | | | | |

N ↕ S

1) No Facilities
2) Wal-Mart is 6 miles west of exit on TX 358

Interstate 40 in Texas runs east to west for 177 miles from the Oklahoma state line to the New Mexico state line. Eastbound travelers should read up the chart. Westbound travelers read down the chart.

| Exit(mm) | ⬈ | ★ | 🛣 | 🚻 | ☎ | ⛱ | ⛽ | 🚮 | 🏨 | 🐴 | W | S | K | T | C | Am | FJ | Lo | Pe | Pi | TA |
|---|---|---|---|---|---|---|---|---|---|---|---|---|---|---|---|---|---|---|---|---|---|
| (175) | wb | | T | | | • | | | | | | | | | | | | | | | |
| (173) | eb | | T | | | • | | | | | | | | | | | | | | | |
| (150) | wb | | T | | | • | | | | | | | | | | | | | | | |
| (149) | eb | | T | | | • | | | | | | | | | | | | | | | |
| (131) | wb | | R | • | • | • | • | | | • | | | | | | | | | | | |
| (129) | eb | | R | • | • | • | • | | | • | | | | | | | | | | | |
| (108) | wb | 1 | T | | | | | | | | | | | | | | | | | | |
| (106) | eb | | T | | | • | | | | | | | | | | | | | | | |
| 96 | b | | | | | | | | | | | | | | | | | | • | | |
| (87) | b | | T | | | • | | | | | | | | | | | | | | | |
| 81 | b | | | | | | | | | | | | | | | | | • | | | |
| 76 | b | | | | | | | | | | | | | | | | | • | | | |
| (76) | b | | W | • | • | • | | | | | | | | | | | | | | | |
| 75 | b | | | | | | | | | | | | | | | | | | • | • | |
| 74 | b | | | | | | | | | | | | | | | | | • | | | • |
| 72b | b | | | | | | | | | | s | | | | | | | | | | |
| 72a | b | | | | | | | | | | | | | | n | | | | | | |
| 71 | b | | | | | | | | | | | s | | | | | | | | | |
| 68b | b | | | | | | | | | | | | s | | | | | | | | |
| 64 | b | | | | | | | | | | | | s | s | | | | | | | |
| 60 | b | | | | | | | | | | | | | | | | | | • | | |
| (55) | wb | 1 | T | | | | | | | | | | | | | | | | | | |
| (53) | eb | 1 | T | | | | | | | | | | | | | | | | | | |
| (32) | b | | T | | | • | | | | | | | | | | | | | | | |
| (13) | b | | T | | | • | | | | | | | | | | | | | | | |

*1) No Facilities*

Interstate 44 is an east/west route that is 15 miles long in Texas. It travels from the Oklahoma state line to Wichita Falls. Eastbound travelers should read up the chart. Westbound travelers read down the chart.

| Exit(mm) | ⬈ | ★ | 🛣 | 🚻 | ☎ | ⛱ | ⛽ | 🚮 | 🏨 | 🐴 | W | S | K | T | C | Am | FJ | Lo | Pe | Pi | TA |
|---|---|---|---|---|---|---|---|---|---|---|---|---|---|---|---|---|---|---|---|---|---|
| 13 | b | | | | | | | | | | n | | | | | | | | | | |
| (9) | b | | T | | | • | | | | | | | | | | | | | | | |
| 3c | b | | | | | | | | | | n | | | | | | | | | | |
| 1c | b | | W | • | • | • | | | | | | | | | | | | | | | |

**45** Interstate 45 in Texas runs north to south for about 286 miles from Dallas to TX Highway 87 in Galveston. Northbound travelers should read up the chart. Southbound travelers read down the chart.

| Exit(mm) | | * | [dir] | [restroom] | [phone] | [picnic] | [box] | [box] | [pet] | W | S | K | T | C | Am | FJ | Lo | Pe | Pi | TA |
|---|---|---|---|---|---|---|---|---|---|---|---|---|---|---|---|---|---|---|---|---|
| 251 | b | | | | | | | | | w | | | | | | | | | | |
| (217) | b | | R | • | • | • | • | | • | | | | | | | | | | | |
| 198 | b | | | | | | | | | | | | | | | | | • | | |
| (187) | b | | T | | • | | | | | | | | | | | | | | | |
| (160) | sb | | T | | • | | | | | | | | | | | | | | | |
| (155) | nb | | T | | • | | | | | | | | | | | | | | | |
| (126) | sb | | R | • | • | • | • | | • | | | | | | | | | | | |
| (124) | nb | | R | • | • | • | • | | • | | | | | | | | | | | |
| (121) | nb | 1 | T | | | | | | | | | | | | | | | | | |
| 118 | b | | | | | | | | | | | | | | | • | | | • | |
| 116 | b | | | | | | | | | w | | | | | | | | | | |
| (105) | b | | T | | • | | | | | | | | | | | | | | | |
| 91 | b | | | | | | | | | | | | | w | | | | | | |
| 88 | b | | | | | | | | | w | w | | | | | | | | | |
| 87 | b | | | | | | | | | | | | w | | | | | | | |
| 84 | b | | | | | | | | | | | w | | | | | | | | |
| 79 | b | | | | | | | | | w | | | | | | | | | | |
| 77 | b | | | | | | | | | | e | | w | | | | | | | |
| 68 | b | | | | | | | | | e | | | w | | | | | | | |
| 64 | b | | | | | | | | | | | e | | | | | • | | | |
| 63 | b | | | | | | | | | | | | | w | | | | | | |
| 61 | b | | | | | | | | | | | | w | | | | | | | |
| 60a | b | | | | | | | | | w | | | | | | | | | | |
| 59 | b | | | | | | | | | | | w | | | | | | | | |
| 50 | sb | 2 | | | | | | | | | | | | | | | | | • | |
| 50a | nb | 2 | | | | | | | | | | | | | | | | | • | |
| 41b | b | | | | | | | | | | | w | | | | | | | | |
| 34 | b | | | | | | | | | | | w | w | | | | | | | |
| 33 | b | | | | | | | | | w | w | | | | | | | | | |
| 27 | b | | | | | | | | | w | w | | | | | | | | | |
| 26 | b | | | | | | | | | | | | w | | | | | | | |
| 25 | b | | | | | | | | | w | | e | | | | | | | | |
| 23 | b | | | | | | | | | | | | | w | | | | | | |
| 15 | b | | | | | | | | | w | | | | | | | | | | |
| 1a | b | | | | | | | | | | | w+ | e | | | | | | | |

1) No Facilities

2) Pilot Travel Center is on Patton St

Interstate 410 is a 53-mile loop around San Antonio. Part of it is also shared with I-35. Exit numbers increase in a clockwise direction.

| Exit(mm) | ↗ | * | | | | | | | | W | S | K | T | C | Am | FJ | Lo | Pe | Pi | TA |
|---|---|---|---|---|---|---|---|---|---|---|---|---|---|---|---|---|---|---|---|---|
| 35 | b | | | | | | | | | e | | | | | | | | | | |
| 164a | b | | | | | | | | | | | | e | | | | | | | |
| 25 | b | | | | | | | | | s | | | | | | | | | | |
| 17 | b | | | | | | | | | | | n | | | | | | | | |
| 15 | b | | | | | | | | | | | w | e | | | | | | | |
| 14 | b | | | | | | | | | w | w | | | | | | | | | |
| 13a | b | | | | | | | | | | | | e | | | | | | | |
| 9 | b | | | | | | | | | w | | | | | | | | | | |
| 7 | b | | | | | | | | | | | w | w | | | | | | | |

Interstate 610 is a 38-mile loop around Houston. Exit numbering begins at Knight Road in southern Houston and increases in a clockwise direction.

| Exit(mm) | ↗ | * | | | | | | | | W | S | K | T | C | Am | FJ | Lo | Pe | Pi | TA |
|---|---|---|---|---|---|---|---|---|---|---|---|---|---|---|---|---|---|---|---|---|
| 24a | b | | | | | | | | | | | | | | • | | | | | |
| 9a | b | | | | | | | | | | | | e | | | | | | | |
| 4a | b | | | | | | | | | s | | | | | | | | | | |
| 1b | b | | | | | | | | | | s | | | | | | | | | |

Interstate 635 is a 37-mile route in Dallas. Exit numbering begins in Balch Springs and increases in a counter-clockwise direction.

| Exit(mm) | ↗ | * | | | | | | | | W | S | K | T | C | Am | FJ | Lo | Pe | Pi | TA |
|---|---|---|---|---|---|---|---|---|---|---|---|---|---|---|---|---|---|---|---|---|
| 31 | b | | | | | | | | | n | n | s | | | | | | | | |
| 23 | b | | | | | | | | | n | | | | | | | | | | |
| 22a | b | | | | | | | | | | | n | | | | | | | | |
| 13 | b | | | | | | | | | | w | | | | | | | | | |
| 12 | sb | | | | | | | | | e | | | | | | | | | | |
| 11a | b | | | | | | | | | | | e | | | | | | | | |
| 9a | b | | | | | | | | | | | | w | | | | | | | |
| 7 | b | | | | | | | | | | | e | | | | | | | | |
| 6b | b | | | | | | | | | e | | | | | | | | | | |
| 2 | b | | | | | | | | | w | | | | | | | | | | |

Interstate 820 is a 35-mile route in Fort Worth. Exit numbering begins in Benbrook and increases in a clockwise direction.

| Exit(mm) | ↗ | ★ | ◩ | 👫 | ) | 🍽 | 🛏 | 🏨 | ✈ | W | S | K | T | C | Am | FJ | Lo | Pe | Pi | TA |
|----------|---|---|---|----|---|----|---|----|----|---|---|---|---|---|----|----|----|----|----|----|
| 24a | b | | | | | | | | | w | | | | | | | | | | |
| 23 | b | | | | | | | | | | e | | | | | | | | | |
| 20b | b | | | | | | | | | n | | | | | | | | | | |
| 10a | b | | | | | | | | | w | | | | | | | | | | |

# Utah

| Interstate | Page |
|:---:|:---:|
| 15 | 198 |
| 70 | 199 |
| 80 | 199 |
| 84 | 200 |
| 215 | 200 |

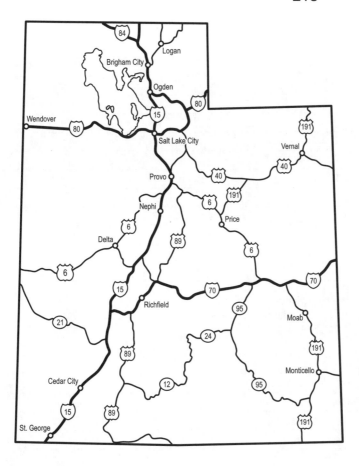

Interstate 15 in Utah runs north to south for about 403 miles from the Idaho state line to the Arizona state line. Parts are shared with I-80 and I-84. Northbound travelers should read up the chart. Southbound travelers read down the chart.

| Exit(mm) | dir | * | [1] | [2] | [3] | [4] | [5] | [6] | [7] | [8] | W | S | K | T | C | Am | FJ | Lo | Pe | Pi | TA |
|---|---|---|---|---|---|---|---|---|---|---|---|---|---|---|---|---|---|---|---|---|---|
| (370) | sb | | W | • | • | • | • | | | • | | | | | | | | | | | |
| 364 | b | | | | | | | | | | e | | | | | | • | | | | |
| (363) | nb | | R | • | • | • | • | | | • | | | | | | | | | | | |
| 360 | b | | | | | | | | | | | | | | | | • | | | | |
| 347 | b | | | | | | | | | | | | | | | | | | | • | |
| 346 | b | | | | | | | | | | | | | | | | • | | | | |
| 342 | b | | | | | | | | | | e | | | e | | | | | | | |
| 335 | b | | | | | | | | | | | | | e | e | | | | | | |
| 334 | b | | | | | | | | | | w | w | | | | | | | | | |
| (329) | b | 1 | T | | | | | | | | | | | | | | | | | | |
| 322 | b | | | | | | | | | | | | | e | | | | | | | |
| 309 | b | | | | | | | | | | e | | | | | | | | | | |
| 308 | b | | | | | | | | | | | | | | | | • | | | | |
| 306 | b | | | | | | | | | | | w | | | | | | | | | |
| 297 | b | | | | | | | | | | e | | | e | | | | | | | |
| 281 | b | | | | | | | | | | e | | | e | | | | | | | |
| 272 | b | | | | | | | | | | e | | | | | | | | | | |
| 266 | b | | | | | | | | | | | | e | e | | | | | | | |
| 265 | b | | | | | | | | | | | | | | | | • | | | | |
| 263 | b | | | | | | | | | | e | | | w | | | | | | | |
| 261 | sb | | | | | | | | | | | | | e | | | | | | | |
| 254 | b | | | | | | | | | | | | | | | | • | | | | |
| 252 | b | | | | | | | | | | e | | | | | | | | | | |
| 222 | b | | | | | | | | | | | | | | | • | • | | | | |
| (153) | sb | 2 | T | | | | | | | | | | | | | | | | | | |
| (151) | nb | 2 | T | | | | | | | | | | | | | | | | | | |
| (137) | sb | | R | • | | • | • | | | • | | | | | | | | | | | |
| (126) | nb | | R | • | | • | • | | | • | | | | | | | | | | | |
| (88) | b | | R | • | • | • | | | | • | | | | | | | | | | | |
| 78 | b | | | | | | | | | | | | | | | | | | | | • |
| 57 | b | | | | | | | | | | w | | | | | | | | | | |
| (44) | b | | R | • | • | • | | | | • | | | | | | | | | | | |
| 10 | b | | | | | | | | | | e | | | | | | | | | | |
| 8 | b | | | | | | | | | | | | | e | | | | | | | |
| 4 | b | | | | | | | | | | w | | | | | | • | | | | |
| (2) | nb | | W | • | • | • | | | | • | | | | | | | | | | | |

*1) No Facilities. 2) Scenic Vista*

Interstate 70 in Utah runs east to west for 232 miles from the Colorado state line to I-15 exit 132 near Beaver. Eastbound travelers should read up the chart. Westbound travelers read down the chart.

| Exit(mm) | | * | ⬀ | 🚻 | ☎ | ⛱ | 🛢 | 🏪 | 🐾 | W | S | K | T | C | Am | FJ | Lo | Pe | Pi | TA |
|---|---|---|---|---|---|---|---|---|---|---|---|---|---|---|---|---|---|---|---|---|
| (226) | wb | 1 | R | • | | | | | | | | | | | | | | | | |
| (188) | wb | | W | • | • | • | | | | | | | | | | | | | | |
| (180) | eb | 1 | R | • | • | • | | | | | | | | | | | | | | |
| 162 | b | | | | | | | | | | | | | | | • | | | | | |
| 158 | b | | | | | | | | | | | | | | | • | | | | | |
| (144) | wb | 1 | R | • | | | | | | | | | | | | | | | | |
| (141) | eb | 1 | R | • | | | | | | | | | | | | | | | | |
| (120) | b | | R | • | | | | | | | | | | | | | | | | |
| 114 | b | | R | • | | | | | | | | | | | | | | | | |
| (102) | b | 1 | R | • | | | | | | | | | | | | | | | | |
| 84 | b | | R | • | | • | | | | • | | | | | | | | | | |
| 40 | b | | | | | | | | | | | | | | | | • | | | | |
| 37 | b | | | | | | | | | | | s+ | | | | | | | | | |

*1) Scenic Vista*

Interstate 80 in Utah runs east to west for 197 miles from the Wyoming state line to the Nevada state line. Part of it is also I-15. Eastbound travelers should read up the chart. Westbound travelers read down the chart.

| Exit(mm) | | * | ⬀ | 🚻 | ☎ | ⛱ | 🛢 | 🏪 | 🐾 | W | S | K | T | C | Am | FJ | Lo | Pe | Pi | TA |
|---|---|---|---|---|---|---|---|---|---|---|---|---|---|---|---|---|---|---|---|---|
| (170) | b | 1 | W | • | • | • | • | | | • | | | | | | | | | | | |
| (166) | b | 2 | T | | | | | | | | | | | | | | | | | | |
| (147) | wb | | R | • | • | • | • | | | • | | | | | | | | | | | |
| 145 | b | | | | | | | | | | | s | | | | | | | | | |
| (144) | eb | 2 | T | | | | | | | | | | | | | | | | | | |
| 308 | b | | | | | | | | | | | | | | | | • | | | | |
| 309 | b | | | | | | | | | | | n | | | | | | | | | |
| (101) | wb | 2 | T | | | | | | | | | | | | | | | | | | |
| 99 | b | | | | | | | | | | | | | | | | • | | | | • |
| (54) | b | | R | • | • | • | • | | | • | | | | | | | | | | | |
| (10) | b | | R | • | • | • | • | | | • | | | | | | | | | | | |

*1) Welcome Center (westbound), Rest Area (eastbound)*
*2) Scenic Vista*

Interstate 84 in Utah runs east to west for about 120 miles from I-80 near Coalville to the Idaho state line. Portions are shared with I-15. Eastbound travelers should read up the chart. Westbound travelers read down the chart.

| Exit(mm) | ↗ | * | ◩ | 👥 | ☏ | ⛺ | 🛢 | 🗑 | 🐾 | W | S | K | T | C | Am | FJ | Lo | Pe | Pi | TA |
|---|---|---|---|---|---|---|---|---|---|---|---|---|---|---|---|---|---|---|---|---|
| (111) | b | 1 | T | | | | | | | | | | | | | | | | | |
| (94) | wb | | R | • | | • | | | • | | | | | | | | | | | |
| (91) | eb | | R | • | | • | | | • | | | | | | | | | | | |
| 81 | b | | | | | | | | | n | n | | n | | | | | | | |
| 346 | b | | | | | | | | | | | | | | | | • | | | |
| 347 | b | | | | | | | | | | | | | | | | | | • | |
| 360 | b | | | | | | | | | | | | | | | | • | | | |
| (363) | wb | | R | • | • | • | • | | • | | | | | | | | | | | |
| 364 | b | | | | | | | | | | n | | | | | | • | | | |
| (370) | eb | | R | • | • | • | • | | • | | | | | | | | | | | |
| 7 | b | | | | | | | | | | | | | | | | • | | | |

E ↕ W

*1) Scenic Vista*

Interstate 215 in Utah is 29 miles long. It forms a partial loop around Salt Lake City. Exit numbers increase in a clockwise direction.

| Exit(mm) | ↗ | * | ◩ | 👥 | ☏ | ⛺ | 🛢 | 🗑 | 🐾 | W | S | K | T | C | Am | FJ | Lo | Pe | Pi | TA |
|---|---|---|---|---|---|---|---|---|---|---|---|---|---|---|---|---|---|---|---|---|
| 28 | b | | | | | | | | | | | | | | | | | • | | |
| 18 | sb | | | | | | | | | | | | | e | | | | | | |
| 18a | nb | | | | | | | | | | | | | e | | | | | | |
| 13 | b | | | | | | | | | n | | | | | | | | | | |
| 11 | wb | | | | | | | | | | n | | | | | | | | | |
| 10 | eb | | | | | | | | | | n | | | | | | | | | |
| 9 | b | | | | | | | | | n | | n | | | | | | | | |

# Vermont

| Interstate | Page |
|------------|------|
| 89 | 201 |
| 91 | 202 |
| 93 | 202 |

Interstate 89 in Vermont runs north to south for 130 miles from the United States/Canada border to the New Hampshire state line. Exit numbers are based on the consecutive numbering system. Northbound travelers should read up the chart. Southbound travelers read down the chart.

| Exit(mm) | ↗ | ★ | ↗ | 👪 | 🚹 | 🍴 | ⛽ | 🏨 | 🛫 | W | S | K | T | C | Am | FJ | Lo | Pe | Pi | TA |
|----------|---|---|---|---|---|---|---|---|---|---|---|---|---|---|----|----|----|----|----|----|
| (129) | sb | | R | • | • | • | | | • | | | | | | | | | | | |
| (111) | b | | R | • | • | • | • | | • | | | | | | | | | | | |
| 13 | b | | | | | | | | | | | w+ | | | | | | | | |
| 12 | b | | | | | | | | | e | | | | | | | | | | |
| (82) | b | | R | • | • | • | • | | • | | | | | | | | | | | |
| (67) | sb | 1 | T | | | | | | | | | | | | | | | | | |

| Exit(mm) | ⤢ | ★ | ◰ | 👥 | 📞 | 🍽 | ⛽ | 🏪 | 🐾 | W | S | K | T | C | Am | FJ | Lo | Pe | Pi | TA |
|---|---|---|---|---|---|---|---|---|---|---|---|---|---|---|---|---|---|---|---|---|
| N (66) | nb | 1 | T | | | | | | | | | | | | | | | | | |
| (34) | b | | R | • | • | • | | • | | | | | | | | | | | | |
| S (9) | b | | R | • | • | • | • | | | | | | | | | | | | | |

*1) No Facilities*

Interstate 91 in Vermont runs north to south for 178 miles from the United States/Canada border to the Massachusetts state line. Exit numbers are based on the consecutive numbering system. Northbound travelers should read up the chart. Southbound travelers read down the chart.

| Exit(mm) | ⤢ | ★ | ◰ | 👥 | 📞 | 🍽 | ⛽ | 🏪 | 🐾 | W | S | K | T | C | Am | FJ | Lo | Pe | Pi | TA |
|---|---|---|---|---|---|---|---|---|---|---|---|---|---|---|---|---|---|---|---|---|
| (176) | sb | | W | • | • | • | | • | | | | | | | | | | | | |
| (167) | b | | T | | • | | | | | | | | | | | | | | | |
| (154) | nb | 1 | T | | | | | | | | | | | | | | | | | |
| (143) | nb | 2 | T | | | | | | | | | | | | | | | | | |
| (141) | sb | | R | • | • | • | | | | | | | | | | | | | | |
| N (122) | nb | 2 | T | | | | | | | | | | | | | | | | | |
| (115) | sb | 1 | T | | | | | | | | | | | | | | | | | |
| (114) | nb | 1 | T | | | | | | | | | | | | | | | | | |
| S (100) | nb | 3 | R | • | • | • | | • | | | | | | | | | | | | |
| (68) | b | | R | • | • | • | • | • | | | | | | | | | | | | |
| (39) | b | | T | | • | | | | | | | | | | | | | | | |
| (24) | b | 1 | T | | | | | | | | | | | | | | | | | |
| (20) | nb | 1 | T | | | | | | | | | | | | | | | | | |
| (6) | nb | | W | • | • | • | • | • | | | | | | | | | | | | |

*1) No Facilities*
*2) Scenic Vista*
*3) Rest Area (northbound), Turnout (southbound - no facilities)*

Interstate 93 in Vermont is 11 miles long. It runs between I-91 and the New Hampshire state line. Exit numbers are based on the consecutive numbering system. Northbound travelers should read up the chart. Southbound travelers read down the chart.

| Exit(mm) | ⤢ | ★ | ◰ | 👥 | 📞 | 🍽 | ⛽ | 🏪 | 🐾 | W | S | K | T | C | Am | FJ | Lo | Pe | Pi | TA |
|---|---|---|---|---|---|---|---|---|---|---|---|---|---|---|---|---|---|---|---|---|
| (1) | nb | | W | • | • | • | • | | • | | | | | | | | | | | |

# Virginia

| Interstate | Page |
|---|---|
| 64 | 203 |
| 66 | 204 |
| 77 | 205 |
| 81 | 205 |
| 85 | 206 |
| 95 | 206 |
| 264 | 207 |
| 295 | 207 |

Interstate 64 in Virginia runs east to west for 299 miles from I-264 in Chesapeake to the West Virginia state line. Part of it is shared with I-81. Eastbound travelers should read up the chart. Westbound travelers read down the chart.

| Exit(mm) | ⤴ | ★ | ⤴ | 👫 | 🚻 | ⛱ | ⛽ | 🏨 | 🐾 | W | S | K | T | C | Am | FJ | Lo | Pe | Pi | TA |
|---|---|---|---|---|---|---|---|---|---|---|---|---|---|---|---|---|---|---|---|---|
| 290b | b | | | | | | | | | s | s | s | | | | | | | | |
| 289b | b | | | | | | | | | | | | s | | | | | | | |
| 281 | b | | | | | | | | | | | n | s | | | | | | | |
| 279 | b | | | | | | | | | | | n | | | | | | | | |
| 263b | b | | | | | | | | | n | | n | | | | | | | | |
| 263a | b | | | | | | | | | | | | s | | | | | | | |

E ↑↓ W

| Exit(mm) | ↗ | * | ⤡ | 🚻 | 📞 | 🧺 | ⛽ | 🏪 | 🐕 | W | S | K | T | C | Am | FJ | Lo | Pe | Pi | TA |
|---|---|---|---|---|---|---|---|---|---|---|---|---|---|---|---|---|---|---|---|---|
| 255b | b | | | | | | | | | n | n | | | | | | | | | |
| 255a | b | | | | | | | | | | | s | s | | | | | | | |
| 238 | b | | | | | | | | | | | | s+ | | | | | | | |
| 234a | wb | | | | | | | | | s+ | | | | | | | | | | |
| 234 | eb | | | | | | | | | s+ | | | | | | | | | | |
| (213) | b | 1 | W | • | • | • | • | | • | | | | | | | | | | | |
| 183 | b | | | | | | | | | | | n | | | | | | | | |
| 180b | b | | | | | | | | | | n | | | | | | | | | |
| 178a | b | | | | | | | | | s+ | | s+ | | | | | | | | |
| (169) | eb | | R | • | • | • | • | | • | | | | | | | | | | | |
| (168) | wb | | R | • | • | • | • | | • | | | | | | | | | | | |
| (113) | wb | | R | • | • | • | • | | • | | | | | | | | | | | |
| (105) | eb | | R | • | • | • | • | | • | | | | | | | | | | | |
| (104) | eb | 2 | T | | | | | | | | | | | | | | | | | |
| (100) | eb | 2 | T | | | | | | | | | | | | | | | | | |
| 213a | wb | | | | | | | | | | | | | | | | | | • | |
| 213 | eb | | | | | | | | | | | | | | | | | | • | |
| 205 | b | | | | | | | | | | | | | | | | • | | | |
| (199) | wb | | R | • | • | • | • | | • | | | | | | | | | | | |
| 55 | b | | | | | | | | | n | | | | | | | | | | |
| 16 | b | | | | | | | | | | | s | | | | | | | | |
| 14 | b | | | | | | | | | s | | | | | | | | | | |
| (2) | eb | 3 | W | • | • | • | • | | • | | | | | | | | | | | |

(Left-margin travel-direction segments, top to bottom: E ↕ W; E ↕ W; E ↕ W)

1) Welcome Center (eastbound), Rest Area (westbound)
2) Scenic Vista
3) No Trucks

Interstate 66 in Virginia runs east to west for 77 miles from Washington, D.C. to I-81 exit 300 near Strasburg. Eastbound travelers should read up the chart. Westbound travelers read down the chart.

| Exit(mm) | ↗ | * | ⤡ | 🚻 | 📞 | 🧺 | ⛽ | 🏪 | 🐕 | W | S | K | T | C | Am | FJ | Lo | Pe | Pi | TA |
|---|---|---|---|---|---|---|---|---|---|---|---|---|---|---|---|---|---|---|---|---|
| 55 | b | | | | | | | | | n | | n | | | | | | | | |
| (48) | b | 1 | W | • | • | • | | | • | | | | | | | | | | | |
| 47b | wb | | | | | | | | | | | | n | | | | | | | |
| 47a | wb | | | | | | | | | s | s | | | | | | | | | |
| 47 | eb | | | | | | | | | s | s | | n | | | | | | | |
| 43a | b | | | | | | | | | | | | s | | | | | | | |

(Left-margin travel-direction segment: E ↕ W)

1) Welcome Center (westbound), Rest Area (eastbound)

Interstate 77 in Virginia runs north to south for 67 miles from the West Virginia state line to the North Carolina state line. Part of it is also I-81. Northbound travelers should read up the chart. Southbound travelers read down the chart.

*(N ↕ S indicator shown in left margin)*

| Exit(mm) | ↗ | ★ | 🚗 | 🚻 | ☎ | ⛺ | 🚮 | 🥤 | 🐕 | W | S | K | T | C | Am | FJ | Lo | Pe | Pi | TA |
|---|---|---|---|---|---|---|---|---|---|---|---|---|---|---|---|---|---|---|---|---|
| (61) | sb | | W | • | • | • | • | | • | | | | | | | | | | | |
| (59) | nb | | R | • | • | • | • | | • | | | | | | | | | | | |
| 41 | b | | | | | | | | | | | | | | | | | | | • |
| 73 | b | | | | | | | | | | | | | w | | | | | | |
| 77 | b | | | | | | | | | | | | | | | • | | | | | |
| 80 | b | | | | | | | | | | | | | | | • | | | | | |
| (1) | nb | | W | • | • | • | • | | • | | | | | | | | | | | |

Interstate 81 in Virginia runs north to south for 325 miles from the West Virginia state line to the Tennessee state line. Portions are shared with I-64 and I-77. Northbound travelers should read up the chart. Southbound travelers read down the chart.

*(N ↕ S indicators shown in left margin)*

| Exit(mm) | ↗ | ★ | 🚗 | 🚻 | ☎ | ⛺ | 🚮 | 🥤 | 🐕 | W | S | K | T | C | Am | FJ | Lo | Pe | Pi | TA |
|---|---|---|---|---|---|---|---|---|---|---|---|---|---|---|---|---|---|---|---|---|
| 323 | b | | | | | | | | | | | | | | | | • | | | | |
| 313b | sb | | | | | | | | | w | | w | w | | | | | | | |
| 313a | sb | | | | | | | | | | | | | e | | | | | | |
| 313 | nb | | | | | | | | | w | | w | w | e | | | | | | |
| (320) | sb | | W | • | • | • | • | | • | | | | | | | | | | | |
| 291 | b | | | | | | | | | | | | | | | | • | | | | |
| 283 | b | | | | | | | | | w | | | | | | | | | | | |
| (262) | b | | R | • | • | • | • | | • | | | | | | | | | | | |
| 247 | b | | | | | | | | | e | | e | | | | | | | | |
| 243 | b | | | | | | | | | | | | w | | | | | | | |
| (232) | b | | R | • | • | • | • | | • | | | | | | | | | | | |
| 222 | b | | | | | | | | | w | | | | e | | | | | | |
| 213a | sb | | | | | | | | | | | | | | | | | | • | |
| 213 | nb | | | | | | | | | | | | | | | | | | • | |
| 205 | b | | | | | | | | | | | | | | • | | | | | |
| (199) | sb | | R | • | • | • | • | | • | | | | | | | | | | | |
| (158) | sb | | R | • | • | • | • | | • | | | | | | | | | | | |
| 150a | b | | | | | | | | | | | | | e | | | | | • | • |
| 143 | b | | | | | | | | | e+ | | e+ | | | | | | | | |
| 137 | b | | | | | | | | | e | | | | | | | | | | |
| (129) | nb | | R | • | • | • | • | | • | | | | | | | | | | | |

| Exit(mm) | | ★ | | | | | | | | | W | S | K | T | C | Am | FJ | Lo | Pe | Pi | TA |
|---|---|---|---|---|---|---|---|---|---|---|---|---|---|---|---|---|---|---|---|---|---|
| 118 | b | | | | | | | | | | | | | | e | | | | | | |
| (108) | b | | R | • | • | • | • | | • | | | | | | | | | | | | |
| 84 | b | | | | | | | | | | | | | | | | | | | • | |
| 80 | b | | | | | | | | | | | | | | | | | | • | | |
| 77 | b | | | | | | | | | | | | | | | | | | • | | |
| 73 | b | | | | | | | | | | | | | | | e | | | | | | |
| 72 | b | 1 | | | | | | | | | | | | | | | | | | | • |
| 70 | b | | | | | | | | | | | e | | | | | | | | | | |
| (61) | nb | 2 | R | • | • | • | • | | • | | | | | | | | | | | | |
| (53) | sb | | R | • | • | • | • | | • | | | | | | | | | | | | |
| 47 | b | | | | | | | | | | | | | w | | | | | | | | |
| 29 | b | | | | | | | | | | | | | | | | | | | | • | |
| 19 | b | | | | | | | | | | | | | | w | | | | | | | |
| 17 | b | | | | | | | | | | | | | w | | | | | | | | |
| (13) | nb | 3 | R | • | • | • | • | | • | | | | | | | | | | | | |
| 1 | b | | | | | | | | | | | e+ | | | | | | | | | | |
| (1) | nb | 2 | W | • | • | • | • | | • | | | | | | | | | | | | |

*1) TA Travel Center is off I-77 Exit 41. 2) No Trucks. 3)Truckers Only*

Interstate 85 in Virginia is 69 miles long. It runs north to south from I-95 in Petersburg to the North Carolina state line. Northbound travelers should read up the chart. Southbound travelers read down the chart.

| Exit(mm) | | ★ | | | | | | | | | W | S | K | T | C | Am | FJ | Lo | Pe | Pi | TA |
|---|---|---|---|---|---|---|---|---|---|---|---|---|---|---|---|---|---|---|---|---|---|
| (55) | b | | R | • | • | • | • | | • | | | | | | | | | | | | |
| (32) | b | | R | • | • | • | • | | • | | | | | | | | | | | | |
| 12 | b | | | | | | | | | | | e | | | | | | | | | | |
| (.5) | nb | | W | • | • | • | • | | • | | | | | | | | | | | | |

Interstate 95 in Virginia runs north to south for 179 miles from the Maryland state line to the North Carolina state line. Northbound travelers should read up the chart. Southbound travelers read down the chart.

| Exit(mm) | | ★ | | | | | | | | | W | S | K | T | C | Am | FJ | Lo | Pe | Pi | TA |
|---|---|---|---|---|---|---|---|---|---|---|---|---|---|---|---|---|---|---|---|---|---|
| 169 | b | | | | | | | | | | | | | w | | | | | | | | |
| 156 | b | | | | | | | | | | | | | w | | | | | | | | |
| (155) | b | 1 | R | • | • | • | • | | • | | | | | | | | | | | | |

| Exit(mm) | ↗ | ★ | ♿ | 🚻 | ☎ | ⛱ | 🏪 | 🛗 | 🐕 | W | S | K | T | C | Am | FJ | Lo | Pe | Pi | TA |
|---|---|---|---|---|---|---|---|---|---|---|---|---|---|---|---|---|---|---|---|---|
| (154) | b | 2 | R | • | • | • | • |  | • |  |  |  |  |  |  |  |  |  |  |  |
| 152 | b |  |  |  |  |  |  |  |  |  |  |  | w |  |  |  |  |  |  |  |
| 143b | b |  |  |  |  |  |  |  |  | w |  | w |  |  |  |  |  |  |  |  |
| (131) | sb |  | W | • | • | • | • |  | • |  |  |  |  |  |  |  |  |  |  |  |
| 130b | b |  |  |  |  |  |  |  |  | w |  | w | w | w |  |  |  |  |  |  |
| 126 | sb |  |  |  |  |  |  |  |  | w |  |  | w |  |  |  |  |  |  |  |
| 126b | nb |  |  |  |  |  |  |  |  | w |  |  | w |  |  |  |  |  |  |  |
| (107) | b |  | R | • | • | • | • |  | • |  |  |  |  |  |  |  |  |  |  |  |
| 104 | b |  |  |  |  |  |  |  |  |  |  |  |  |  |  | • |  | • | • |  |
| 92 | sb |  |  |  |  |  |  |  |  |  |  |  | w |  |  |  |  |  |  | • |
| 92b | nb |  |  |  |  |  |  |  |  |  |  |  | w |  |  |  |  |  |  | • |
| 89 | b |  |  |  |  |  |  |  |  |  |  |  |  |  |  |  |  |  |  | • |
| 86 | b |  |  |  |  |  |  |  |  |  |  |  | w |  |  |  |  |  |  |  |
| 83b | b |  |  |  |  |  |  |  |  | w |  |  |  |  |  |  |  |  |  |  |
| 61b | b |  |  |  |  |  |  |  |  |  |  | w | w | w |  |  |  |  |  |  |
| 54 | b |  |  |  |  |  |  |  |  | e | e | e | e |  |  |  |  |  |  |  |
| (37) | nb |  | R | • | • | • | • |  | • |  |  |  |  |  |  |  |  |  |  |  |
| 33 | b |  |  |  |  |  |  |  |  |  |  |  |  |  | • |  |  |  |  |  |
| 11a | b |  |  |  |  |  |  |  |  | e |  |  |  |  |  |  |  |  |  |  |
| 4 | b |  |  |  |  |  |  |  |  |  |  |  |  |  |  |  | • |  |  |  |
| (1) | nb | 1 | W | • | • | • | • |  | • |  |  |  |  |  |  |  |  |  |  |  |

*1) No Trucks. 2) Truckers Only.*

Interstate 264 runs east to west for about 22 miles from Virginia Beach to I-64 west of Norfolk. Eastbound travelers should read up the chart. Westbound travelers read down the chart.

| Exit(mm) | ↗ | ★ | ♿ | 🚻 | ☎ | ⛱ | 🏪 | 🛗 | 🐕 | W | S | K | T | C | Am | FJ | Lo | Pe | Pi | TA |
|---|---|---|---|---|---|---|---|---|---|---|---|---|---|---|---|---|---|---|---|---|
| 21 | b |  |  |  |  |  |  |  |  |  |  | n |  |  |  |  |  |  |  |  |
| 18 | b |  |  |  |  |  |  |  |  |  |  | s |  |  |  |  |  |  |  |  |

Interstate 295 in the Richmond area is 53 miles long. It primarily runs north to south, between I-64 near Richmond with I-95 near Petersburg.

| Exit(mm) | ↗ | ★ | ♿ | 🚻 | ☎ | ⛱ | 🏪 | 🛗 | 🐕 | W | S | K | T | C | Am | FJ | Lo | Pe | Pi | TA |
|---|---|---|---|---|---|---|---|---|---|---|---|---|---|---|---|---|---|---|---|---|
| 43 | b |  |  |  |  |  |  |  |  |  |  | s+ |  |  |  |  |  |  |  |  |
| 37a | b |  |  |  |  |  |  |  |  |  |  | e |  | e | e |  |  |  |  |  |

# Washington

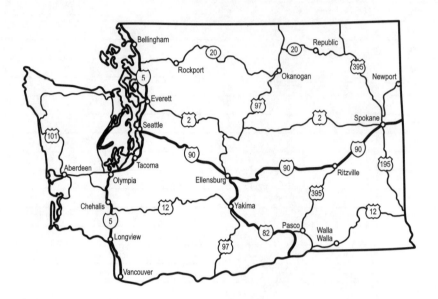

| Interstate | Page |
|:---:|:---:|
| 5 | 208 |
| 82 | 209 |
| 90 | 210 |
| 182 | 211 |
| 405 | 211 |

**5**

Interstate 5 in Washington runs north to south for 277 miles from the United States/Canada border to the Oregon state line. Northbound travelers should read up the chart. Southbound travelers read down the chart.

| Exit(mm) | ⤢ | ★ | 🏞 | 👪 | 🚻 | ⛽ | 🏧 | 🏪 | 🐕 | W | S | K | T | C | Am | FJ | Lo | Pe | Pi | TA |
|---|---|---|---|---|---|---|---|---|---|---|---|---|---|---|---|---|---|---|---|---|
| (269) sb | W | • | | • | • | • | | • | | | | | | | | | | | | |
| (267) nb | R | • | | • | • | • | | • | | | | | | | | | | | | |
| 256a b | | | | | | | | | | | e | | e | | | | | | | |
| 255 b | | | | | | | | | | | | e | | | | | | | | |

N ↑ ↓ S

| Exit(mm) | ↗ | * | ↗ | 🚻 | 📞 | ⛱ | 🏪 | 🗑 | 🐎 | W | S | K | T | C | Am | FJ | Lo | Pe | Pi | TA |
|---|---|---|---|---|---|---|---|---|---|---|---|---|---|---|---|---|---|---|---|---|
| (238) | b |  | R | • | • | • |  |  | • |  |  |  |  |  |  |  |  |  |  |  |
| 230 | b |  |  |  |  |  |  |  |  |  |  |  | e |  |  |  |  |  |  |  |
| 229 | b |  |  |  |  |  |  |  |  |  |  | e |  |  |  |  |  |  |  |  |
| 227 | b |  |  |  |  |  |  |  |  | e |  |  |  |  |  |  |  |  |  |  |
| (207) | b |  | R | • | • | • | • | • | • |  |  |  |  |  |  |  |  |  |  |  |
| 200 | b |  |  |  |  |  |  |  |  | w |  |  |  |  |  |  |  |  |  |  |
| 189 | b | 1 |  |  |  |  |  |  |  |  |  | w+ |  |  |  |  |  |  |  |  |
| (188) | sb |  | R | • | • | • | • | • |  |  |  |  |  |  |  |  |  |  |  |  |
| 183 | b |  |  |  |  |  |  |  |  | e |  |  |  |  |  |  |  |  |  |  |
| 182 | b |  |  |  |  |  |  |  |  |  |  |  | w |  |  |  |  |  |  |  |
| 174 | nb |  |  |  |  |  |  |  |  |  | w+ | w+ |  |  |  |  |  |  |  |  |
| 173 | b |  |  |  |  |  |  |  |  |  |  |  | e |  |  |  |  |  |  |  |
| 154b | b |  |  |  |  |  |  |  |  |  |  |  | e |  |  |  |  |  |  |  |
| 142b | b |  |  |  |  |  |  |  |  |  |  |  |  |  |  | • |  |  |  |  |
| (141) | nb |  | R | • | • | • | • | • |  |  |  |  |  |  |  |  |  |  |  |  |
| 136 | sb |  |  |  |  |  |  |  |  |  | e |  |  |  |  | • |  |  |  |  |
| 136b | nb |  |  |  |  |  |  |  |  |  |  |  |  |  |  | • |  |  |  |  |
| 136a | nb |  |  |  |  |  |  |  |  |  | e |  |  |  |  |  |  |  |  |  |
| 111 | b |  |  |  |  |  |  |  |  | e |  |  |  |  |  |  |  |  |  |  |
| 109 | b |  |  |  |  |  |  |  |  |  |  | w |  |  |  |  |  |  |  |  |
| 108 | b |  |  |  |  |  |  |  |  |  |  |  | e |  |  |  |  |  |  |  |
| (93) | sb |  | R | • | • | • | • |  | • |  |  |  |  |  |  |  |  |  |  |  |
| (90) | nb |  | R | • | • | • | • |  | • |  |  |  |  |  |  |  |  |  |  |  |
| 79 | b |  |  |  |  |  |  |  |  | w |  | w |  |  |  |  |  |  |  |  |
| (54) | b |  | R | • | • | • |  |  | • |  |  |  |  |  |  |  |  |  |  |  |
| 39 | b |  |  |  |  |  |  |  |  |  |  |  | w |  |  |  |  |  |  |  |
| (12) | sb |  | R | • | • | • | • | • | • |  |  |  |  |  |  |  |  |  |  |  |
| (11) | nb |  | R | • | • | • | • | • | • |  |  |  |  |  |  |  |  |  |  |  |
| 5 | b |  |  |  |  |  |  |  |  | e |  |  | w |  |  |  |  |  |  |  |

Direction markers along the left: N ↕ S (at exits 189–182), N ↕ S (at exits 111–108).

*1) K-Mart is on Evergreen Way*

Interstate 82 in Washington runs east to west for 133 miles from the Oregon state line to I-90 exit 110 near Ellensburg. Eastbound travelers should read up the chart. Westbound travelers read down the chart.

| Exit(mm) | ↗ | * | ↗ | 🚻 | 📞 | ⛱ | 🏪 | 🗑 | 🐎 | W | S | K | T | C | Am | FJ | Lo | Pe | Pi | TA |
|---|---|---|---|---|---|---|---|---|---|---|---|---|---|---|---|---|---|---|---|---|
| 113 | b |  |  |  |  |  |  |  |  |  | n |  |  |  |  |  |  |  |  |  |
| 80 | b |  | R | • | • | • |  |  | • |  |  |  |  |  |  |  |  |  |  |  |
| 69 | b |  |  |  |  |  |  |  |  |  | n |  |  |  |  |  |  |  |  |  |

Direction markers along the left: E ↑↓ W.

| Exit(mm) | ⇱ | ★ | ↗ | 👫 | ☎ | ⛺ | 🛢 | 🔋 | 🐕 | W | S | K | T | C | Am | FJ | Lo | Pe | Pi | TA |
|---|---|---|---|---|---|---|---|---|---|---|---|---|---|---|---|---|---|---|---|---|
| 36 | b | | | | | | | | | | | | | | • | | | | | |
| 34 | b | | | | | | | | | | | | n | | | | | | | |
| 33 | b | | | | | | | | | | | n | | s | | | | | | |
| (24) | eb | | R | • | • | • | | • | • | | | | | | | | | | | |
| (22) | wb | | R | • | • | • | | • | • | | | | | | | | | | | |
| (8) | b | 1 | T | | | | | | | | | | | | | | | | | |

*E ↕ W*

1) Scenic Vista

Interstate 90 in Washington runs east to west for about 300 miles from the Idaho state line to I-5 in Seattle. Eastbound travelers should read up the chart. Westbound travelers read down the chart.

| Exit(mm) | ⇱ | ★ | ↗ | 👫 | ☎ | ⛺ | 🛢 | 🔋 | 🐕 | W | S | K | T | C | Am | FJ | Lo | Pe | Pi | TA |
|---|---|---|---|---|---|---|---|---|---|---|---|---|---|---|---|---|---|---|---|---|
| (299) | wb | | R | • | • | • | | | • | | | | | | | | | | | |
| 291b | b | | | | | | | | | | | s | | s | | | | | | |
| 286 | b | | | | | | | | | | | | | | | | | • | | | |
| 285 | b | | | | | | | | | | | | n | | | | | | | |
| 276 | b | | | | | | | | | | | | | | | | | • | | | |
| (242) | b | 1 | R | • | • | • | • | • | • | | | | | | | | | | | |
| (199) | b | 2 | R | • | • | • | • | • | • | | | | | | | | | | | |
| (162) | wb | | R | • | • | • | | • | • | | | | | | | | | | | |
| (161) | eb | | R | • | • | • | | • | • | | | | | | | | | | | |
| (139) | b | 3 | T | | | | | | | | | | | | | | | | | |
| (126) | b | | R | • | • | • | • | | • | | | | | | | | | | | |
| 109 | b | | | | | | | | | | | | | | | | • | | | | |
| 106 | b | | | | | | | | | | | | | | | | | | • | | |
| (89) | b | | R | • | • | • | • | • | • | | | | | | | | | | | |
| 34 | b | | | | | | | | | | | | | | | | | | | • | |
| 15 | b | | | | | | | | | | | | | s | | | | | | | |

*E ↕ W*

1) RV Dump Station (eastbound)
2) RV Dump Station (westbound)
3) Scenic Vista

Interstate 182 in Washington is 15 miles long. It runs east to west from US 12 in Pasco to Interstate 82. Eastbound travelers should read up the chart. Westbound travelers read down the chart.

| Exit(mm) | ↗ | ★ | ◧ | ⛹ | ☎ | ⛺ | 🛏 | 🍽 | 🐾 | W | S | K | T | C | Am | FJ | Lo | Pe | Pi | TA |
|---|---|---|---|---|---|---|---|---|---|---|---|---|---|---|---|---|---|---|---|---|
| 12a | b | | | | | | | | | | | s | | | | | | | | |
| 3 | b | | | | | | | | | | n | | | | | | | | | |

 Interstate 405 in Washington is 30 miles long. It forms a partial loop around Seattle. Exit numbering begins at WA 181 and increases in a counter-clockwise direction.

| Exit(mm) | ↗ | ★ | ◧ | ⛹ | ☎ | ⛺ | 🛏 | 🍽 | 🐾 | W | S | K | T | C | Am | FJ | Lo | Pe | Pi | TA |
|---|---|---|---|---|---|---|---|---|---|---|---|---|---|---|---|---|---|---|---|---|
| 10 | b | 1 | | | | | | | | | | | e+ | | | | | | | |
| 2 | b | | | | | | | | | | w | | w | | | | | | | |
| 1 | b | | | | | | | | | | | | e | | | | | | | |

*1) Target is on Factoria Blvd*

# West Virginia

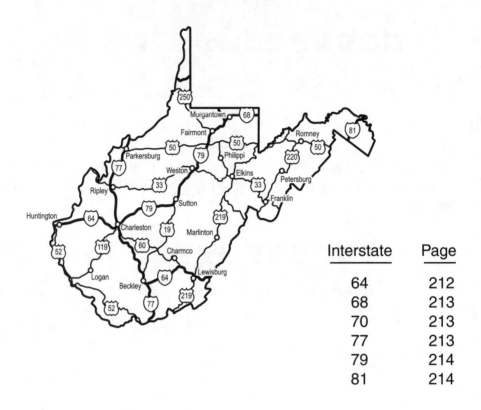

| Interstate | Page |
| --- | --- |
| 64 | 212 |
| 68 | 213 |
| 70 | 213 |
| 77 | 213 |
| 79 | 214 |
| 81 | 214 |

**64** Interstate 64 in West Virginia runs east to west for 189 miles from the Virginia state line to the Kentucky state line. Portions are shared with I-77 and the West Virginia Turnpike. Eastbound travelers should read up the chart. Westbound travelers read down the chart.

| Exit(mm) | ↗ | ★ | 🚗 | 🚻 | 🍴 | 🍽 | ⛽ | 🏪 | ✈ | W | S | K | T | C | Am | FJ | Lo | Pe | Pi | TA |
| --- | --- | --- | --- | --- | --- | --- | --- | --- | --- | --- | --- | --- | --- | --- | --- | --- | --- | --- | --- | --- |
| (179) | wb | | W | • | • | • | | | • | | | | | | | | | | | |
| 169 | b | | | | | | | | | | s | | | | | | | | | |
| 44 | b | | | | | | | | | | | | | s | | | | | | |
| (45) | b | 1 | S | • | • | • | • | | | | | | | | | | | | | |
| 48 | b | | | | | | | | | | n+ | | | | | | | | | |
| (69) | eb | | R | • | • | • | • | | • | | | | | | | | | | | |
| (72) | wb | 1 | S | • | • | • | • | • | | | | | | | | | | | | |
| 95 | b | | | | | | | | | | | | n | s | | | | | | |
| 56 | b | | | | | | | | | | | | n | | | | | | | |
| 47 | wb | | | | | | | | | | s | | | s | | | | | | |

| Exit(mm) | ↗ | ✲ | ► | 👫 | ☎ | ⛱ | ⛽ | 🏪 | 🐾 | W | S | K | T | C | Am | FJ | Lo | Pe | Pi | TA |
|---|---|---|---|---|---|---|---|---|---|---|---|---|---|---|---|---|---|---|---|---|
| 47a | eb | | | | | | | | | | s | | | s | | | | | | |
| 45 | b | | | | | | | | | | | | | | | | | | • | |
| 39 | b | | | | | | | | | | | s | | | | | | | • | |
| (35) | b | | R | • | • | • | • | • | • | | | | | | | | | | | |
| 20 | wb | | | | | | | | | | n | | | s | | | | | | |
| 20a | eb | | | | | | | | | | | | | s | | | | | | |
| 20b | eb | | | | | | | | | | n | | | | | | | | | |
| 18 | b | | | | | | | | | | | | n | | | | | | | |
| 15 | b | | | | | | | | | | s | | | | | | | | | |
| (10) | eb | | W | • | • | • | • | | • | | | | | | | | | | | |

*E ↕ W*

1) Gas, Food

---

## 68

Interstate 68 in West Virginia is 32 miles long. It runs east to west from the Maryland state line to I-79 exit 148 near Morgantown. Eastbound travelers should read up the chart. Westbound travelers read down the chart.

| Exit(mm) | ↗ | ✲ | ► | 👫 | ☎ | ⛱ | ⛽ | 🏪 | 🐾 | W | S | K | T | C | Am | FJ | Lo | Pe | Pi | TA |
|---|---|---|---|---|---|---|---|---|---|---|---|---|---|---|---|---|---|---|---|---|
| (31) | wb | | W | • | • | • | • | • | • | | | | | | | | | | | |

---

## 70

Interstate 70 in West Virginia runs east to west for 14 miles from the Pennsylvania state line to the Ohio state line. Eastbound travelers should read up the chart. Westbound travelers read down the chart.

| Exit(mm) | ↗ | ✲ | ► | 👫 | ☎ | ⛱ | ⛽ | 🏪 | 🐾 | W | S | K | T | C | Am | FJ | Lo | Pe | Pi | TA |
|---|---|---|---|---|---|---|---|---|---|---|---|---|---|---|---|---|---|---|---|---|
| (13) | wb | | W | • | • | • | • | • | • | | | | | | | | | | | |
| 11 | b | | | | | | | | | | | | | | | • | | | | | • |

---

## 77

Interstate 77 in West Virginia runs north to south for 187 miles from the Ohio state line to the Virginia state line. Portions are also I-64 and the West Virginia Turnpike. Northbound travelers should read up the chart. Southbound travelers read down the chart.

| Exit(mm) | ↗ | ✲ | ► | 👫 | ☎ | ⛱ | ⛽ | 🏪 | 🐾 | W | S | K | T | C | Am | FJ | Lo | Pe | Pi | TA |
|---|---|---|---|---|---|---|---|---|---|---|---|---|---|---|---|---|---|---|---|---|
| 170 | b | | | | | | | | | | | | | | w | | | | | | |
| (166) | b | 1 | W | • | • | • | • | • | • | | | | | | | | | | | |
| 138 | b | | | | | | | | | | e | | | | | | | | | | |
| 95 | b | | | | | | | | | | | e | | | w | | | | | | |

*N ↕ S*

| Exit(mm) | ⤢ | ★ | 🔀 | 🚻 | ☎ | ⛺ | 🛢 | 🚮 | 🐾 | W | S | K | T | C | Am | FJ | Lo | Pe | Pi | TA |
|---|---|---|---|---|---|---|---|---|---|---|---|---|---|---|---|---|---|---|---|---|
| (72) | nb | 2 | S | • | • | • | • | • | | | | | | | | | | | | |
| (69) | sb | | R | • | • | • | • | | • | | | | | | | | | | | |
| 48 | b | | | | | | | | | e+ | | | | | | | | | | |
| (45) | b | 2 | S | • | • | • | • | | | | | | | | | | | | | |
| 44 | b | | | | | | | | | | | | | w | | | | | | |
| (18) | sb | 3 | T | | | | | | | | | | | | | | | | | |
| (17) | nb | 4 | S | • | • | • | • | • | | | | | | | | | | | | |
| 9 | b | | W | • | • | • | • | | • | | | w | | w | | | | | | |

1) Welcome Center (southbound), Rest Area (northbound)
2) Gas, Food
3) Scenic Vista
4) Gas, Food, Scenic Vista

 Interstate 79 in West Virginia runs north to south for 161 miles from the Pennsylvania state line to I-77 exit 104 near Charleston. Northbound travelers should read up the chart. Southbound travelers read down the chart.

| Exit(mm) | ⤢ | ★ | 🔀 | 🚻 | ☎ | ⛺ | 🛢 | 🚮 | 🐾 | W | S | K | T | C | Am | FJ | Lo | Pe | Pi | TA |
|---|---|---|---|---|---|---|---|---|---|---|---|---|---|---|---|---|---|---|---|---|
| (159) | sb | | W | • | • | • | • | • | • | | | | | | | | | | | |
| 152 | b | | | | | | | | | | | w | | | | | | | | |
| 133 | b | | | | | | | | | | | | | e | | | | | | |
| 132 | b | | | | | | | | | e | e | | | | | | | | | |
| (123) | b | | R | • | • | • | • | • | • | | | | | | | | | | | |
| 121 | b | | | | | | | | | w | | | | | | | | | | |
| 119 | b | | | | | | | | | | | e | | | | | | | | |
| 117 | b | | | | | | | | | e | | | | | | | | | | |
| 99 | b | | | | | | | | | e | | | | | | | | | | |
| (85) | b | | R | • | • | • | • | • | • | | | | | | | | | | | |
| (49) | b | | R | • | • | • | • | • | • | | | | | | | | | | | |
| 9 | b | | | | | | | | | | | w | | | | | | | | |

 Interstate 81 in West Virginia runs north to south for 26 miles from the Maryland state line to the Virginia state line. Northbound travelers should read up the chart. Southbound travelers read down the chart.

| Exit(mm) | ⤢ | ★ | 🔀 | 🚻 | ☎ | ⛺ | 🛢 | 🚮 | 🐾 | W | S | K | T | C | Am | FJ | Lo | Pe | Pi | TA |
|---|---|---|---|---|---|---|---|---|---|---|---|---|---|---|---|---|---|---|---|---|
| (25) | sb | | W | • | • | • | | | • | | | | | | | | | | | |
| 13 | b | | | | | | | | | | | e | | e | | | | | | |
| (2) | nb | | W | • | • | • | • | | • | | | | | | | | | | | |

# Wisconsin

| Interstate | Page |
| --- | --- |
| 39 | 215 |
| 43 | 216 |
| 90 | 217 |
| 94 | 217 |
| 894 | 218 |

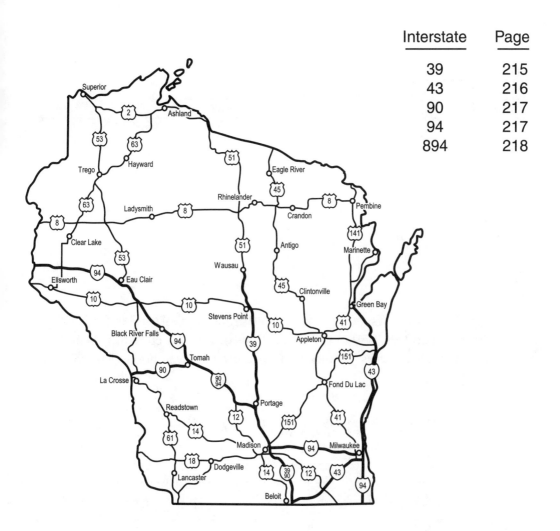

Interstate 39 in Wisconsin is about 205 miles long. It runs north to south from US 51 in Merrill to the Illinois state line. Part of it is also shared with I-90 and I-94. Northbound travelers should read up the chart. Southbound travelers read down the chart.

| Exit(mm) | ↗ | * | ⬗ | 🚻 | 🧍 | ☎ | ⛱ | 🛢 | 🏨 | 🐾 | W | S | K | T | C | Am | FJ | Lo | Pe | Pi | TA |
| --- | --- | --- | --- | --- | --- | --- | --- | --- | --- | --- | --- | --- | --- | --- | --- | --- | --- | --- | --- | --- | --- |
| N  208 | b | | | | | | | | | | | | w | | | | | | | | |
| 188 | b | | | | | | | | | | | e | e | | | | | | | | |
| S (183) | sb | T | | • | | | • | | | | | | | | | | | | | | |

| Exit(mm) | ↗ | ★ | 🔀 | 🚻 | ☎ | ⛱ | 🛢 | 🏪 | 🐾 | | W | S | K | T | C | Am | FJ | Lo | Pe | Pi | TA |
|---|---|---|---|---|---|---|---|---|---|---|---|---|---|---|---|---|---|---|---|---|---|
| (178) | nb | T | • | | • | | | | | | | | | | | | | | | | |
| 158 | b | | | | | | | | | | e | | e | | | | | | | | |
| (120) | sb | R | • | • | • | • | | | • | | | | | | | | | | | | |
| (118) | nb | R | • | • | • | • | | | • | | | | | | | | | | | | |
| 92 | b | | | | | | | | | | e | | | | | | | | | | |
| (113) | b | R | • | • | • | • | | | • | | | | | | | | | | | | |
| 132 | b | | | | | | | | | | | | | | | | | | | | • |
| 135a | b | | | | | | | | | | | | w | | w | | | | | | |
| 160 | b | | | | | | | | | | | | | | | | | | • | | |
| (168) | sb | R | • | • | • | • | | | • | | | | | | | | | | | | |
| 171a | b | | | | | | | | | | w | | w | w | e | | | | | | |
| 171b | nb | | | | | | | | | | w | | w | w | | | | | | | |
| 171c | b | | | | | | | | | | | | | | | | | | | | • |
| 185a | b | | | | | | | | | | w | | | | | | | | | • | |
| (187) | nb | W | • | • | • | • | | | • | | | | | | | | | | | | |

Interstate 43 in Wisconsin runs north to south for 192 miles from US 41 in Green Bay to I-90/I-39 in Beloit. Portions of it is shared with I-94 and I-894. Northbound travelers should read up the chart. Southbound travelers read down the chart.

| Exit(mm) | ↗ | ★ | 🔀 | 🚻 | ☎ | ⛱ | 🛢 | 🏪 | 🐾 | | W | S | K | T | C | Am | FJ | Lo | Pe | Pi | TA |
|---|---|---|---|---|---|---|---|---|---|---|---|---|---|---|---|---|---|---|---|---|---|
| 183 | b | | | | | | | | | | w+ | | w+ | | | | | | | | |
| (168) | b | R | • | • | • | • | | | • | | | | | | | | | | | | |
| 149 | b | | | | | | | | | | e | | | | | | | | | | |
| 126 | b | | | | | | | | | | e | | | | | | | | | | |
| 96 | b | | | | | | | | | | e | | | | | | | | | | |
| 92 | b | | | | | | | | | | | | | w | | | | | | | |
| 314a | b | | | | | | | | | | | | e | | | | | | | | |
| 9a | sb | | | | | | | | | | | | e | e | | | | | | | |
| 9 | nb | | | | | | | | | | | | e | e | | | | | | | |
| 60 | b | sb | | | | | | | | | w | | e | | | | | | | | |
| 57 | b | | | | | | | | | | w+ | | | w | | | | | | | |
| 43 | b | | | | | | | | | | w | | | | | | | | | | |
| (32) | b | R | • | • | • | • | | | • | | | | | | | | | | | | |
| 21 | b | | | | | | | | | | e | | w | | | | | | | | |

Interstate 90 in Wisconsin runs east to west for 188 miles from the Illinois state line to the Minnesota state line. Parts of it are shared with I-39 and I-94. Eastbound travelers should read up the chart. Westbound travelers read down the chart.

| Exit(mm) | | ⤴ | ★ | 🅿 | 🚻 | ☎ | 🍽 | ⛽ | 🏪 | 🐾 | W | S | K | T | C | Am | FJ | Lo | Pe | Pi | TA |
|---|---|---|---|---|---|---|---|---|---|---|---|---|---|---|---|---|---|---|---|---|---|
| (187) | wb | W | • | • | • | • | • | | | • | | | | | | | | | | | |
| 185a | b | | | | | | | | | | s | | | | | | | | | • | |
| 171c | b | | | | | | | | | | | | | | | | | | | | • |
| 171b | wb | | | | | | | | | | s | | s | s | | | | | | | |
| 171a | b | | | | | | | | | | s | | s | s | n | | | | | | |
| (168) | eb | R | • | • | • | • | • | | | • | | | | | | | | | | | |
| 160 | b | | | | | | | | | | | | | | | • | | | | | |
| 135a | b | | | | | | | | | | | | s | | s | | | | | | |
| 132 | b | | | | | | | | | | | | | | | | | | | | • |
| (113) | b | R | • | • | • | • | • | | | • | | | | | | | | | | | |
| 108a | b | | | | | | | | | | | | | | | | | • | | | |
| 92 | b | | | | | | | | | | | | | | n | | | | | | |
| 89 | b | | | | | | | | | | s | | | | | | | | | | |
| (75) | wb | R | • | • | • | • | • | | | • | | | | | | | | | | | |
| (74) | eb | R | • | • | • | • | • | | | • | | | | | | | | | | | |
| 69 | b | | | | | | | | | | s | | s | | | | | | | • | |
| 25 | b | | | | | | | | | | n+ | | | | | | | | | | |
| (22) | wb | R | • | • | • | • | • | | | • | | | | | | | | | | | |
| (20) | eb | R | • | • | • | • | • | | | • | | | | | | | | | | | |
| 5 | b | | | | | | | | | | n | | | s | | | | | | | |
| 4 | b | | | | | | | | | | | | s | s | | | | | | | |
| (1) | eb | W | • | • | • | • | • | | | • | | | | | | | | | | | |

Interstate 94 runs east to west for about 350 miles from the Illinois state line to the Minnesota state line. Portions are shared with I-39, I-43, and I-90. Eastbound travelers should read up the chart. Westbound travelers read down the chart.

| Exit(mm) | | ⤴ | ★ | 🅿 | 🚻 | ☎ | 🍽 | ⛽ | 🏪 | 🐾 | W | S | K | T | C | Am | FJ | Lo | Pe | Pi | TA |
|---|---|---|---|---|---|---|---|---|---|---|---|---|---|---|---|---|---|---|---|---|---|
| 347 | b | W | • | • | • | • | • | | | • | | | | | | | | | | | |
| 344 | b | | | | | | | | | | | | | w | | | | | | | |
| 333 | b | | | | | | | | | | | | | | | | | | | • | |
| 329 | b | | | | | | | | | | | | | | | | | | | | • |
| 322 | b | | | | | | | | | | | | | | | | | | • | | • |

| Exit(mm) | ↗ | * | ⬈ | 🚻 | ☎ | ⛱ | ♿ | ⛽ | 🐾 | W | S | K | T | C | Am | FJ | Lo | Pe | Pi | TA |
|---|---|---|---|---|---|---|---|---|---|---|---|---|---|---|---|---|---|---|---|---|
| 314a | b | | | | | | | | | | | n | | | | | | | | |
| 297 | b | | | | | | | | | | | n+ | s | | | | | | | |
| 287 | b | | | | | | | | | | s | | s | | | | | | | |
| (264) | wb | | R | • | • | • | • | | • | | | | | | | | | | | |
| (261) | eb | | R | • | • | • | • | | • | | | | | | | | | | | |
| 135a | b | | | | | | | | | | | s | | s | | | | | | |
| 132 | b | | | | | | | | | | | | | | | | | | | • |
| (113) | b | | R | • | • | • | • | | • | | | | | | | | | | | |
| 108a | b | | | | | | | | | | | | | | | | | • | | |
| 92 | b | | | | | | | | | | | | n | | | | | | | |
| 89 | b | | | | | | | | | | s | | | | | | | | | |
| (75) | wb | | R | • | • | • | • | | • | | | | | | | | | | | |
| (74) | eb | | R | • | • | • | • | | • | | | | | | | | | | | |
| 69 | b | | | | | | | | | | s | s | | | | | | | • | |
| 143 | b | | | | | | | | | | s | | | | | | | | | |
| (124) | eb | | R | • | • | • | • | | • | | | | | | | | | | | |
| (122) | wb | 1 | R | • | • | • | • | | • | | | | | | | | | | | |
| 116 | b | | | | | | | | | | s | | | | | | • | | | |
| 88 | b | | | | | | | | | | | | | | • | | | | | |
| 70 | b | | | | | | | | | | n | n | n | | | | | | | |
| (43) | b | | R | • | • | • | • | | • | | | | | | | | | | | |
| 41 | b | | | | | | | | | | | n | s | | | | | | | |
| 4 | b | | | | | | | | | | | | | | | | | | | • |
| 2 | b | | W | • | • | • | • | | • | | s | | n | | | | | | | |

(Left margin direction indicators: E ↕ W segments)

1) Scenic Vista

Interstate 894 is a 10-mile route in Milwaukee between Interstate 94 and Interstate 43. Exit numbering increases in a counter-clockwise direction.

| Exit(mm) | ↗ | * | ⬈ | 🚻 | ☎ | ⛱ | ♿ | ⛽ | 🐾 | W | S | K | T | C | Am | FJ | Lo | Pe | Pi | TA |
|---|---|---|---|---|---|---|---|---|---|---|---|---|---|---|---|---|---|---|---|---|
| 9a | wb | | | | | | | | | | | | s | s | | | | | | | |
| 9 | eb | | | | | | | | | | | | s | s | | | | | | | |
| 2a | b | | | | | | | | | | | | w | | | | | | | | |
| 1d | b | | | | | | | | | | | w | | | | | | | | | |

# Wyoming

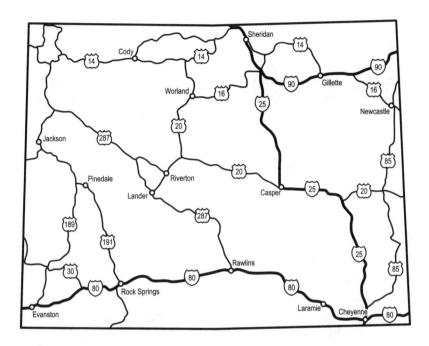

| Interstate | Page |
| --- | --- |
| 25 | 219 |
| 80 | 220 |
| 90 | 221 |

**25**  Interstate 25 in Wyoming runs north to south for 300 miles from I-90 in Buffalo to the Colorado state line. Northbound travelers should read up the chart. Southbound travelers read down the chart.

| Exit(mm) | ⤢ | ★ | ⬈ | 👫 | 🚹 | ⛽ | 🍴 | 🛏 | 🏨 | 🌃 | W | S | K | T | C | Am | FJ | Lo | Pe | Pi | TA |
| --- | --- | --- | --- | --- | --- | --- | --- | --- | --- | --- | --- | --- | --- | --- | --- | --- | --- | --- | --- | --- | --- |
| N (274) | b | 1 | T | | | | | | | | | | | | | | | | | | |
| 254 | b | | R | • | • | • | | | • | | | | | | | | | | | | |
| S (219) | b | 1 | T | | | | | | | | | | | | | | | | | | |

| Exit(mm) | ↗ | ✱ | ⬩ | 🚻 | ☎ | 🏕 | 🏪 | 🚐 | 🐎 | W | S | K | T | C | Am | FJ | Lo | Pe | Pi | TA |
|---|---|---|---|---|---|---|---|---|---|---|---|---|---|---|---|---|---|---|---|---|
| 185 | b | | | | | | | | | w | w | w | w | | • | | | | | |
| (175) | sb | 1 | T | | | | | | | | | | | | | | | | | |
| (171) | nb | 1 | T | | | | | | | | | | | | | | | | | |
| (153) | b | 1 | T | | | | | | | | | | | | | | | | | |
| (129) | b | 1 | T | | | | | | | | | | | | | | | | | |
| 126 | b | | R | • | • | • | | • | • | | | | | | | | | | | |
| (91) | b | | R | • | | • | | | • | | | | | | | | | | | |
| (67) | nb | 1 | T | | | | | | | | | | | | | | | | | |
| (65) | b | 1 | T | | | | | | | | | | | | | | | | | |
| 54 | b | | R | • | • | • | | • | • | | | | | | | | | | | |
| 7 | b | | W | • | • | • | | • | • | | | | | | | | | | • | • |

(Left margin, direction: N ↕ S)

*1) No Facilities*

Interstate 80 in Wyoming runs east to west for about 403 miles from the Nebraska state line to the Utah state line. Eastbound travelers should read up the chart. Westbound travelers read down the chart.

| Exit(mm) | ↗ | ✱ | ⬩ | 🚻 | ☎ | 🏕 | 🏪 | 🚐 | 🐎 | W | S | K | T | C | Am | FJ | Lo | Pe | Pi | TA |
|---|---|---|---|---|---|---|---|---|---|---|---|---|---|---|---|---|---|---|---|---|
| 401 | b | | W | • | • | • | • | | • | | | | | | | | | | | |
| 377 | b | | | | | | | | | | | | | | | | | | | • |
| (343) | b | 1 | T | | | | | | | | | | | | | | | | | |
| (341) | b | 1 | T | | | | | | | | | | | | | | | | | |
| (333) | b | 1 | T | | | | | | | | | | | | | | | | | |
| 323 | b | | R | • | • | • | | | • | | | | | | | | | | | |
| 316 | b | | | | | | | | | n+ | | | | | | | | | | |
| 310 | b | | | | | | | | | | | n+ | | | | | | | • | • |
| (307) | b | 1 | T | | | | | | | | | | | | | | | | | |
| 267 | b | | R | • | • | • | | | • | | | | | | | | | | | |
| (262) | b | 1 | T | | | | | | | | | | | | | | | | | |
| 228 | b | | R | • | • | • | | | • | | | | | | | | | | | |
| 214 | b | | | | | | | | | | | | | | | | | | | • |
| 209 | b | | | | | | | | | | | | | | | | • | | | |
| (190) | wb | 1 | T | | | | | | | | | | | | | | | | | |
| (189) | eb | | T | | | • | | | | | | | | | | | | | | |
| 173 | b | | | | | | | | | | | | | | | | • | | | |
| (144) | b | | R | • | • | • | | | • | | | | | | | | | | | |
| (143) | b | 1 | T | | | | | | | | | | | | | | | | | |
| (135) | b | 1 | T | | | | | | | | | | | | | | | | | |
| 104 | b | | | | | | | | | | | | | | | | • | | | |

(Left margins, directions: E ↕ W / E ↕ W)

| Exit(mm) | ↗ | * | Facilities | W | S | K | T | C | Am | FJ | Lo | Pe | Pi | TA |
|---|---|---|---|---|---|---|---|---|---|---|---|---|---|---|
| 102 | b | | | s | | | | | | | | | | |
| (71) | b | 1 | T | | | | | | | | | | | |
| (60) | b | 1 | T | | | | | | | | | | | |
| (54) | eb | 1 | T | | | | | | | | | | | |
| (49) | wb | 1 | T | | | | | | | | | | | |
| 41 | b | | R • • •  • | | | | | | | | | | | |
| (33) | eb | 1 | T | | | | | | | | | | | |
| 30 | b | | | | | | | | | | | | | • |
| (27) | b | 1 | T | | | | | | | | | | | |
| (14) | b | 1 | T | | | | | | | | | | | |
| 6 | b | | W • • • • • • • | | | | | | | | | • | | |
| 5 | b | | | n | | | | | | | | | | |
| 3 | b | | | | | | | | • | | | | | |

E ↕ W

*1) No Facilities*

Interstate 90 in Wyoming runs east to west for 208 miles from the South Dakota state line to the Montana state line. Eastbound travelers should read up the chart. Westbound travelers read down the chart.

| Exit(mm) | ↗ | * | Facilities | W | S | K | T | C | Am | FJ | Lo | Pe | Pi | TA |
|---|---|---|---|---|---|---|---|---|---|---|---|---|---|---|
| 189 | b | | W • • • •  • | | | | | | | | | | | |
| (177) | b | 1 | T | | | | | | | | | | | |
| (171) | b | 1 | T | | | | | | | | | | | |
| (163) | b | 1 | T | | | | | | | | | | | |
| 153 | b | | R • • •  • | | | | | | | | | | | |
| (138) | b | 1 | T | | | | | | | | | | | |
| 126 | b | | | s | | s | | | • | | | | | |
| (110) | b | 1 | T | | | | | | | | | | | |
| 88 | b | | R • • •  • | | | | | | | | | | | |
| (68) | b | 1 | T | | | | | | | | | | | |
| (59) | b | 1 | T | | | | | | | | | | | |
| (39) | wb | 2 | T | | | | | | | | | | | |
| (31) | eb | 1 | T | | | | | | | | | | | |
| 25 | b | | | s | | | | | | | | | | |
| 23 | b | | W • • •  • • | | | | | | | | | | | |
| 20 | b | | | | | s | | | | | | | | |
| (15) | wb | 1 | T | | | | | | | | | | | |

E ↕ W

*1) No Facilities*
*2) Scenic Vista*

# RV Dump Station Locator

With this RV Dump Station Locator, you can easily find dump stations along Interstate highways for emptying your RV's holding tanks. Most dump stations listed here are located in travel centers like Flying J. Others are in rest areas or welcome centers, city and county parks, gas stations, and other places.

Like the rest of this book, the list is arranged alphabetically by state and Interstate highway. Southbound and westbound travelers should read down the chart. Northbound and eastbound travelers read up the chart. Exit or mile marker numbers are provided for each listing; mile markers are surrounded by parentheses.

To learn about dump stations not along Interstate highways or to obtain up-to-date information, please visit our web site: www.rvdumps.com

## Alabama I-10

| | |
|---|---|
| (66) | Welcome Center (wb) |
| 53 | Oasis Travel Center |
| 44 | Econ Family Center |
| 44 | Love's Travel Stop |
| 22 | Shady Acre RV Park, no fee. *Comments:* From exit go south on AL 163 to first light, turn on Old Military Rd, one block on the right. |
| (1) | Welcome Center (eb) |

## Alabama I-20

| | |
|---|---|
| (213) | Welcome Center (wb) |
| 104 | Flying J Travel Plaza |
| (85) | Rest Area |
| 77 | TA Travel Center |
| (39) | Rest Area (wb) |
| (38) | Rest Area (eb) |
| (.5) | Welcome Center (eb) |

## Alabama I-59

| | |
|---|---|
| (241) | Welcome Center (sb) |
| (168) | Rest Area (sb) |
| (165) | Rest Area (nb) |
| 104 | Flying J Travel Plaza |
| (85) | Rest Area |
| 77 | TA Travel Center |
| (39) | Rest Area (sb) |
| (38) | Rest Area (nb) |
| (.5) | Welcome Center (nb) |

## Alabama I-65

| | |
|---|---|
| (364) | Welcome Center (sb) |
| 334 | Pilot Travel Center |
| (302) | Rest Area |
| 264 | Flying J Travel Plaza |
| (213) | Rest Area |
| (134) | Rest Area |
| (89) | Rest Area (sb) |

(85)   Welcome Center (nb)
69     Conoco Minute Stop
19     Pilot Travel Center

## Alabama I-85

(78)   Welcome Center (sb)
(44)   Rest Area

## Arizona I-8

119    Holt's Shell Truck Stop
115    Love's Travel Stop
115    McDonalds
115    Subway
115    Texaco

## Arizona I-10

340    Rip Griffin Travel Center
302    Gas City Truck Stop
268    Mr T's Self Serve. *Comments:* Dump is
       to the back on the west end.
268    Triple T Truck Stop
254    Arizona Roadrunner RV Service Center,
       free. *Comments:* From exit go east to
       third traffic light, turn left on Flowing
       Wells Rd and go north about one mile.
208    Flying J Travel Plaza
208    Pilot Travel Center
203    TA Travel Center
200    Love's Travel Stop
137    Flying J Travel Plaza
114    Love's Travel Stop
94     El Dorado Hot Springs. *Comments:*
       Dump is free with purchase of a hot
       mineral water soak, located 1/4 mile west
       of 411th Ave.
45     Tomahawk Auto & Truck Plaza, $5 fee
17     Love's Travel Stop
1      Flying J Travel Plaza

## Arizona I-17

287    Shell Gas Station, $5 fee
205    Grand Service Station, $5 fee.
       *Comments:* On N 35th Ave, one mile
       west of exit.

## Arizona I-40

255    Flying J Travel Plaza

253    Pilot Travel Center
201    Unocal 76, $8 or free with fuel
198    Conoco, free
59     Love's Travel Stop
53     Flying J Travel Plaza
48     Mobile Service Station, free

## Arkansas I-30

46     Love's Travel Stop
44     Rip Griffin Travel Center
7      Flying J Travel Plaza

## Arkansas I-40

280    Flying J Travel Plaza
280    Pilot Travel Center
278    Flash Market
233    Love's Travel Stop
193    T Ricks RV Park, $4
150    Burns Park (city park), $5 fee
84     Flying J Travel Plaza
84     Pilot Travel Center
55     Highway 109 Truck Plaza

## Arkansas I-55

63     Phoenix Truck Plaza
278    Flash Market
4      Flying J Travel Plaza
4      Pilot Travel Center

## Arkansas I-530

34     Big Red Travel Plaza

## Arkansas I-540

29     Silver Bridge Auto & Truck Plaza

## California I-5

681b   Exxon Service Station. *Comments:*
       Northbound travelers use Exit 680 (CA
       299 / Lake Blvd) and go west to N
       Market St, then north to Caterpillar Rd.
667    Shell Service Station
630    TA Travel Center
(608)  Willows Rest Area
537    Bill Lowe's Tires, free.
537    Yolo County Fairgrounds, free
485    Flying J Travel Plaza

(445)  Westley Rest Area
407  TA Travel Center
257  TA Travel Center
219  Petro Stopping Center
219  TA Travel Center
205  Flying J Travel Plaza
(204)  Tejon Pass Rest Area
110  Anaheim Resort RV Park, a fee is charged. *Comments:* From exit follow Ball Rd east to Anaheim Blvd and then south to Midway Dr, turn right (west).
96  El Toro RV Service Center
96  McMahon RV
79  Doheny State Beach, must pay day-use fee
(60)  Aliso Creek Rest Area
54c  Oceanside Harbor Boat Ramp, free. *Comments:* On west side of harbor, circle around south side to approach, across from boat launch area.
41b  San Elijo State Beach, $4 fee. *Comments:* From exit, follow Encinitas Blvd west to Pacific Coast Hwy 101, turn south and go approximately two miles to state beach.
22  Mission Bay Information Center, free
21  South Shores Boat Launch. *Comments:* Follow Sea World Dr to South Shores Boat Launch just before Sea World on right.

## California I-8

166  Sleepy Hollow RV Park, $5. *Comments:* Located 1.25 miles south of exit.
164  Shell Service Station, fee varies
115  Imperial 8 Travel Center
(108)  Sunbeam Rest Area
51  Buckman Springs Rest Area
20  Vacationer RV Resort, $10

## California I-10

222  Wiley's Well Rest Area
146  Love's Travel Stop
146  TA Travel Center
130  Flying J Travel Plaza, free with fuel purchase, $5 without. *Comments:* Very difficult access for large vehicles. There is little turn room to maneuver. Suggest checking it out before entering.
104  Shell Gas Station

76  Mission RV Park, $8
50  Arrow Trailer Supply, $3. *Comments:* Two miles south of exit on W Holt Blvd.
50  Green's Trailer Supply, $2. *Comments:* Two miles south of exit on N Benson Ave.

## California I-15

246  Ultra Gas Station, $5
178  Flying J Travel Plaza
178  Rip Griffin Travel Center
122  Glen Helen Regional Park, $5. *Comments:* You must go to the main entrance to pay the fee.
58  Pechanga Casino RV Park, $6. *Comments:* From exit go east to Pechanga Pkwy and turn right to Casino. Pay fee at office before dumping.
58  Temecula Valley RV Service Center

## California I-80

109  Loomis RV Park, $7. *Comments:* North on Sierra College Blvd to Taylor Rd and turn right.
105a  Chevron Station, $4. *Comments:* Free dump with propane or fuel purchase.
94a  Arco Gas Station, $3.50. *Comments:* Take Watt Ave exit off I-80 or Capital City Freeway (Bus I-80) and go south across Auburn Blvd, entrance on right.
85  Sacramento 49er Travel Plaza
63  Arco Gas Station, free
41  Camping World

## California I-880

16  Shell Service Station, $8. *Comments:* Dump is free with with $50 fill-up.

## Colorado I-25

269b  Fort Collins CoOp, no fee. *Comments:* CoOp is on NW Service Road, just north of CO 14. Dump station is free but the business appreciates you buying fuel or other items if you use dump.
269b  Phillips 66 gas station, $2. *Comments:* Dump is free with fill-up.
184  Town of Castle Rock Service Center,

free. *Comments:* From exit, go west to Santa Fe Dr and turn south (left), follow to Justice Way and turn east (left). Watch for one story brick building on right, go thru gate, dump is on right, open Mon-Fri 8am to 5pm

161   Conoco Fuel Stop, $5. *Comments:* Dump is closed in winter. No set schedule for opening and closing. Best to call ahead (719-481-2128) in the fall or early spring.

139   Pikes Peak Traveland, $8. *Comments:* From exit go east to Academy Blvd. Go north on Academy Blvd to Platte Ave and then east one mile.

(115)  Rest Area (nb)
(112)  Rest Area (sb)
101    Amoco

## Colorado I-70

(437)  Welcome Center (wb)
405    Shady Grove Campground, $5
383    Rest Area
285    Flying J Travel Plaza
278    TA Travel Center
267    Shell Gas Station, $5. *Comments:* Dump is free with gas purchase.
163    Rest Area
90     Rest Area. *Comments:* From exit, go north and follow rest area signs. Dump is located on the right as you exit the rest area.
19     Welcome Center

## Colorado I-76

180    Welcome Center
125    Rest Area
22     Co-op, no fee. *Comments:* From exit travel west about 4 miles to Co-op.

## Colorado I-225

4      Cherry Creek State Park, $5

## Connecticut I-84

71     TA Travel Center
(85)   Welcome Center (wb)
(42)   Rest Area (eb). *Comments:* Dump station

is closed Nov 1 to Apr 1.
2      Welcome Center (eb)

## Connecticut I-91

(22)   Rest Area (nb)
(15)   Rest Area (sb)

## Connecticut I-95

56     TA Travel Center

## Florida I-4

10     Flying J Travel Plaza
7      Singh 301

## Florida I-10

303    Lake City KOA, $6. *Comments:* One mile north of exit.
258    Yogi Bear's Jellystone Park & RV Resort, $8. *Comments:* From exit, go south 200 feet to Old Saint Augustine Rd and then west about 1 mile to park.
192    Flying J Travel Plaza
192    Pilot Truck Stop, free. *Comments:* Dump station is adjacent to the large propane tank to the north of the building with plenty of turning room.
31     KOA north of exit, $10

## Florida I-75

368    Petro Stopping Center
285    Flying J Travel Plaza
9a     C.B. Smith Park (county park)

## Florida I-95

305    Flying J Travel Plaza
273    Texaco Fuel Stop
131b   Flying J Travel Plaza
31     Easterlin Park (county park)
21     Topeekeegee Yugnee Park (county park)

## Georgia I-16

(46)   Rest Area (wb)
(44)   Rest Area (eb)

## Georgia I-20

| | |
|---|---|
| (201) | Welcome Center (wb) |
| (182) | Rest Area |
| 114 | Pilot Travel Center |
| (108) | Rest Area (wb) |
| (103) | Rest Area (eb) |
| 9 | Love's Travel Stop |

## Georgia I-75

| | |
|---|---|
| 326 | Pilot Travel Center |
| 320 | Flying J Travel Plaza |
| (319) | Rest Area (sb) |
| (308) | Rest Area (nb) |
| 296 | TA Travel Center |
| 201 | Flying J Travel Plaza |
| 138 | Happy Store |
| 135 | Perry Welcome Center, free |
| (118) | Rest Area (sb) |
| (108) | Rest Area (nb) |
| 101 | Pilot Travel Center |
| (85) | Rest Area (nb) |
| (76) | Rest Area (sb) |
| 60 | Pilot Travel Center |
| (48) | Rest Area (sb) |
| (47) | Rest Area (nb) |
| 11 | Wilco Travel Plaza |
| 5 | Eagles Roost RV Resort, $5 |
| 2 | Flying J Travel Plaza |

## Georgia I-85

| | |
|---|---|
| (176) | Welcome Center (sb) |
| 160 | Flying J Travel Plaza |
| 160 | Petro Stopping Center |
| 147 | Pilot Travel Center |
| 41 | Pilot Travel Center |
| (.5) | Welcome Center (nb) |

## Georgia I-95

| | |
|---|---|
| (41) | Rest Area (sb) |
| 29 | Flying J Travel Plaza |
| 3 | Pilot Travel Center |
| 1 | Welcome Center (nb) |
| 1 | Cisco Travel Plaza |

## Georgia I-185

| | |
|---|---|
| 12 | Welcome Center |

## Georgia I-475

| | |
|---|---|
| (8) | Rest Area (nb) |

## Idaho I-15

| | |
|---|---|
| 167 | Scoggins RV Camp |
| 119 | Grandview Texaco |
| 113 | Yellowstone Truck Stop |
| 108 | North Bingham Recreation Site (County Park) |
| 93 | Chevron |
| 93 | Flying J Travel Plaza |
| 71 | Bannock County Fairgrounds. *Comments:* From exit go east on Pocatello Creek Rd, north on Olympus Dr, and west on Fairway Dr. |
| 71 | Willie's Chevron |
| 47 | McCammon Chevron |
| 31 | Flags West Truck Stop |

## Idaho I-84

| | |
|---|---|
| 216 | Village of Trees RV Resort |
| 208 | Cassia County Fairgrounds, free. *Comments:* Just north of intersection of US 30 and Hiland Ave. |
| 194 | Greenwood Pioneer Stop |
| 168 | Honker's Mini Mart |
| 157 | Burt Harbaugh Motors. *Comments:* One mile north of exit. |
| 157 | Intermountain Motor Homes & RV Park |
| 157 | City maintained RV dump station. *Comments:* Located at 210 S Shohone St, one block west of N Idaho St (ID 46). |
| 157 | Wendell Gas & Oil |
| 71 | Boise Stage Stop |
| 54 | Flying J Travel Plaza |
| 36 | Jackson Food Store |
| 29 | Flying J Travel Plaza |
| 29 | Sage Travel Plaza |

## Idaho I-86

| | |
|---|---|
| 61 | Big Bear Chevron |
| 58 | City Water Treatment Plant. *Comments:* On Batiste Rd. |

## Idaho I-90

| | |
|---|---|
| 49 | RV dump station. *Comments:* RV dump station on Bunker Ave across from Silver |

Mountain Gondola Base.
45     KOA, $10
43     Exxon Station
15     Big Y Truck Stop
12     Jifi Stop-N-Shop
5      Conoco Gas Station and Convenience
       Store. *Comments:* North on Spokane St,
       right on Seltice Way to Conoco.
2      Flying J Travel Plaza

## Illinois I-39

1      Flying J Travel Plaza
99     Petro Stopping Center

## Illinois I-55

241    Public campground. *Comments:* In Des
       Plaines Fish & Wildlife Area.
109    Love's Travel Stop, no fee
82     Auburn Travel Center

## Illinois I-57

(332)  Welcome Center
283    R&R RV Sales, $10
160    Flying J Travel Plaza
83     Love's Travel Stop

## Illinois I-70

160    Flying J Travel Plaza

## Illinois I-74

160a   TA Travel Center
(114)  Rest Area
(30)   Rest Area (wb)
(28)   Rest Area (eb)

## Illinois I-80

130    Empress Casino and RV Park, no fee.
       *Comments:* Directly behind the hotel,
       easy entry and exit with tow vehicle.
77     Flying J Travel Plaza
75     Tiki Truck Stop

## Illinois I-90

1      Flying J Travel Plaza

## Illinois I-94

1      TA Travel Center

## Illinois I-270

6b     Flying J Travel Plaza

## Indiana I-64

25b    Flying J Travel Plaza
25b    Pilot Travel Center
(7)    Welcome Center (eb)

## Indiana I-65

175    Lafayette Travel Trailer Sales, $5.
       *Comments:* 1/2 mile west of exit.
139    Flying J Travel Plaza
99     Pilot Travel Center
95     Flying J Travel Plaza

## Indiana I-69

78     Crazy D's

## Indiana I-70

149b   Love's Travel Stop
149a   Tom Raper RVs, free. *Comments:* Dump
       station is just off Rich Rd, near the Body
       Shop and Trailers Division building.
123    Flying J Travel Plaza
115    Gas America

## Indiana I-74

4      Flying J Travel Plaza
(1)    Welcome Center (eb)

## Indiana I-80

(126)  Rest Area
(90)   Rest Area
(56)   Rest Area
9a     Flying J Travel Plaza

## Indiana I-90

(126)  Rest Area
(90)   Rest Area
(56)   Rest Area

## Indiana I-94

43   Welcome Center (wb)
22a  Pilot Travel Center
9a   Flying J Travel Plaza

## Indiana I-465

4    Flying J Travel Plaza

## Iowa I-29

(139)  Welcome Center (sb) / Rest Area (nb)
(110)  Rest Area
(80)   Rest Area (sb)
(78)   Rest Area (nb)
(38)   Rest Area
10     Cross Roads Texaco
10     Sapp Brothers Truck Stop

## Iowa I-35

(214)  Welcome Center
(159)  Rest Area
(120)  Rest Area (nb)
(119)  Rest Area (sb)
126    Pilot Travel Center
(32)   Rest Area
(7)    Welcome Center

## Iowa I-80

292    Flying J Travel Plaza
(270)  Welcome Center (wb) / Rest Area (eb)
259    Amoco Travel Plaza
254    Kum 'n Go, no fee. *Comments:* one-half mile south of Hoover Presidential Library, no charge but you must go inside gas station to ask for the key.
(237)  Rest Area
(208)  Rest Area
197    Brooklyn 80 Amoco
(180)  Rest Area
(147)  Rest Area
126    Pilot Travel Center
(119)  Rest Area
(81)   Rest Area (eb)
(80)   Rest Area (wb)
40     Wings America Travel Center
(19)   Welcome Center (eb) / Rest Area (wb)

## Iowa I-380

70     Deerwood City Park, $1. *Comments:* North of exit and west of River Forest Rd.
68     Flying J Travel Plaza
(13)   Rest Area

## Kansas I-35

(175)  Rest Area
127    Flying J Travel Plaza, free

## Kansas I-70

41b    Cabela's, free. *Comments:* Use I-435 Exit 13b
341    Maple Hill Truck Stop
(336)  Rest Area
(310)  Rest Area
295    Sapp Brothers Truck Stop
(294)  Rest Area
(265)  Rest Area
253    Flying J Travel Plaza
252    Thomas Park (city park). *Comments:* About 1/2 mile south of exit. Overnight parking is permitted.
(224)  Rest Area
206    The Waterin' Hole
(187)  Rest Area
(132)  Rest Area
(97)   Rest Area
53     Oasis Travel Center
(48)   Rest Area
17     Mid America Camp Inn, $5
(7)    Welcome Center (eb) / Rest Area (wb)

## Kansas I-135

(68)   Rest Area
40     Sav-A-Trip
31     Newell Truck Plaza
(23)   Rest Area
2      Wichita Wastewater Treatment Plant. *Comments:* On Industrial Dr, one mile north of exit.

## Kansas I-435

13     Cabela's, free

## Kentucky I-24

86    Flying J Travel Plaza
86    Pilot Travel Center

## Kentucky I-64

185    Flying J Travel Plaza
43    Flying J Travel Plaza
43    Waddy '76 Travel Plaza

## Kentucky I-65

116    Love's Travel Stop
81    Davis Brothers Travel Plaza
58    KOA campground, $3
28    Camping World. *Comments:* From exit
       go south on US 31W; follow signs; turn
       right on Beech Bend Rd
6    Pilot Travel Center
2    Flying J Travel Plaza

## Kentucky I-75

171    Flying J Travel Plaza
120    Kentucky Horse Park campground
41    Tourist Information Center, free
11    Pilot Travel Center

## Louisiana I-10

(270)    Rest Area (wb)
239    Big Easy Travel Plaza
236    Mardi Gras Truck Stop. *Comments:*
       Eastbound use Exit 236b, westbound use
       Exit 237.
139    Bayou Texaco Truck Stop
(121)    Rest Area
87    Frog City Travel Plaza
(67)    Rest Area
64    Jennings Travel Center

## Louisiana I-20

(184)    Welcome Center (wb) / Rest Area (eb)
171    Love's Travel Stop
(150)    Rest Area
112    Pilot Travel Center
(97)    Rest Area (wb)
(95)    Rest Area (eb)
(58)    Rest Area
5    Kelly's Truck Terminal

3    Flying J Travel Plaza
(2)    Welcome Center (eb)

## Louisiana I-49

138    Shop-A-Lott
(35)    Rest Area

## Louisiana I-55

(65)    Welcome Center (sb)

## Louisiana I-59

(1)    Welcome Center (sb)

## Maine I-95

180    Dysart's Truck Stop. *Comments:* Free
       with fuel purchase.
132    Truckers International, $2

## Maryland I-70

(39)    Welcome Center

## Maryland I-81

5    AC&T Fuel Center

## Maryland I-95

109b    TA Travel Center
100    Flying J Travel Plaza
(37)    Rest Area
25    Cherry Hill Park, $5. *Comments:* From
       exit, south to Cherry Hill Rd, turn right
       and go north one mile to park.

## Maryland I-97

10a    Washington NE KOA, $15. *Comments:*
       Located at 768 Cecil Ave N. Northbound
       travelers should use Exit 10.

## Massachusetts I-91

22    Diamond RV Centre, $7. *Comments:*
       Closed in winter. Note: Southbound
       travelers use Exit 23.

## Massachusetts I-495

53    Wastewater treatment plant, $10.
*Comments:* Located at 50 Federal Way

## Michigan I-69

184    Bisco's Truck Stop
155    Water Tower Park (city park), $3.
*Comments:* Located at 1552 N Main St, 2
1/2 miles north of exit.
81    Flying J, free

## Michigan I-75

290    Andy's Mobile, $10
251    Charlie's Country Corner
144    TA Travel Center, $2
101    Yogi Bear's Jellystone Park, $5.
*Comments:* The dump station is outside
the park's gate on the exit side of the
drive. In winter there is a drop bax at the
office door for the fee.
79    A&S RV Center, $7. *Comments:* From
exit follow University Dr west .2 miles
to N Opdyke Rd and turn right (north).
Travel north one mile to dealership.
63    Oakland County Sewage Disposal
System, free. *Comments:* Located at
29132 Stephenson Hwy. Open 7:30-3:30
Mon-Fri (except when raining).

## Michigan I-94

159    Mobil Gas Station, $2. *Comments:* Dump
is free with fill up of gas or propane

## Michigan I-96

90    Flying J, 7800 W Grand River Ave, free
52    R2C Road Service, $5. *Comments:* Site
is two miles south of exit at 6445 Alden
Nash (MI 50).

## Minnesota I-35

249    Holiday Gas Station, free. *Comments:*
Located at 9314 W Skyline Pkwy.
169    Pump N Munch
135    Citgo Gas Station, $3. *Comments:* Dump
is free with fill-up.
69    Big Steer Travel Center

45    Cabela's, free
42a    Wastewater treatment plant, no charge.
*Comments:* About one mile east of exit at
1150 Industrial Rd.
11    TA Travel Center

## Minnesota I-90

233    Amish Market Square
73    Burger King restaurant, free
45    Blue Line Travel Center

## Minnesota I-94

207    TA Travel Center
178    Clearwater Travel Plaza, $5. *Comments:*
Dump is free with fuel purchase.
171    Holiday Station
171    Pleasureland RV Center, free
147    Holiday Gas Station, free
135    Sauk River Park (city park)
103    Tom Thumb Amoco, $3. *Comments:*
Dump is free with fuel purchase.
54    Holiday Station. *Comments:* One mile
east of exit, free with fuel purchase.
50    Interstate Fuel & Food
24    Wagner City Park campground

## Minnesota I-694

43a    Shoreview Amoco. *Comments:* Free with
fill-up.

## Mississippi I-10

(74)    Welcome Center (wb)
(63)    Rest Area
44    Pilot Travel Center
31    Flying J Travel Plaza
31    Love's Travel Stop
(2)    Welcome Center

## Mississippi I-20

(164)    Welcome Center (wb)
129    Spaceway Truck Stop
(90)    Rest Area (eb)
(75)    Rest Area (wb)
68    Super Stop
47    Flying J Travel Plaza
47    Pilot Travel Center
11    Bovina Truck Stop

## Mississippi I-55

(279)  Welcome Center (sb)
(276)  Rest Area (nb)
(240)  Rest Area
174  Vaiden KOA Shell
(173)  Rest Area (sb)
(163)  Rest Area (nb)
119  Love's Travel Stop
(54)  Rest Area
51  County Junction Truck Stop
(3)  Welcome Center (nb)

## Mississippi I-59

(164)  Welcome Center (sb)
113  JR's I-59 Truck Stop
(3)  Welcome Center (nb)

## Missouri I-35

114  Walter Brothers
54  Jones Travel Mart

## Missouri I-44

226  Flying J Travel Plaza
163  Voss Truck Port
88  Speedy's Phillips 66
11a  Flying J Travel Plaza
4  Love's Travel Stop

## Missouri I-55

174b  One Stop, $4. *Comments:* Located about two miles southwest of exit.
58  Flying J Travel Plaza
19  Pilot Travel Center

## Missouri I-70

188  Flying J Travel Plaza
148  Petro Stopping Center
121  Midway Auto & Truck Plaza
49  Pilot Travel Center
28  Petro Stopping Center
28  TA Travel Center
24  Apple Travel Trailer Center

## Montana I-15

339  Cenex Gas Station, no fee

290  Valley Country Store, no fee
278  Sinclair Service Station. *Comments:* On Fox Farm Rd. Free with fuel purchase.
192  High Country Travel Plaza
164  Boulder City Park, no fee. *Comments:* No charge for use of dump but donations are accepted. City park also has free overnight parking, water, and restrooms.
63  Rocky Mountain Supply. *Comments:* Store is one mile from exit at 700 N Montana St (I-15 Bus).

## Montana I-90

495  Flying J Travel Plaza
455  Flying J Travel Plaza
437  Pelican Truck Plaza
408  Town Pump
306  Conoco Grantree Convenience Store, $3. *Comments:* Dump is free with fill-up.
298  Rocky Mountain Supply Co
278  Mable's Laundry, $5. *Comments:* From I-90 exit go south into town.
184  Pizza Hut. *Comments:* Site is one mile from exit at 202 N Main St (I-90 Bus).
101  Bretz RV & Marine, free
101  Deano's Travel Plaza
101  Harvest States Cenex
96  Crossroads Travel Center
96  Muralt's Travel Plaza

## Montana I-94

138  Cenex General Store

## Nebraska I-80

432  Flying J Travel Plaza
430  Leach Camper Sales, no fee. *Comments:* Dealer is three miles south of exit.
353  Petro Stopping Center
332  Love's Travel Stop, free
332  Streeter Park (city park). *Comments:* Located in Aurora about 3 miles north of exit. Small campground with 15 RV sites also available. Donation requested.
312  Bosselman Travel Center
312  Rich and Sons Camper Sales, $3. *Comments:* Dealer is three miles north of exit.
305  TA Travel Center

| | |
|---|---|
| 190 | Fort McPherson Campground, $3. *Comments:* Located at 12568 S Valleyview Rd, on gravel road two miles south and one mile west of exit. |
| 179 | Flying J Travel Plaza |
| 177 | Time Savers Texaco. *Comments:* About one mile north of exit. |
| 164 | Tomahawk Auto & Truck Plaza |
| 126 | TA Travel Center |
| 59 | Cabela's, free |

## Nevada I-15

| | |
|---|---|
| 122 | Virgin River Casino |
| 122 | Virgin River Food Mart |
| 46 | Hallmark Truck Center |
| 33 | TA Travel Center |
| 27 | Vegas Valley Travel Center |
| 1 | Whiskey Pete's Casino & Truck Stop |

## Nevada I-80

| | |
|---|---|
| 352 | Flying J Travel Plaza |
| 280 | Pilot Travel Center |
| (258) | Rest Area |
| 231 | Flying J Travel Plaza. *Comments:* Can also be accessed from Exit 229 or Exit 233. |
| (216) | Rest Area |
| (187) | Rest Area |
| 176 | Flying J Travel Plaza |
| (158) | Rest Area |
| 46 | Love's Travel Stop |
| (42) | Rest Area (wb) |
| 19 | TA Travel Center |

## New Hampshire I-93

| | |
|---|---|
| 34c | Cannon RV Park at Echo Lake |
| 32 | Goodie's Mobil, $5. *Comments:* One mile east of exit on Kancamagus Hwy. |
| 13 | City of Concord wastewater treatment station, $5. *Comments:* Must sign in at main office and get a pass. |

## New Hampshire I-293

| | |
|---|---|
| 2 | Wastewater treatment plant, no fee. *Comments:* South 1/4 mile on Route 3A, first right to end, follow signs, closed weekends. |

## New Jersey I-295

| | |
|---|---|
| 2c | Flying J Travel Plaza |

## New Mexico I-10

| | |
|---|---|
| 139 | TA Travel Center |
| 20 | Love's Travel Stop |

## New Mexico I-25

| | |
|---|---|
| (374) | Rest Area (nb) |
| 252 | San Felipe Pueblo Travel Center |
| 227a | TA Travel Center |
| 156 | Roadrunner Travel Center |
| 115 | Santa Fe Diner & Truck Stop |
| 75 | Public dump station. *Comments:* Maintained by the Village of Williamsburg. From exit go east .6 mile to Hyde Ave and turn south. |

## New Mexico I-40

| | |
|---|---|
| 329 | Ortega Shell Plaza |
| 277 | Love's Travel Stop |
| 194 | Phillip's 66, free |
| 194 | Rip Griffin Travel Center |
| 153 | Flying J Travel Plaza |
| 39 | Giant Travel Center |
| (22) | Welcome Center |

## New York I-90

| | |
|---|---|
| 41 | Petro Stopping Center, free |
| 48a | Flying J Travel Plaza |
| 48a | TA Travel Center |

## New York I-190

| | |
|---|---|
| 22 | Junior's Fuel Plaza |

## New York I-390

| | |
|---|---|
| 5 | TA Travel Center |

## North Carolina I-40

| | |
|---|---|
| 150 | Flying J Travel Plaza |
| (82) | Rest Area |

## North Carolina I-85

150   Flying J Travel Plaza
5     Kings Mountain Truck Plaza

## North Carolina I-95

106   TA Travel Center
75    Sadler Travel Plaza
1     Porky's Truck Stop

## North Carolina I-440

13b   College Park RV, $15

## North Dakota I-29

141   E-Z Stop Truck Stop, no fee
141   StaMart Travel Plaza
138   Big Sioux Travel Plaza
66    StaMart Travel Center, no fee
62    Flying J Travel Plaza

## North Dakota I-94

348   Petro Stopping Center
157   Cenex Station, no fee
157   Conoco/MVP, no fee
147   Freeway 147 Truck Stop
61    The General Store

## Ohio I-70

160   Love's Travel Stop
122   Flying J Travel Plaza

## Ohio I-71

218   Avalon RV Center, free
209   TA Travel Center
140   Pilot Travel Center
131   Flying J Travel Plaza
69    Flying J Travel Plaza

## Ohio I-75

135   Flying J Travel Plaza
135   Pilot Travel Center
36    Shell Gas Station

## Ohio I-76

1     TA Travel Center

## Ohio I-77

111   Beggs RV Center

## Ohio I-80

234    Flying J Travel Plaza
223    TA Travel Center
(197)  Rest Area
180    Kamper City, $10. *Comments:* From exit,
       follow OH 8 south to OH 303/Akron-
       Cleveland Rd exit. Continue straight
       through the light about one mile. Kamper
       City is on the left.
(139)  Rest Area
(77)   Rest Area
34     Fulton County Fairgrounds, $7.
       *Comments:* Dump station is in the
       southwest part of fairground. Pay the care
       takers at the mobile home in park.
(21)   Rest Area (wb)

## Ohio I-90

223    Flying J Travel Plaza
(139)  Rest Area
(77)   Rest Area
34     Fulton County Fairgrounds, $7.
       *Comments:* Dump station is in the
       southwest part of fairground. Pay the care
       takers at the mobile home in park.
(21)   Rest Area (wb)

## Ohio I-280

1b    Flying J Travel Plaza

## Oklahoma I-35

(225)  Welcome Center (sb) / Rest Area (nb)
185    Sooner's Corner Texaco
137    Flying J Travel Plaza
137    Love's Travel Stop
(59)   Rest Area

## Oklahoma I-40

(316)  Rest Area (eb)
(314)  Welcome Center (wb)
264b   Flying J Travel Plaza
(197)  Rest Area
142    TA Travel Center

| | |
|---|---|
| 140 | Flying J Travel Plaza |
| 140 | Pilot Travel Center |
| 101 | Hinton Travel Plaza |
| 20 | Flying J Travel Plaza |
| (10) | Welcome Center (eb) / Rest Area (wb) |
| 7 | Texaco Log Cabin |
| 1 | Double D Fuel Stop |

## Oklahoma I-44

| | |
|---|---|
| 248 | Dave's Claremore RV, free. *Comments:* Dealer is three miles south of Claremore on Hwy 66. |
| 236a | Flying J Travel Plaza |
| 137 | Flying J Travel Plaza |
| 137 | Love's Travel Stop |

## Oklahoma I-244

| | |
|---|---|
| 15 | Flying J Travel Plaza |

## Oregon I-5

| | |
|---|---|
| 307 | Jubitz Travel Center |
| (240) | Rest Area between Albany and Jefferson |
| 238 | McKay Truck and RV Center, $5. *Comments:* One mile west of exit. |
| 234 | Knox Butte RV Park, $5. *Comments:* Southbound travelers use Exit 234a |
| 199 | TA Travel Center |
| 136 | McGuffies BP Gas Station, $3 |
| 129 | Kamper Korner RV Center, $3. *Comments:* From exit go north on Hwy 99 1 1/2 miles to dealership. |
| 123 | Douglas County Fairgrounds ($3 fee) |
| 119 | Love's Travel Stop |
| 99 | Stanton County Park ($3 fee) |
| 86 | Meadow Wood RV Park, $5. *Comments:* From southbound I-5 take Exit 86, go east over Interstate to dead end, right 3 miles to Barton Rd, left 500 feet to Autumn Ln, right one mile to park office. |
| 83 | Meadow Wood RV Park, $5. *Comments:* From northbound I-5 take Exit 83, right 500 feet to Autumn Ln, right one mile to park office. |
| 58 | 76 service station, free |
| 45 | Rest Area in Valley of the Rogue State Park |
| 14 | Shell Service Station, $3. *Comments:* Dump is free with fuel purchase. |

## Oregon I-84

| | |
|---|---|
| 376 | Pilot Travel Center |
| 374 | Rest Area in Ontario State Park |
| 304 | Baker Truck Corral |
| 304 | Jackson's Food Mart |
| (269) | Rest Area |
| (228) | Rest Area |
| (73) | Rest Area (eb) |
| 63 | Hood River Waste Treatment Plant. *Comments:* Located at 818 Riverside Dr. |
| 17 | Flying J Travel Plaza |

## Oregon I-205

| | |
|---|---|
| 9 | Clackamette RV Park (city park) |

## Pennsylvania I-70

| | |
|---|---|
| 49 | Penn Station Travel Plaza |
| 6 | Petro Stopping Center |

## Pennsylvania I-76

| | |
|---|---|
| 350 | Walt Whitman Truck Stop |
| (325) | Rest Area (eb) |
| (259) | Rest Area (wb) |
| (172) | Rest Area |

## Pennsylvania I-78

| | |
|---|---|
| 29b | Cabela's, free |

## Pennsylvania I-80

| | |
|---|---|
| 215 | Petro Stopping Center |
| 173 | Flying J Travel Plaza |
| 78 | Flying J Travel Plaza |
| 78 | TA Travel Center |

## Pennsylvania I-81

| | |
|---|---|
| 219 | Flying J Travel Plaza |
| 178b | Petro Stopping Center |
| 52 | Flying J Travel Plaza |

## Pennsylvania I-90

| | |
|---|---|
| 35 | TA Travel Center |

## Pennsylvania I-95

| | |
|---|---|
| 19 | Walt Whitman Truck Stop |

## Pennsylvania I-99

23    CoGo's Travel Center

## Pennsylvania I-276

(352)  Welcome Center (wb) / Rest Area (eb)

## Pennsylvania I-476

(56)   Lehigh Valley Service Plaza

## Rhode Island I-95

8     Arlington RV, $5

## South Carolina I-20

70    Flying J Travel Plaza

## South Carolina I-26

205a  KOA campground, $10. *Comments:* One mile west of exit.

## South Carolina I-77

34    Best Stop

## South Ca1rolina I-85

102   Flying J Travel Plaza

## South Carolina I-95

1     Porky's Truck Stop. *Comments:* Exit is in North Carolina.
181   Flying J Travel Plaza
181   Wilco Travel Plaza
169   Petro Stopping Center
119   TA Travel Center
77    Rainbow Gas Garden

## South Dakota I-29

213   Rest Area east of exit
177   Stone's Truck Stop
(161) Rest Area
121   Rest Area east of exit
83    Flying J Travel Plaza
26    Welcome Center east of exit

## South Dakota I-90

(412) Welcome Center (wb)
(363) Rest Area
332   Cabela's, free
(302) Rest Area (wb)
(301) Rest Area (eb)
(264) Rest Area
(221) Rest Area (wb)
(218) Rest Area (eb)
(167) Rest Area (wb)
(165) Rest Area (eb)
(100) Rest Area
66    Flying J Travel Plaza
61    Flying J Travel Plaza
58    Conoco
55    Windmill Truck Stop
(42)  Rest Area
30    Cenex Station
(1)   Welcome Center (eb)

## Tennessee I-40

369   Petro Stopping Center, free
288   Middle Tennessee Auto & Truck Plaza
238   Pilot Travel Center
182   Flying J Travel Plaza
172   Pilot Travel Center
126   North Forty Truck Stop
87    Love's Travel Stop

## Tennessee I-75

369   Petro Stopping Center, free

## Tennessee I-81

4     Pilot Travel Center

## Texas I-10

873   Flying J Travel Plaza
(590) Rest Area
583   Flying J Travel Plaza
583   TA Travel Center
(514) Rest Area
(394) Rest Area
372   Circle Bar Auto & Truck Plaza
212   I-10 Fina
87    Tiger Travel Plaza
0     Flying J Travel Plaza
0     Pilot Travel Center

## Texas I-20

| | |
|---|---|
| 503 | Rip Griffin Travel Center |
| 472 | Flying J Travel Plaza |
| 472 | TA Travel Center |
| 466 | Love's Travel Stop |
| 410 | Love's Travel Stop |
| 277 | Flying J Travel Plaza |
| 42 | Flying J Travel Plaza |

## Texas I-27

| | |
|---|---|
| 14 | New Deal Truck Stop |

## Texas I-30

| | |
|---|---|
| 223a | Simons Mid-Continent Travel Plaza |
| 70 | Love's Travel Stop |

## Texas I-35

| | |
|---|---|
| 368a | Love's Travel Stop |
| 331 | Flying J Travel Plaza |
| 328 | Pilot Travel Center |
| 306 | Love's Travel Stop |
| 304 | Cefco Travel Center |
| 193 | Rip Griffin Travel Center |
| (180) | Rest Area |
| 144 | Love's Travel Stop |

## Texas I-35W

| | |
|---|---|
| 65 | Pilot Travel Center |
| 40 | Love's Travel Stop |

## Texas I-37

| | |
|---|---|
| 3a | Corpus Christi Truck Stop |

## Texas I-40

| | |
|---|---|
| 76 | Flying J Travel Plaza |
| 75 | Pilot Travel Center |
| 74 | Love's Travel Stop |
| 74 | TA Travel Center |
| 36 | Texas Quick Stop |

## Texas I-45

| | |
|---|---|
| 238 | Corner Food Mart |
| 198 | Love's Travel Stop |
| 64 | Flying J Travel Plaza |
| 1c | Harborside Food Mart |

## Utah I-15

| | |
|---|---|
| 364 | Flying J Travel Plaza |
| 360 | Flying J Travel Plaza |
| 348 | Flying J Travel Plaza |
| 320 | RB's One Stop |
| 308 | Flying J Travel Plaza |
| 254 | Flying J Travel Plaza |
| 222 | Circle C Car & Truck Plaza |
| 222 | Flying J Travel Plaza |
| 222 | Tri-Mart Fuel Stop |
| 78 | TA Travel Center |
| 8 | Premium Oil. *Comments:* Located two miles west of exit. |

## Utah I-70

| | |
|---|---|
| 162 | West Winds Truck Stop. *Comments:* Westbound travelers use this exit. |
| 158 | West Winds Truck Stop. *Comments:* Eastbound travelers use this exit. |
| 40 | Flying J Travel Plaza |

## Utah I-80

| | |
|---|---|
| 164 | Holiday Hills |
| 308 | Flying J Travel Plaza |
| 99 | Flying J Travel Plaza |
| 99 | TA Travel Center |

## Utah I-84

| | |
|---|---|
| 346 | Flying J Travel Plaza |
| 360 | Flying J Travel Plaza |
| 364 | Flying J Travel Plaza |
| 40 | Golden Spike Travel Plaza |
| 7 | Flying J Travel Plaza |

## Utah I-215

| | |
|---|---|
| 18 | State Trailer Supply, no fee. *Comments:* From exit, go east on UT 171 to Redwood Rd and turn south. |
| 28 | Flying J Travel Plaza |

## Vermont I-89

| | |
|---|---|
| 14e | Pete's RV Center, free |

## Virginia I-64

| | |
|---|---|
| 250b | Newport News City Park campground, |

$3. *Comments:* Located at 13564 Jefferson Ave. Dump is free if camping.

120    The Sleep Inn
195    Lee Hi Travel Plaza

## Virginia I-77

41     TA Travel Center
77     Flying J Travel Plaza

## Virginia I-81

323    Flying J Travel Plaza
195    Lee Hi Travel Plaza
84     Love's Travel Stop
77     Flying J Travel Plaza
72     TA Travel Center. *Comments:* Located off exit 41 from I-77.
67     Wilco Travel Plaza

## Virginia I-95

152    Prince William Trailer Village, $5. *Comments:* 2.5 miles west of exit on VA 234.
104    Flying J Travel Plaza
98     Doswell All American Plaza
89     TA Travel Center
11b    Public dump station, no fee. *Comments:* Dump station is in the corner of lot for Burger King/Citgo station on US 58.
4      Love's Travel Stop, free

## Washington I-5

258    Yorky's Exxon, $4. *Comments:* Free with fuel purchase.
256a   Meridian Shell. *Comments:* Located behind car wash, limited to RVs up to 32 feet long.
254    Iowa Street Chevron, $3. *Comments:* Free with fuel purchase.
232    Cook Road Texaco
227    Lions Park
(207)  Rest Area
(188)  Rest Area (sb)
176⁻   Evergreen RV Supply, $1.50. *Comments:* Go west at exit and then south on Aurora Ave.
(141)  Rest Area (nb)
(12)   Rest Area (sb)
(11)   Rest Area (nb)

## Washington I-82

80     Rest Area
80     Horse Heaven Hills Travel Plaza
54     City-maintained dump station. *Comments:* On First Ave across from supermarket on west end of town, donation requested.
52     City-maintained dump station. *Comments:* On First Ave across from supermarket on west end of town, donation requested.
(24)   Rest Area (eb)
(22)   Rest Area (wb)

## Washington I-90

(242)  Rest Area (eb)
(199)  Rest Area (wb)
179    Husky Hillstop
179    Moses Lake Exxon
(162)  Rest Area (wb)
(161)  Rest Area (eb)
(89)   Rest Area
85     Shell Service Station. *Comments:* Free with fuel purchase.
31     Public dump station, $3.75. *Comments:* From exit, go north through second light, over bridge, next right, 2/3 block, right into car wash end bay. Dump is at end of wall next to street.
15     Lake Sammamish State Park, $10

## Washington I-182

5b     Columbia Point, no fee. *Comments:* From exit go north to first stop light and then east about one mile to city-owned boat launch.

## West Virginia I-64

(72)   Turnpike Service Area (wb)
(44)   Beckley Travel Plaza
(35)   Rest Area

## West Virginia I-68

(31)   Welcome Center (wb)

## West Virginia I-70

(13)   Welcome Center (wb)

11    Dallas Pike Travel Express

## West Virginia I-77

(166)  Welcome Center (sb) / Rest Area (nb)
(72)   Turnpike Service Area (nb)
(44)   Beckley Travel Plaza
(17)   Turnpike Service Area (nb)

## West Virginia I-79

(159)  Welcome Center (sb)
(123)  Rest Area
(85)   Rest Area
(49)   Rest Area

## Wisconsin I-39

188   Rib Mountain Travel Center
132   Token Creek Park (county park), $2
132   Wisconsin RV World

## Wisconsin I-43

187   Bay Beach City Park
157   Fun-N-Fast Travel Center

## Wisconsin I-90

132   Token Creek Park (county park), $2
132   Wisconsin RV World
69    Kwik Trip
61    New Lisbon Travel Center
61    The Bunk House

## Wisconsin I-94

322   Flying J Travel Plaza.
319   Prosser RV / Cruise America, $35.
      *Comments:* Full-service dump (no do-
      it-yourself) by appointment only. From
      exit, go east to WI 38 (Howell Ave) and
      turn left (north); one block on east side of
      street.
306   Wisconsin State Fair Park, $7
132   Token Creek Park (county park), $2
132   Wisconsin RV World
69    Kwik Trip

61    New Lisbon Travel Center
61    The Bunk House
143   Kwik Trip
116   Black River Crossing Oasis
116   Flying J Travel Plaza

## Wyoming I-25

299   Big Horn Travel Plaza, $3
299   Cenex Truck Stop, free
185   Flying J Travel Plaza
182   Eastgate Travel Plaza
126   Rest Area
126   Orin Junction Truck Stop
(54)  Rest Area
7     Welcome Center
7     Flying J Travel Plaza, free
7     Love's Travel Stop, free

## Wyoming I-80

370   Sapp Brothers Truck Stop, $5
311   High Country Sportsman
214   Rip Griffin Travel Center
209   Flying J Travel Plaza
173   Sinclair Fuel Stop
173   Wamsutter Conoco Service
104   Flying J Travel Plaza, free
68    Little America Truck Stop
(6)   Welcome Center

## Wyoming I-90

126   Dalbey Memorial Park. *Comments:* One
      mile south of exit.
      Flying J Travel Plaza, free
25    Holiday Gas Station, free. *Comments:*
      Best accessed by smaller RVs. May be
      closed in winter.
25    Washington City Park. *Comments:* From
      I-90 exit proceed west to first traffic light
      and turn right. Proceed about one mile
      and cross Little Goose Creek bridge.
      Park is about 1/4 mile beyond the bridge
      on the right.
23    Visitor Information Center. *Comments:*
      Closed in winter.

# Online Resources

## RoadNotes
www.RoadNotes.com

The RoadNotes web site offers free travel information and a monthly online newsletter. At RoadNotes you'll find:

- Current rest area and welcome center information
- Over 200 scenic byways
- Articles about buying an RV, boondocking, solar power, and many more
- A list of AM and FM radio stations and a TV station list
- Plus much more

The monthly online newsletter is about camping and traveling in America. Each issue explores unique and interesting places to visit, fun things to see and do, and the scenic byways in between. Read articles that cover a variety of subjects from the RV lifestyle to legends of America. Learn about Corps of Engineers lakes, National Forests, National Parks, and other public recreation areas. You'll also find book reviews, gadgets and gizmos, interesting web sites to visit, and other tidbits of information.

## RV Dump Stations
www.rvdumps.com

The RV Dump Stations web site makes it easy to find public dump stations. Nearly 2,000 locations across the United States are listed and include places like truck stops and travel centers, city and county parks, gas stations, rest areas, and more.

Dump stations easily accessed from Interstate highways are listed by exit or mile marker number, making it easy to find one as you travel. Those in other locations are listed alphabetically by city or town.

## Travel Books
www.TravelBooksUSA.com

Visit our online book store for a variety of unique travel books.